THE LAWS OF LARGE NUMBERS

Probability and Mathematical Statistics

A Series of Monographs and Textbooks

Edited by

Z. W. Birnbaum
University of Washington
Seattle, Washington

E. Lukacs
Catholic University
Washington, D.C.

---

1. Thomas Ferguson. Mathematical Statistics: A Decision Theoretic Approach. 1967
2. Howard Tucker. A Graduate Course in Probability. 1967
3. K. R. Parthasarathy. Probability Measures on Metric Spaces. 1967
4. P. Révész. The Laws of Large Numbers. 1968

In preparation

B. V. Gnedenko, Yu. K. Belyayev, and A. D. Solovyev. Mathematical Methods of Reliability Theory

THE LAWS OF LARGE NUMBERS

by

PÁL RÉVÉSZ

Mathematical Institute
Hungarian Academy of Sciences
Budapest, Hungary

1968

ACADEMIC PRESS

NEW YORK AND LONDON

ACADEMIC PRESS INC.
111 Fifth Avenue, New York, New York 10003

United Kingdom Edition published by
ACADEMIC PRESS INC. (LONDON) LTD.
Berkeley Square House, London W.1

Library of Congress Catalog Card Number: 68-26629

JOINT EDITION PUBLISHED BY
ACADEMIC PRESS, NEW YORK AND LONDON
AND
AKADÉMIAI KIADÓ, BUDAPEST

PRINTED IN THE UNITED STATES OF AMERICA

CONTENTS

INTRODUCTION

For most people the idea of probability is closely related to that of relative frequency. Therefore, it is natural that an attempt was made to construct a mathematical theory of probability using this concept. Such an approach was tried for instance by Mises [1], [2] in the first three decades of this century. Unfortunately it did not produce sufficiently deep results,[1] and it was necessary to find another approach.

This was accomplished in Kolmogorov's axiomatic treatment of probability. However, if we wish to be sure that this theory adequately represents our natural ideas of probability, then we must investigate the relationships between probability and relative frequency. The results of this investigation are called the laws of large numbers.

Similarly, the relationships between other theoretical and practical concepts of probability theory, e.g. the concepts of expectation and sample mean, can also be investigated by using the laws of large numbers.

These remarks show the theoretical importance of this field; its practical importance is no less. If we want to estimate the unknown probability of a random event or the unknown expectation of a random variable, then we have to show that the relative frequency or the sample mean converges to the probability or to the expectation.

The statistical application of the laws of large numbers raises two other questions: what is the rate of convergence of the relative frequency or of the sample mean and what is the behaviour of the sample mean if the elements of the sample are not necessarily independent and identically distributed random variables. If we are working with a class of stochastic processes then it is necessary to know how to estimate the parameters of this process, or in other words, it is necessary to give the corresponding laws of large numbers.

To define exactly the field of the laws of large numbers seems to be very difficult. We can say, in an attempt to obtain a definition, that

[1] This way was tried again very recently by Kolmogorov [3] and Martin-Löf [1]. Their results are based on very deep mathematical methods and in some sense can solve the problem of Mises.

a law of large numbers asserts the convergence, in a certain sense, of the average

$$\eta_n = \frac{\xi_1 + \xi_2 + \ldots + \xi_n}{n}$$

of the random variables $\xi_1, \xi_2, \ldots$ to a random variable η. Actually, this class of theorems contains many theorems which are not related to probability, for example the classical theorems of Fejér about the Cesaro summability of Fourier series. Therefore, we will say that laws of large numbers are theorems stating the convergence of η_n which are interesting from the point of view of probability. Evidently it is very difficult to say exactly what theorems are of interest in probability theory. It may happen that the author investigates some problems in which he is especially interested but which are not that closely related to probability theory and he omits others, more closely related.

If we study the convergence of η_n, making use of different modes of convergence, then we obtain different types of the laws of large numbers. In this book we consider three types of laws of large numbers according to the following kinds of convergence:[1]

1°. Stochastic convergence: $\mathbf{P}(|\eta_n - \eta| \geqq \varepsilon) \to 0$,
2°. Mean convergence: $\mathbf{E}[(\eta_n - \eta)^2] \to 0$,
3°. Convergence with probability 1 : $\mathbf{P}(\eta_n \to \eta) = 1$.

In connection with the resulting types of laws of large numbers we will investigate the rate of convergence. In the first two cases the definition of the rate of convergence is clear. In the third case the rate of convergence will be characterized by the "largest" function $f(n)$ for which $\mathbf{P}\big(f(n)|\eta_n - \eta| \to 0\big) = 1$. More precisely, we investigate the class of functions $f(n)$ for which the last mentioned formula holds. Hence, the laws of the iterated logarithm will also be treated in this book.

Theorems on the convergence of a series of the form $\sum_{k=1}^{\infty} c_k \xi_k$, where, $\{\xi_k\}$ is a sequence of random variables and $\{c_k\}$ is a sequence of real numbers cannot be considered as a law of large numbers. However, this class of theorems will occasionally be studied here, because the convergence of a series of the above form immediately implies a law of large numbers by Theorem 1.2.2.

Let us mention some types of theorems which could be considered as laws of large numbers but which will not be investigated in this book.

First, the theory of large deviations will be completely omitted, though these theorems also give results about the rate of convergence in case 1°. In general, we intend to distinguish the laws of large numbers and the limit theorems. Of course, it is not possible to succeed in every case.

[1] The exact definitions are given in § 1.1.

Another class of theorems which will not be treated here is the laws of large numbers for stochastic processes with a continuous parameter.

Likewise, the problems of double sequences are not investigated. This question was recently treated in several papers (see e.g. GNEDENKO–KOLMOGOROV [1] and CHOW [1]).

The aim of the author is to give a general survey of the results and the most important methods of proof in this field. Occasionally, when the proof of a theorem requires very special methods, the proof will be omitted. For instance, one can prove some laws of large numbers for certain classes of stochastic processes making use only of general methods of proof, but at times it is necessary to apply the deeper special properties of the class of stochastic process in question. In such cases we will not give the proof, because we do not intend to study the special methods of stochastic processes. For example, the theory of martingales which, can be applied as a method of proof to obtain laws of large numbers, will be omitted.

In Chapter 0 we have collected the most important definitions and theorems which are applied in this book. We emphasize that it is not the aim of this chapter to give a systematic treatment. The reader should be familiar with the most fundamental results and concepts of probability (FISZ [1], GNEDENKO [1], LOÈVE [1], RÉNYI [1]),[1] stochastic processes (DOOB [1]), measure theory (HALMOS [1]), ergodic theory (HALMOS [2], or JACOBS [1], [2]), functional analysis (RIESZ–SZ.-NAGY [1], YOSIDA [1], etc. The aim of Chapter 0 is to give some help to the reader by presenting the necessary preliminary material.

Chapter 1 deals with the special concepts and general theorems of the laws of large numbers. Chapters 2, 3, 4, 6, 7 discuss the laws of large numbers of different classes of stochastic processes. Chapter 5 gives laws of large numbers for subsequences of sequences of random variables. Chapter 8 contains some general laws of large numbers which are not related to any concrete class of stochastic processes. Chapters 9 and 10 treat some special questions.

In Chapter 11 we give some examples of the applications of the theorems of this book. It is evident that many more quite different applications can be found.

I am deeply indebted to Professors Á. CSÁSZÁR, A. RÉNYI and K. TANDORI for their valuable advice and criticism. My thanks are due to Mr. G. EAGLESON for correcting the text linguistically and for his valuable remarks.

[1] The numbers in brackets refer to some books containing the necessary fundamental knowledge. (See the "References" at the end of the book.)

CHAPTER 0

MATHEMATICAL BACKGROUND

§ 0.1. Measure theory

The fundamental concept of measure theory is that of a measure space.

Let X be an arbitrary abstract (non-empty) set, sometimes called the *basic space*. A class $\mathcal{S}$ of the subsets of X is called a *σ-algebra* if

$$X \in \mathcal{S},$$

$$A\bar{B} \in \mathcal{S} \quad \text{whenever} \quad A \in \mathcal{S} \text{ and } B \in \mathcal{S}$$

and

$$\sum_{i=1}^{\infty} A_i \in \mathcal{S} \quad \text{whenever} \quad A_i \in \mathcal{S} \quad (i = 1, 2, \ldots).$$

Here (and in the following) the product AB of two sets A and B denotes their common part (intersection). The union of two sets A and B will be denoted by addition $A + B$. Finally $\bar{B}$ is the complement of B, i.e. $\bar{B}$ contains those points of X which do not belong to B.

The elements of $\mathcal{S}$ are called *measurable sets*. A set function μ defined on $\mathcal{S}$ is called a *measure* if

$$\mu(A) \geq 0 \quad \text{whenever} \quad A \in \mathcal{S}$$

and

$$\mu\left(\sum_{i=1}^{\infty} A_i\right) = \sum_{i=1}^{\infty} \mu(A_i) \text{ whenever } A_i \in \mathcal{S} \text{ and } A_i A_j = \emptyset \text{ (if } i \neq j)$$

where $\emptyset$ denotes the empty set. A measure μ is called *σ-finite* if there exists a sequence $A_1, A_2, \ldots$ of measurable sets such that

$$X = \sum_{i=1}^{\infty} A_i \text{ and } \mu(A_i) < \infty \quad (i = 1, 2, \ldots).$$

The ordered pair $\{X, \mathcal{S}\}$ is called a *measurable space*. The ordered triple $\{X, \mathcal{S}, \mu\}$ (where X is an abstract non-empty set, $\mathcal{S}$ is a σ-algebra of the subsets of X ($X \in \mathcal{S}$) and μ is a measure defined on $\mathcal{S}$) is called a *measure space*.

A class $\mathcal{R}$ of the subsets of X is called an *algebra* if

$$X \in \mathcal{R}$$

$$A\bar{B} \in \mathcal{R} \text{ whenever } A \in \mathcal{R} \text{ and } B \in \mathcal{R}$$

and

$$A + B \in \mathcal{R} \text{ whenever } A \in \mathcal{R} \text{ and } B \in \mathcal{R}.$$

Evidently, for every algebra $\mathcal{R}$ there is a unique smallest σ-algebra $\mathcal{S} = \mathcal{S}(\mathcal{R})$ containing $\mathcal{R}$. ("Smallest" means: if $\mathcal{S}^*$ is a σ-algebra containing $\mathcal{R}$ then $\mathcal{S}^*$ also contains $\mathcal{S}(\mathcal{R})$.)

A real valued function $f(x)$ defined on X is called *measurable* (with respect to $\mathcal{S}$) if for each real z

$$\{x : f(x) < z\} \in \mathcal{S}.$$

Let $f_1(x)$, $f_2(x), \ldots$ be a finite or infinite sequence of measurable functions defined on a measurable space $\{X, \mathcal{S}\}$. $\mathcal{B}(f_1, f_2, \ldots) \in \mathcal{S}$ *denotes the smallest σ-algebra with respect to which the functions $f_1, f_2, \ldots$ are measurable. If the function $g(x)$ is measurable with respect to the σ-algebra $\mathcal{B}(f_1, f_2, \ldots)$ then there exists a function $h(., ., \ldots)$ such that $g = h(f_1, f_2, \ldots)$. In particular, if $f_1, f_2, \ldots$ is a finite sequence of n elements then h is a Borel-measurable*[1] *function defined on the n-dimensional Cartesian space.* g is called a *Baire-function* of $f_1, f_2, \ldots$.

A measurable function $f(x)$ is called *integrable* if it is integrable over the space X (with respect to the measure μ) in the sense of Lebesgue, and its integral is finite. The integral of $f(x)$ over the whole space X will be denoted in the following different ways:

$$\int_X f(x)\, d\mu = \int_X f d\mu = \int f d\mu = \int f.$$

Among the properties of the Lebesgue integral we mention here only two theorems.

THEOREM 0.1.1 (LEBESGUE THEOREM). *If $f_1, f_2, \ldots$ is a sequence of integrable functions and there exists an integrable function $b(x)$ such that $|f_n| \leq b(x)$ $(n = 1, 2, \ldots)$ then*

$$\lim_{n\to\infty} \int f_n = \int \lim_{n\to\infty} f_n$$

provided that $\lim_{n\to\infty} f_n$ exists almost everywhere (i.e. for each x except a set of measure 0).

[1] The Borel sets of the n-dimensional Cartesian space are the elements of the smallest σ-algebra containing the n-dimensional intervals. A function $g(x_1, x_2, \ldots, x_n)$ is called Borel-measurable if it is measurable with respect to this σ-algebra.

THEOREM 0.1.2 (BEPPO-LEVI THEOREM). *If $f_1, f_2, \ldots$ is a sequence of non-negative integrable functions for which $\sum_{n=1}^{\infty} \int f_n < \infty$ then the series $\sum_{n=1}^{\infty} f_n$ is convergent almost everywhere and*

$$\int \sum_{n=1}^{\infty} f_n = \sum_{n=1}^{\infty} \int f_n .$$

A set function λ (defined on $\mathcal{S}$) is called a *signed measure* if

$$\lambda\left(\sum_{i=1}^{\infty} A_i\right) = \sum_{i=1}^{\infty} \lambda(A_i) \quad \text{whenever} \quad A_i \in \mathcal{S} \text{ and } A_i A_j = \varnothing \text{ (if } i \neq j)$$

and $\lambda(A)$ can take on at most one of the values $+\infty$ and $-\infty$. The signed measure λ is called σ-finite if there exists a sequence $A_1, A_2, \ldots$ of measurable sets such that

$$X = \sum_{i=1}^{\infty} A_i \quad \text{and} \quad |\lambda(A_i)| < \infty \ (i = 1, 2, \ldots).$$

Henceforth we assume that all measures and all signed measures are σ-finite.

We can characterize signed measures by

THEOREM 0.1.3. *If λ is a signed measure then there exist two measures λ^+ and λ^- such that*

$$\lambda(A) = \lambda^+(A) - \lambda^-(A) \quad \textit{if} \quad A \in \mathcal{S}.$$

The measures λ^+ (resp. λ^-) are called the upper (resp. lower) variation of λ. The measure $|\lambda|(A) = \lambda^+(A) + \lambda^-(A)$ is called the total variation of λ.

We will say that a signed measure ν is *absolutely continuous* with respect to a signed measure μ (in symbols $\nu \ll \mu$) if $\nu(A) = 0$ for every measurable set A for which $|\mu|(A) = 0$.

We mention only two fundamental results of measure theory.

THEOREM 0.1.4 (EXTENSION THEOREM). *If we have a σ-additive, and σ-finite non-negative set function*[1] *μ defined on an algebra $\mathcal{R}$ then there exists a unique measure μ^* defined on $\mathcal{S}(\mathcal{R})$ such that*

$$\mu^*(A) = \mu(A) \ \textit{whenever} \ A \in \mathcal{R}.$$

This theorem implies that if two measures μ_1 and μ_2 are equal to each other on an algebra $\mathcal{R}$ then they are equal on $\mathcal{S}(\mathcal{R})$.

[1] That is $\mu(\sum_{i=1}^{\infty} A_i) = \sum_{i=1}^{\infty} \mu(A_i)$ whenever $A_i \in \mathcal{R}$, $\sum_{i=1}^{\infty} A_i \in \mathcal{R}$ and $A_i A_j = \varnothing$ $(i \neq j)$, and there exists a sequence $A_1, A_2, \ldots$ of elements of $\mathcal{R}$ such that $\sum_{i=1}^{\infty} A_i = X$ and $\mu(A_i) < \infty$.

THEOREM 0.1.5 (RADON–NIKODYM THEOREM). *If the signed measure ν is absolutely continuous with respect to a signed measure μ then there exists a measurable function f, (on X), such that*

$$\nu(E) = \int_E f(x)\, d\mu$$

whenever $E \in \mathcal{S}$. The function f is unique in the sense that if also $\nu(E) = \int_E g(x) d\mu$ then $\mu \{x : f(x) \neq g(x)\} = 0$.

The function $f(x)$ is called the Radon–Nikodym derivative of ν with respect to μ. In symbols:

$$f(x) = \frac{d\nu}{d\mu} .$$

We say that the sequence $f_1, f_2, \ldots$ of measurable functions *converges in measure* to a function f if

$$\lim_{n\to\infty} \mu \{x : |f_n - f| \geq \varepsilon\} = 0$$

for any $\varepsilon > 0$. In symbols $f_n \Rightarrow f$.

In connection with the properties of almost everywhere convergence we have

THEOREM 0.1.6 (EGOROV'S THEOREM). *If $f_n(x) \to f(x)$, almost everywhere on a space X of finite measure (i.e. $f_n(x) \to f(x)$ for all x except a set of measure 0), then for any $\varepsilon > 0$ there exists* a *set $F \in \mathcal{S}$ such that $\mu(\bar{F}) < \varepsilon$ and f_n converges to f uniformly on F, i.e. for any $\delta > 0$ there exists an $n = n_0(\delta)$ such that*

$$\mu \{x : |f_n - f| < \delta, x \in F\} = \mu(F)$$

if $n \geq n_0$.

We now define the *Cartesian product* of two, or more, measure spaces.

Let $\{X, \mathcal{S}, \mu\}$ and $\{Y, \mathcal{T}, \nu\}$ be two measure spaces. The product $X \times Y$ means the set of the ordered pairs (x, y) $(x \in X,\ y \in Y)$. If $A \subset X$ and $B \subset Y$ then $A \times B \subset X \times Y$ is defined by

$$A \times B = \{(x, y) : x \in A, y \in B\}.$$

The product $\mathcal{S} \times \mathcal{T}$ of the σ-algebras $\mathcal{S}$ and $\mathcal{T}$ is the smallest σ-algebra containing the sets $A \times B$ where $A \in \mathcal{S}$ and $B \in \mathcal{T}$. We can define the product measure $\mu \times \nu$ on $\mathcal{S} \times \mathcal{T}$ by

$$\mu \times \nu(A \times B) = \mu(A)\, \nu(B) \quad (A \in \mathcal{S},\ B \in \mathcal{T}).$$

The measure of other elements of $\mathcal{S} \times \mathcal{T}$ can be obtained by extension. The measure space $\{X \times Y,\ \mathcal{S} \times \mathcal{T},\ \mu \times \nu\}$ is called the Cartesian product of $\{X, \mathcal{S}, \mu\}$ and $\{Y, \mathcal{T}, \nu\}$.

If $\{X_1, \mathcal{S}_1, \mu_1\}$, $\{X_2, \mathcal{S}_2, \mu_2\}$, ... is a sequence of measure spaces with $\mu_i(X_i) = 1$ $(i = 1, 2, \ldots)$ then the Cartesian product of them can be defined as follows:

$$X_1 \times X_2 \times \ldots = \mathop{X}_{n=1}^{\infty} X_n$$

is the set of all infinite sequences $(x_1, x_2, \ldots)$ $(x_i \in X_i)$ $\cdot \mathscr{S}_1 \times \mathscr{S}_2 \times \ldots$ is the smallest σ-algebra containing the sets

$$A_1 \times A_2 \times \ldots \times A_n \times X_{n+1} \times X_{n+2} \times \ldots = \{(x_1, x_2, \ldots) : x_i \in A_i \text{ if } i \leqq n\}$$

$(n = 1, 2, \ldots)$. The product measure $\mu = \mu_1 \times \mu_2 \times \ldots$ on $\mathscr{S}_1 \times \mathscr{S}_2 \times \ldots$ can be defined by

$$\mu(A_1 \times A_2 \times \ldots \times A_n \times X_{n+1} \times X_{n+2} \times \ldots) = \prod_{i=1}^{n} \mu_i(A_i) \quad (n=1, 2, \ldots).$$

The measure of other elements of $\mathscr{S}_1 \times \mathscr{S}_2 \times \ldots$ can be obtained by extension.

§ 0.2. Probability theory

A measure space $\{X, \mathscr{S}, \mu\}$ such that the measure of the basic space is 1 $(\mu(X) = 1)$, is called a *probability space.* Generally in this case the basic space X will be denoted by Ω, the measure will be denoted by $\mathbf{P}$ and will be called a *probability measure.*

Thus a probability space is a measure space $\{\Omega, \mathscr{S}, \mathbf{P}\}$ with the restriction $\mathbf{P}(\Omega) = 1$. In this case the expressions "almost everywhere" and "with probability 1" are used in the same sense.

The elements of $\mathscr{S}$ will be called *events* and they will be denoted by capital letters: $A, B, C, \ldots$

A measurable function $\xi(\omega)$ $(\omega \in \Omega)$ defined on the probability space $\{\Omega, \mathscr{S}, \mathbf{P}\}$ will be called a *random variable.* The random variables will be denoted by greek letters: $\xi = \xi(\omega)$, $\zeta = \zeta(\omega)$, $\eta = \eta(\omega), \ldots$.

The Lebesgue-integral of a random variable ξ is called the *expectation* (or the *mean value)* of ξ. It will be denoted by

$$\mathbf{E}(\xi) = \int \xi \, d\mathbf{P}.$$

The *variance* $\mathbf{D}^2(\xi)$ of ξ is defined by

$$\mathbf{D}^2(\xi) = \mathbf{E}\left((\xi - \mathbf{E}(\xi))^2\right) = \mathbf{E}(\xi^2) - \mathbf{E}^2(\xi).$$

The following inequality is obvious:

$$\mathbf{D}^2(\xi) \leqq \mathbf{E}\left[(\xi - a)^2\right] \tag{0.2.1}$$

for any real a.

The symbol $\mathbf{P}(\cdot)$ denotes the probability, or the probability measure, of the event in the brackets. For instance

$$\mathbf{P}(\xi < x)$$

(x is a real number) means the probability measure of the set of those $\omega \in \Omega$ for which $\xi(\omega) < x$. The function $\mathbf{P}(\xi < x) = F_\xi(x) = F(x)$ is called the *distribution function* of ξ.

A distribution function $F(x)$ has the following properties:
1. $F(x)$ is a non-decreasing function;
2. $F(x-0) = \lim_{h \searrow 0} F(x-h) = F(x)$;
3. $F(-\infty) = \lim_{x \to -\infty} F(x) = 0$; $F(+\infty) = \lim_{x \to \infty} F(x) = 1$.

A distribution function $F(x)$ generates a measure μ_F on the real line in the following way: the measure of an interval $[a, b)$ is defined by

$$\mu_F([a, b)) = F(b) - F(a).$$

We obtain the measure of the Borel sets of the real line by extension.

The Lebesgue integral of a function $g(x)$ with respect to the measure μ_F is called the Stieltjes (Lebesgue–Stieltjes) integral of g. In symbols

$$\int g(x)\, d\mu_F = \int_{-\infty}^{+\infty} g(x)\, dF(x) = \int g\, dF.$$

In particular if $F_\xi(x)$ is absolutely continuous, i.e. the measure μ_F is absolutely continuous with respect to the ordinary Lebesgue measure, then the derivative f of F will be called the *density function* of ξ and in this case

$$\int g\, dF = \int g f\, dx$$

for any g for which the integral exists.

If $F(x)$ is the distribution function of a random variable ξ then

$$\mathbf{E}(\xi) = \int x\, dF(x).$$

In general, if $h(x)$ is a Borel measurable function then

$$\mathbf{E}(h(\xi)) = \int h(x)\, dF(x).$$

The expectation $\mathbf{E}(\xi^n) = \int x^n dF$ is called the *n-th moment* of ξ.

The real number m for which $F_\xi(m) \leq \frac{1}{2}$ and $F_\xi(m+0) \geq \frac{1}{2}$ is called the *median* of ξ. If more than one real number has this property then any one of them is called as the median. The median of ξ will be denoted by $m(\xi)$.

A simple but important property of the median is given by

THEOREM 0.2.1. *If $\xi_1, \xi_2, \ldots$ is a sequence of random variables tending in measure to a random variable η ($\xi_n \Rightarrow \eta$) then*

$$m(\xi_n) \to m(\eta)$$

provided that the medians are chosen suitably.

If $\xi_1, \xi_2, \ldots, \xi_n$ are arbitrary random variables then the function

$$F_n(x_1, x_2, \ldots, x_n) = \mathbf{P}(\xi_1 < x_1, \xi_2 < x_2, \ldots, \xi_n < x_n)$$

is called the *joint distribution function* of the random variables $\xi_1, \xi_2, \ldots, \xi_n$.

The random variables $\xi_1, \xi_2, \ldots, \xi_n$ are called *independent* if

$$\mathbf{P}(\xi_1 < x_1, \xi_2 < x_2, \ldots, \xi_n < x_n) = \mathbf{P}(\xi_1 < x_1)\,\mathbf{P}(\xi_2 < x_2)\ldots\mathbf{P}(\xi_n < x_n)$$

where $x_1, x_2, \ldots, x_n$ are arbitrary real numbers. Clearly if $\xi_1, \xi_2, \ldots, \xi_n$ are independent then any k of them are also independent.

The random variables $\xi_1, \xi_2, \ldots$ are independent if any n of them are independent for $n = 1, 2, \ldots$.

The events $A_1, A_2, \ldots$ are independent if their indicator functions $\alpha_1(\omega), \alpha_2(\omega), \ldots$ are independent. The random variable $\alpha(\omega)$ is called the *indicator function* of the event A if

$$a(\omega) = \begin{cases} 1 \text{ whenever } \omega \in A \\ 0 \text{ whenever } \omega \notin A. \end{cases}$$

The function

$$\varphi(t) = \varphi_\xi(t) = \mathbf{E}(e^{i\xi t}) = \int e^{ixt}\,dF(x) = \mathbf{E}(\cos \xi t) + i\,\mathbf{E}(\sin \xi t) = \\ = \int \cos xt\,dF(x) + i \int \sin xt\,dF(x)$$

is called the *characteristic function* of ξ.

The sequence $\xi_1, \xi_2, \ldots, \xi_n$ of independent random variables has the following properties:

1. $\mathbf{E}(\xi_1 \xi_2 \ldots \xi_n) = \mathbf{E}(\xi_1)\,\mathbf{E}(\xi_2)\ldots\mathbf{E}(\xi_n)$ provided $\mathbf{E}(\xi_i)$ $(i = 1, 2, \ldots, n)$ exists;

2. $\varphi_{\xi_1+\xi_2+\ldots+\xi_n}(t) = \varphi_{\xi_1}(t)\,\varphi_{\xi_2}(t)\ldots\varphi_{\xi_n}(t)$;

3. the random variables $g_1(\xi_1, \xi_2, \ldots, \xi_{i_1})$, $g_2(\xi_{i_1+1}, \xi_{i_1+2}, \ldots, \xi_{i_2}), \ldots,$ $g_{k+1}(\xi_{i_k+1}, \xi_{i_k+2}, \ldots, \xi_n)$ $(1 \leq i_1 < i_2 < \ldots < i_k < n)$ are independent if $g_1, g_2, \ldots, g_{k+1}$ are Borel measurable functions.

Among the properties of the infinite sequences of independent random variables and independent events we mention two:

THEOREM 0.2.2 (ZERO-ONE LAW). *Let $\xi_1, \xi_2, \ldots$ be a sequence of independent random variables. We denote the smallest σ-algebra with respect to which the random variables $\xi_n, \xi_{n+1}, \ldots$ are measurable by $\mathscr{B}_n = \mathscr{B}(\xi_n, \xi_{n+1}, \ldots)$ and $\prod_{n=1}^{\infty} \mathscr{B}_n$ by $\mathscr{B}$. Then if $A \in \mathscr{B}$ it follows that $\mathbf{P}(A) = 0$ or $\mathbf{P}(A) = 1$ and if η is a random variable, measurable with respect to $\mathscr{B}$ then η is constant with probability* 1.

THEOREM 0.2.3 (BOREL–CANTELLI LEMMA).

(a) *If $A_1, A_2, \ldots$ is a sequence of events such that $\sum_{i=1}^{\infty} \mathbf{P}(A_i) < \infty$ then with probability* 1 *only finitely many events may occur or, in other words, for almost all $\omega \in \Omega$, ω belongs to only finitely many A_i' s or, in other words, $\mathbf{P}\left(\sum_{i=1}^{\infty} \alpha_i < \infty\right) = 1$ where α_i is the indicator function of A_i.*

(b) *If* $A_1, A_2, \ldots$ *is a sequence of independent events such that* $\sum_{i=1}^{\infty} \mathbf{P}(A_i) = \infty$ *then with probability* 1 *infinitely many events will have occured or, in other words, almost all* $\omega \in \Omega$ *are elements of infinitely many* A_i*'s or, in other words,* $\mathbf{P}\left(\sum_{i=1}^{\infty} \alpha_i = \infty\right) = 1$.

Some important properties of characteristic functions are given in the following three theorems:

THEOREM 0.2.4. *If* $\xi_1, \xi_2, \ldots$ *is a sequence of random variables then* $\xi_n \Rightarrow a$ *where* a *is a constant if and only if,* $\varphi_{\xi_n}(t) \to e^{iat}$ *for all real* t *uniformly in any finite t-interval.*

THEOREM 0.2.5. *If the n-th moment* $\mathbf{E}(\xi^n)$ *of a random variable exists then*

$$\mathbf{E}(\xi^n) = i^n \varphi_\xi^{(n)}(0)$$

($\varphi^{(n)}(0)$ *is the n-th derivative of* $\varphi(t)$ *in* $t = 0$).

THEOREM 0.2.6 (PITMAN [1]). *Let k be an odd positive integer. Necessary and sufficient conditions for the existence of* $\varphi^{(k)}(0)$ *are that*

$$\lim_{x\to\infty} x^k [F(-x) + 1 - F(x)] = 0$$

and

$$\lim_{T\to\infty} \int_{-T}^{T} x^k \, dF(x)$$

exist. When these two conditions are satisfied

$$\varphi^{(k)}(0) = i^k \lim_{T\to\infty} \int_{-T}^{T} x^k \, dF(x).$$

The easiest way to define an infinite sequence of independent random variables is by the method of product spaces. More exactly if $\{\Omega_1, \mathscr{S}_1, \mathbf{P}_1\}, \{\Omega_2, \mathscr{S}_2, \mathbf{P}_2\}, \ldots$ is an infinite sequence of probability spaces and $\{\Omega, \mathscr{S}, \mathbf{P}\}$ is their Cartesian product, i.e.

$$\Omega = \Omega_1 \times \Omega_2 \times \ldots$$
$$\mathscr{S} = \mathscr{S}_1 \times \mathscr{S}_2 \times \ldots$$
$$\mathbf{P} = \mathbf{P}_1 \times \mathbf{P}_2 \times \ldots$$

then the random variables $\xi_1(\omega_1, \omega_2, \ldots)$, $\xi_2(\omega_1, \omega_2, \ldots), \ldots$ are evidently independent if $\xi_i(\omega_1, \omega_2, \ldots)$ $(i = 1, 2, \ldots)$ depends only on ω_i and does not depend on its other variables.

To complete this section, the definition and some simple properties of the conditional expectation and conditional probability will be given.

DEFINITION. If ξ is a random variable and B is an event of positive probability then the conditional expectation of ξ under the condition B, in symbols $\mathbf{E}(\xi \mid B)$, is defined by

$$\mathbf{E}(\xi \mid B) = \frac{1}{\mathbf{P}(B)} \int_B \xi \, dP.$$

DEFINITION. If A is an event and B is an event of positive probability then the *conditional probability of* A under the condition B (in symbols $\mathbf{P}(A \mid B)$) is defined by

$$\mathbf{P}(A \mid B) = \frac{\mathbf{P}(AB)}{\mathbf{P}(B)}.$$

Evidently, we have

$$\mathbf{P}(A \mid B) = \mathbf{E}(\alpha \mid B)$$

where α is the indicator function of A.

The concept of the conditional expectation is much more complicated if the condition is a random variable or a σ-algebra. Here only the definition is given without any comment on the meaning of this definition.

DEFINITION. Let ξ be an integrable random variable and $\mathscr{F} \subset \mathscr{S}$ a σ-algebra, then the *conditional expectation* of ξ under the condition $\mathscr{F}$ (in symbols $\mathbf{E}(\xi \mid \mathscr{F})$) by definition is a random variable with the following two properties:

(*a*) $\mathbf{E}(\xi \mid \mathscr{F})$ is measurable with respect to $\mathscr{F}$,

(*b*) $\int_A \mathbf{E}(\xi \mid \mathscr{F}) \, d\mathbf{P} = \int_A \xi \, d\mathbf{P}$ for all $A \in \mathscr{F}$.

By the Radon–Nikodym theorem there exists a unique random variable having these properties, in the sense that if η and ζ are two random variables having these properties then $\mathbf{P}(\zeta = \eta) = 1$.

DEFINITION. If A is an event and $\mathscr{F}$ is a σ-algebra then the conditional probability of A under the condition $\mathscr{F}$ is

$$\mathbf{P}(A \mid \mathscr{F}) = \mathbf{E}(\alpha \mid \mathscr{F})$$

where α is the indicator function of A.

If ξ and η are two random variables then by definition

$$\mathbf{E}(\xi \mid \eta) = \mathbf{E}(\xi \mid \mathscr{B})$$

where $\mathscr{B} = \mathscr{B}(\eta)$ is the smallest σ-algebra with respect to which η is measurable. More generally, if ξ and $\eta_1, \eta_2, \ldots, \eta_n$ are random variables then

$$\mathbf{E}(\xi \mid \eta_1, \eta_2, \ldots, \eta_n) = \mathbf{E}(\xi \mid \mathscr{B}_n)$$

where $\mathscr{B}_n = \mathscr{B}(\eta_1, \eta_2, \ldots, \eta_n)$ is the smallest σ-algebra with respect to which the random variables $\eta_1, \eta_2, \ldots, \eta_n$ are measurable. Similarly, we can define the conditional probability:

$$\mathbf{P}(A \mid \eta_1, \eta_2, \ldots, \eta_n) = \mathbf{E}(\alpha \mid \eta_1, \eta_2, \ldots, \eta_n)$$

where α is the indicator function of A.

Let us emphasize that the random variable $\mathbf{E}(\xi \mid \eta)$ is measurable with respect to $\mathscr{B}(\eta)$ and this fact implies the existence of a Borel measurable function $f(x)$ such that $\mathbf{E}(\xi \mid \eta) = f(\eta)$. This means that $\mathbf{E}(\xi \mid \eta)$ is a Baire-function of η. This fact allows us to use the notation $\mathbf{E}(\xi \mid \eta = y) = f(y)$,

Among the properties of the conditional expectation only the following ones are mentioned:[1]

1. $\mathbf{E}(\mathbf{E}(\xi \mid \mathscr{F})) = \mathbf{E}(\xi)$,
2. $\mathbf{E}(c_1 \xi_1 + c_2 \xi_2 \mid \mathscr{F}) = c_1 \mathbf{E}(\xi_1 \mid \mathscr{F}) + c_2 \mathbf{E}(\xi_2 \mid \mathscr{F})$ with probability 1,
3. $\mathbf{E}(\xi g(\eta) \mid \eta) = g(\eta) \mathbf{E}(\xi \mid \eta)$ with probability 1 where $g(x)$ is a Borel-measurable function or in other words,

3a. $\mathbf{E}(\xi \eta \mid \mathscr{F}) = \eta \mathbf{E}(\xi \mid \mathscr{F})$ with probability 1 if η is measurable with respect to $\mathscr{F}$,

4. $\mathbf{E}(\xi \mid \eta) = \mathbf{E}(\xi)$ with probability 1 if ξ and η are independent.

§ 0.3. Stochastic processes

We now define those stochastic processes which are treated in this book.

1. *Markov processes*. The sequence $\xi_1, \xi_2, \ldots$ of random variables is called Markov process if

$$\mathbf{P}(\xi_{n+1} < x \mid \xi_1, \xi_2, \ldots, \xi_n) = \mathbf{P}(\xi_{n+1} < x \mid \xi_n) \quad (n = 1, 2, \ldots)$$

for all real x with probability 1. If the conditional probability

$$\mathbf{P}(\xi_{n+1} < x \mid \xi_n)$$

does not depend on n, the Markov process will be called homogeneous.

In particular if the possible values of ξ_n $(n = 1, 2, \ldots)$ are the numbers $a_1, a_2, \ldots, a_k$, i.e.

$$\sum_{j=1}^{k} \mathbf{P}(\xi_n = a_j) = 1 \quad (n = 1, 2, \ldots)$$

then the conditional probabilities

$$\mathbf{P}(\xi_{n+1} = a_j \mid \xi_n = a_i) = p_{ij}^{(n)}$$

[1] The existence of all expectations below are assumed.

are called the *transition probabilities*. The matrix

$$\Pi_n = \begin{pmatrix} p_{11}^{(n)}, p_{12}^{(n)}, \ldots, p_{1k}^{(n)} \\ p_{21}^{(n)}, p_{22}^{(n)}, \ldots, p_{2k}^{(n)} \\ \ldots\ldots\ldots\ldots \\ \ldots\ldots\ldots\ldots \\ \ldots\ldots\ldots\ldots \\ p_{k1}^{(n)}, p_{k2}^{(n)}, \ldots, p_{kk}^{(n)} \end{pmatrix}$$

is called the *transition probability matrix*. A transition probability matrix is a *stochastic matrix*; i.e. $p_{ij}^{(n)} \geqq 0$ and

$$\sum_{j=1}^{k} p_{ij}^{(n)} = 1 \quad (i = 1, \ 2, \ldots, k)\,.$$

A stochastic matrix $\Pi = (p_{ij})_{i,j=1}^{k}$ is called *doubly stochastic* if $\sum_{i=1}^{k} p_{ij} = 1$ $(j = 1, \ 2, \ldots, k)$.

The conditional probability $\mathbf{P}(\xi_{n+m} = a_j \mid \xi_n = a_i)$ can be obtained as the j-th element of the i-th row of the matrix $\Pi_n \Pi_{n+1} \ldots \Pi_{n+m-1}$.

The distribution function $F_1(x) = \mathbf{P}(\xi_1 < x)$ of ξ_1 is called the *initial distribution*. One then has

$$F_2(x) = \mathbf{P}(\xi_2 < x) = \int_{-\infty}^{+\infty} \mathbf{P}(\xi_2 < x \mid \xi_1 = y)\, dF_1(y)$$

and similarly,

$$F_n(x) = \mathbf{P}(\xi_n < x) = \int_{-\infty}^{+\infty} \mathbf{P}(\xi_n < x \mid \xi_{n-1} = y)\, dF_{n-1}(y) =$$

$$= \int_{-\infty}^{+\infty} \mathbf{P}(\xi_n < x \mid \xi_1 = y)\, dF_1(y).$$

If $F_1(x) = F_2(x) = \ldots$ then $F_1(x)$ is called a *stationary initial distribution function.*

In the homogeneous case the existence of a stationary initial distribution is proved under the so-called Doeblin condition.

Doeblin's condition. There exist a finite-valued measure λ defined on the σ-algebra $\mathcal{B}(\xi_1, \xi_2, \ldots)$ (the smallest σ-algebra with respect to which the elements $\xi_1, \xi_2, \ldots$ of the Markov process are measurable) with $\lambda(\Omega) > 0$, an integer $\nu \geqq 1$ and a positive ε such that

$$\mathbf{P}(\xi_\nu \in A \mid \xi_1 = x) \leqq 1 - \varepsilon \ \text{ if } \ \lambda(A) \leqq \varepsilon$$

for any real x.

If $\xi_1, \xi_2, \ldots$ is a Markov process with possible values $a_1, a_2, \ldots, a_k$ then a probability distribution $q_1, q_2, \ldots, q_k$ $\left(q_k \geqq 0; \sum_{k=1}^{n} q_k = 1\right)$ is a *stationary initial distribution* if

$$\sum_{j=1}^{k} p_{ij}^{(n)} q_i = q_j \quad (j = 1, 2, \ldots, k; n = 1, 2, \ldots)$$

2. *Stationary processes.* The sequence $\xi_1, \xi_2, \ldots$ is called *a stationary process in the strong sense* if the distribution function

$$\mathbf{P}(\xi_{i_1+k} < x_1, \xi_{i_2+k} < x_2, \ldots, \xi_{i_n+k} < x_n) =$$
$$= F_{i_1, i_2, \ldots, i_n}(x_1, x_2, \ldots, x_n). \quad (i_1 < i_2 < \ldots < i_n; n = 1, 2, \ldots)$$

does not depend on k.

The sequence $\xi_1, \xi_2, \ldots$ of square-integrable random variables is called a *stationary process in the weak sense* if

$$\mathbf{E}(\xi_i) = 0, \quad \mathbf{E}(\xi_i^2) = 1 \quad (i = 1, 2, \ldots)$$

and

$$\mathbf{E}(\xi_i \xi_j) = R(|j - i|)$$

depends only on $|j - i|$. The function $R(\cdot)$ is called the *covariance function* of the process.

Obviously, any strongly stationary process $\xi_1, \xi_2, \ldots$ is weakly stationary if ξ_1 is square-integrable with $\mathbf{E}(\xi_1) = 0$, $\mathbf{E}(\xi_1^2) = 1$ (in this case $\xi_2, \xi_3, \ldots$ are also square-integrable).

3. *Symmetrically dependent random variables.* The random variables $\xi_1, \xi_2, \ldots$ are called symmetrically dependent, or equivalent or exchangable, if the distribution function

$$F_n(x_1, x_2, \ldots, x_n) = \mathbf{P}(\xi_{i_1} < x_1, \xi_{i_2} < x_2, \ldots, \xi_{i_n} < x_n)$$

depends only on n and $x_1, x_2, \ldots, x_n$ and it does not depend on the sequence of different integers $i_1, i_2, \ldots, i_n$.

Clearly, a sequence of symmetrically dependent random variables is a stationary process in the strong sense.

The events $A_1, A_2, \ldots$ are called symmetrically dependent if their indicator functions $\alpha_1, \alpha_2, \ldots$ are symmetrically dependent random variables or, in other words, if the probability

$$\mathbf{P}(A_{i_1} A_{i_2} \ldots A_{i_n}) = p_n \qquad (i_1 < i_2 < \ldots < i_n)$$

depends only on n and does not depend on the indices $i_1, i_2, \ldots, i_n$. A generalization of this concept is the following:

The events $A_1, A_2, \ldots$ are called *quasi-independent* if the value of the ratio

$$\frac{\mathbf{P}(A_{i_1} A_{i_2} \ldots A_{i_k})}{\mathbf{P}(A_{i_1}) \mathbf{P}(A_{i_2}) \ldots P(A_{i_k})} = \omega_k \quad (i_1 < i_2 < \ldots < i_k; k = 1, 2, \ldots)$$

depends only on k and does not depend on the indices $i_1, i_2, \ldots, i_k$.

It is clear that any sequence of symmetrically dependent events and any sequence of independent events is a sequence of quasi-independent events. In the first case $\omega_k = \frac{p_k}{p_1^k}$, in the latter case $\omega_k = 1$ $(k = 1, 2, \ldots)$.

§ 0.4. Hilbert and Banach spaces

The notion of Banach space is based on the notion of the vector space.

DEFINITION. A (real) *vector space* V is a set of abstract elements $x, y, z, \ldots$ called vectors. There exists a so-called zero vector denoted by 0. To each vector x, there corresponds a vector $-x$. The following axioms are assumed to hold:

1. For each pair of vectors x, y, there exists a vector called the sum of x and y, denoted by $x + y$. This addition obeys the following rules:

(a) $x + y = y + x$
(b) $x + (y + z) = (x + y) + z$
(c) $x + 0 = x$
(d) $x + (-x) = 0$

2. For each real number λ and each vector x, there exists a vector λx. This multiplication obeys the following rules:

(a) $\lambda(x + y) = \lambda x + \lambda y$
(b) $(\lambda + \mu) x = \lambda x + \mu x$
(c) $(\lambda\mu)x = \lambda(\mu x)$
(d) $1x = x$.

Now the Banach and the Hilbert space can be defined as follows:

DEFINITION. A (real) *Banach space* B is a vector space with the following further restrictions:

1. For each vector x there exists a real number called the norm of x, denoted by $\| x \|$, such that:

(*a*) $\| x \| \geq 0$ and $\| x \| = 0$ if and only if $x = 0$
(*b*) $\| x + y \| \leq \| x \| + \| y \|$
(*c*) $\| \lambda x \| = | \lambda | \| x \|$

2. If $x_1, x_2, \ldots$ is a sequence of elements of B for which $\| x_m - x_n \| \to 0$ as $m, n \to \infty$ then there exists a vector $x \in B$ (called the strong limit of $\{x_n\}$) for which $\| x_n - x \| \to 0$

3. For any $\varepsilon > 0$ there exists a sequence $x_1, x_2, \ldots$ of elements of B such that for any $y \in B$ there is a corresponding x_n for which $\| y - x_n \| \leq \varepsilon$. Such a sequence $x_1, x_2, \ldots$ is called a basis.

DEFINITION. A (real) *Hilbert space* H is a Banach space with the following further restrictions:

1. For each pair of vectors x, y there exists a real number called the *scalar (inner) product* of x and y, denoted by (x, y) obeying the following axioms

(a) $(x, y) = (y, x)$
(b) $(x + y, z) = (x, z) + (y, z)$
(c) $(\lambda x, y) = \lambda(x, y)$
(d) $\sqrt{(x, x)} = \| x \|$

x and y are called *orthogonal* if $(x, y) = 0$.

In the case of Hilbert spaces the third condition in the definition of the Banach spaces can be replaced by the following:

2. There exists a sequence (finite or countably infinite) $x_1, x_2, \ldots$ of elements of H such that if $(y, x_n) = 0$ $(n = 1, 2, \ldots)$ then $y = 0$. This sequence $x_1, x_2, \ldots$ is called a *basis*.[1] The basis $x_1, x_2, \ldots$ is called an *orthonormal basis* if

$$(x_i, x_j) = \begin{cases} 0 \text{ whenever } i \neq j \\ 1 \text{ whenever } i = j. \end{cases}$$

One of the simplest examples of a Hilbert space is the space of the square integrable functions defined in a measure space, $\{X, \mathscr{S}, \mu\}$, where the scalar product of two square integrable functions f, g is defined by

$$(f, g) = \int_X fg \, d\mu.$$

This space will be denoted by $L^2 = L^2 (X, \mu)$. If $\{f_n\} \in L^2$ converges to $f \in L^2$ in the norm of L^2, i.e. $\int (f_n - f)^2 \, d\mu \to 0$, then we say that f_n *converges to f in mean*. In symbols $f_n \xrightarrow{m} f$.

If x and y denote elements of the Hilbert space then the following theorems hold:

THEOREM 0.4.1 (CAUCHY INEQUALITY).

$$|(x, y)| \leq \| x \| \cdot \| y \|.$$

THEOREM 0.4.2.

$$\| x + y \| \leq \| x \| + \| y \|.$$

In particular if $(x, y) = 0$, *then*

$$\| x + y \|^2 = \| x \|^2 + \| y \|^2.$$

THEOREM 0.4.3. *If $x_1, x_2, \ldots$ is a basis then for any $y \in H$ there exists a sequence $c_1, c_2, \ldots$ of real numbers for which*

$$y = c_1 x_1 + c_2 x_2 + \ldots \quad (0.4.1)$$

[1] This concept and the concept of the basis of a Banach space are different.

More exactly

$$\| y - (c_1 x_1 + c_2 x_2 + \ldots + c_n x_n) \| \to 0 \quad (n \to \infty).$$

If $x_1, x_2, \ldots$ is an orthonormal basis then the series (0.4.1) is called the *Fourier expansion* of y.

THEOREM 0.4.4. *In a Hilbert space there exists an orthonormal basis, i.e. a basis $x_1, x_2, \ldots$ such that $(x_i, x_j) = 0$ (if $i \neq j$) and $\| x_i \| = 1$ ($i = 1, 2, \ldots$). If $x_1, x_2, \ldots$ is an orthonormal basis, then the coefficient of* (0.4.1) *can be obtained by $c_n = (y, x_n)$.*

THEOREM 0.4.5 (BESSEL INEQUALITY). *Let $x_1, x_2, \ldots$ be an orthonormal sequence and let*

$$c_n = (y, x_n)$$

where y is an arbitrary element of the Hilbert space; then

$$\sum_{k=1}^{\infty} c_k^2 \leq \| y \|^2 .$$

In particular if the sequence $x_1, x_2, \ldots$ is a basis then

$$\sum_{k=1}^{\infty} c_k^2 = \| y \|^2.$$

DEFINITION. A subset H_1 of the Hilbert space H is called *subspace* if H_1 is also a Hilbert space, i.e. if $z_1 \in H_1$ and $z_2 \in H_1$ implies $\lambda_1 z_1 + \lambda_2 z_2 \in H_1$ (λ_1, λ_2 are real numbers) and if $x_n \in H_1$ ($n = 1, 2, \ldots$) and $\| x_n - x \| \to 0$ (where $x \in H$) then $x \in H_1$.

DEFINITION. If H_1 is a subspace of H and H_2 is the set of those elements of H which are orthogonal to every element of H_1 (i.e. $x \in H_2$ if $(x, y) = 0$ for each $y \in H_1$) then H_2 is a subspace of H, called the *orthogonal complement* of H_1.

DEFINITION. A sequence $x_1, x_2, \ldots,$ of the elements of H, is said to converge weakly to $y \in H$ if $(x_n, z) \to (y, z)$ for each $z \in H$. In symbols $x_n \rightharpoonup y$.

THEOREM 0.4.6. *If H_1 is a subspace of H and H_2 is the orthogonal complement of H_1 then to every $h \in H$ there corresponds a uniquely determined $h_1 \in H_1$ and a uniquely determined $h_2 \in H_2$ such that*

$$h = h_1 + h_2 .$$

THEOREM 0.4.7. *If $x_1, x_2, \ldots$ is a sequence of the elements of H such that*

$$\| x_n \| \leq K$$

(where K is a positive constant) then there exists a subsequence $x_{n_1}, x_{n_2}, \ldots$ of the sequence $x_1, x_2, \ldots$ which converges weakly to a $y \in H$. In particular, if $x_1, x_2, \ldots$ is an orthonormal sequence then $x_n \rightharpoonup 0$.

THEOREM 0.4.8 (RÉNYI [2], SCHMEIDLER [1]). *If $x_1, x_2, \ldots$ is a sequence of the elements of H such that*

$$\| x_n \| \leq K$$

and

$$\lim_{n\to\infty} (x_n, x_k) = \alpha_k \qquad (k = 1, 2, \ldots)$$

(where K is a positive constant and α_k is a sequence of real numbers) then x_n converges weakly to an element y of H, i.e.

$$(x_n, z) \to (y, z)$$

for each $z \in H$.

In particular, if $\alpha_k = 0$ $(k = 1, 2, \ldots)$ then $y = 0$.

DEFINITION. A mapping A of H into itself is called a *bounded linear operator* if

$$A(\lambda x + \mu y) = \lambda A x + \mu A y$$

(for any real λ and μ and for any $x, y \in H$) and

$$\| A x \| \leq K \|x\| \tag{0.4.2}$$

(for $x \in H$) where K is a positive constant. The smallest K for which (0.4.2) holds is called the norm of A, and is denoted by $\| A \|$.

DEFINITION. A bounded linear operator U is called an *isometry* if $\| Ux \| = \| x \|$ for any $x \in H$. An isometry U is called *a unitary operator* if there exists a bounded linear operator U^{-1} such that

$$U^{-1}Ux = U U^{-1}x = x \quad \text{for each } x \in H.$$

§ 0.5. Ergodic theory

Let $\{X, \mathscr{S}, \mu\}$ be a measure space and let T be a transformation defined on X, i.e. T is a mapping from X into X. We assume that

1° T is measurable, i.e. $T^{-1}A \in \mathscr{S}$ whenever $A \in \mathscr{S}$,

2° T is measure preserving, i.e. $\mu(T^{-1}A) = \mu(A)$ whenever $A \in \mathscr{S}$.

The fundamental problem of ergodic theory is to characterize the "wandering" of a point $x \in X$ under the transformation T. More precisely, the properties of the sequence $x, Tx, T^2x, \ldots$ are investigated.

In connection with this question we have the following two theorems.

THEOREM 0.5.1 (INDIVIDUAL ERGODIC THEOREM OF BIRKHOFF). *If T is a measurable and measure preserving transformation on a measure space $\{X, \mathscr{S}, \mu\}$ and if $f(x)$ is an integrable function then*

$$\frac{1}{n} \sum_{k=0}^{n-1} f(T^k x)$$

converges almost everywhere to an integrable function $f^*(x)$ for which $f^*(Tx) = f^*(x)$. In particular, if $\mu(X) < \infty$ then $\int_X f(x)d\mu = \int_X f^*(x)d\mu$.

THEOREM 0.5.2 (STATISTICAL ERGODIC THEOREM OF NEUMANN). *If T is a measurable and measure preserving transformation on a measure space $\{X, \mathscr{S}, \mu\}$ and if $f(x) \in L^2_{(X,\mu)}$ then*

$$\frac{1}{n} \sum_{k=0}^{n-1} f(T^k x)$$

converges in mean to a square integrable function $f^*(x)$ for which $f^*(Tx) = f^*(x)$.

We note that a measurable and measure preserving transformation T determines an isometry U on the space $L^2_{(X,\mu)}$ by

$$U f(x) = f(Tx) .$$

Making use of this fact we can formulate the following generalization of Theorem 0.5.2.

THEOREM 0.5.3 (STATISTICAL ERGODIC THEOREM OF F. RIESZ). *If U is an isometry on a Hilbert space H then*

$$\frac{1}{n} \sum_{j=0}^{n-1} U^j f$$

converges, in the norm of H, to an element f^* of H for which $Uf^* = f^*$.

In the applications of these ergodic theorems the most difficult problem is to say anything about the limit function $f^*(x)$. Under a condition corresponding to the transformation T, it can be stated that $f^*(x)$ is constant almost everywhere. This condition is the following:

DEFINITION. The transformation T is called an *ergodic transformation* if $T^{-1}A = A (A \in \mathscr{S})$ implies that $\mu(A) = 0$ or $\mu(\bar{A}) = 0$. A measurable set A is called an *invariant set* (with respect to T) if $T^{-1}A = A$. Hence a transformation is an ergodic transformation if all invariant sets or their complements are of measure 0.

The fact that $f^*(x)$ is invariant with respect to T (i.e. $f^*(Tx) = f^*(x)$) easily implies that

if $f(x)$ is an integrable (resp. square integrable) function and T is an ergodic measurable and measure preserving transformation then

$$\frac{f(x) + f(Tx) + \ldots + f(T^n x)}{n+1}$$

tends to a constant almost everywhere (resp. in mean).

When the space X is of finite measure, a condition stronger than ergodicity is sometimes used.

DEFINITION. If $\mu(X) = 1$ then the measurable and measure preserving transformation T is called a *mixing transformation* if

$$\mu(T^{-n} A . B) \to \mu(A)\, \mu(B)$$

for any $A \in \mathscr{S}, B \in \mathscr{S}$.

It is easy to see that all mixing transformations are ergodic.

Many generalizations of these theorems are known. Among them the so-called random ergodic theorems are probably closest to the laws of large numbers (see e.g. KAKUTANI [1], RÉVÉSZ [1]). We will not give any details here since in this book these theorems will not be applied.

To see the connection between the above mentioned two theorems and the theory of stochastic processes we mention the following facts.

If $\{\Omega, \mathscr{S}, \mathbf{P}\}$ is a probability space, T a measurable and measure preserving transformation (on Ω) and $\xi(\omega)$ a random variable defined on Ω, then $\xi(\omega)$, $\xi(T\omega)$, $\xi(T^2\omega)$, ... is a stationary sequence in the strong sense. Similarly, if U is an isometry defined on $L^2 = L_{(\Omega, \mathbf{P})}$ and $\xi \in L^2$ with $\mathbf{E}(\xi) = 0$, $\mathbf{E}(\xi^2) = 1$ then $\xi, U\xi, U^2\xi, \ldots$ is a stationary sequence in the weak sense. The converse question is more interesting: can a sequence stationary in the strong (resp. weak) sense, be represented in the form $\xi(\omega)$, $\xi(T\omega)$, ... (resp. $\xi, U\xi, \ldots$)?

We can give the following answer: if $\xi_1, \xi_2, \ldots$ is a stationary sequence in the strong sense and is defined on a probability space $\{\Omega, \mathscr{S}, \mathbf{P}\}$ then we can define a probability space $\{\tilde{\Omega}, \tilde{\mathscr{S}}, \tilde{\mathbf{P}}\}$ a measurable and measure preserving transformation T and a random variable $\tilde{\xi}(\tilde{\omega})$ such that

$$\mathbf{P}(\xi_1 < x_1, \xi_2 < x_2, \ldots, \xi_n < x_n) = \tilde{\mathbf{P}}(\tilde{\xi}_1 < x_1, \tilde{\xi}_2 < x_2, \ldots, \tilde{\xi}_n < x_n)$$
$$(n = 1, 2, \ldots)$$

for any $x_1, x_2, \ldots, x_n$ where $\tilde{\xi}_n = \tilde{\xi}_n(\tilde{\omega}) = \tilde{\xi}(T^{n-1}\tilde{\omega})$.

Similarly if $\xi_1, \xi_2, \ldots$ is a stationary sequence in the weak sense defined on a probability space $\{\Omega, \mathscr{S}, \mathbf{P}\}$ then there exists an isometry U defined on $L^2_{(\Omega, \mathbf{P})}$ such that $U^n \xi_1 = \xi_{n+1}$ almost everywhere.

§ 0.6. Orthogonal series

DEFINITION. The sequence $\xi_1, \xi_2, \ldots$ of random variables is called an orthonormal system if

$$\mathbf{E}(\xi_i \xi_j) = 0 \quad (i \neq j)$$
$$\mathbf{E}(\xi_i^2) = 1 \quad (i = 1, 2, \ldots).$$

DEFINITION. The orthonormal system $\xi_1, \xi_2, \ldots$ is called complete if the relations $\mathbf{E}(\xi_i \eta) = 0$ $(i = 1, 2, \ldots)$ imply $\mathbf{P}(\eta = 0) = 1$, for any square integrable random variable η.

DEFINITION. The Fourier series of a square integrable random variable η (with respect to the orthonormal system $\xi_1, \xi_2, \ldots$) is the series $\sum_{k=1}^{\infty} c_k \xi_k$ where $c_k = \mathbf{E}(\xi_k \eta)$.

The Bessel inequality implies that $\sum_{k=1}^{\infty} c_k^2 \leqq \mathbf{E}(\eta^2)$.

Therefore the fundamental problem of the theory of orthogonal series is to find conditions implying the almost everywhere convergence of a series $\sum_{k=1}^{\infty} c_k \xi_k$ where $\xi_1, \xi_2, \ldots$ is an orthonormal system and $\sum_{k=1}^{\infty} c_k^2 < \infty$.

Strong enough results can be obtained in the case of an equinormed strongly multiplicative system (abbr.: ESMS) (ALEXITS [1]).

DEFINITION. The sequence $\xi_1, \xi_2, \ldots$ of random variables is called a *multiplicative system* if

$$\mathbf{E}(\xi_{i_1} \xi_{i_2} \ldots \xi_{i_k}) = 0 \quad (i_1 < i_2 < \ldots < i_k\,; k = 1, 2, \ldots).$$

DEFINITION. The sequence $\xi_1, \xi_2, \ldots$ of random variables is called a *strongly multiplicative system* if the system $\{\xi_{i_1} \xi_{i_1} \cdot\ \cdot \xi_{i_k}\}$ is an orthogonal system, i.e. if

$$\mathbf{E}(\xi_{i_1}^{r_1} \xi_{i_2}^{r_2} \ldots \xi_{i_k}^{r_k}) = 0 \quad (i_1 < i_2 < \ldots < i_k\,; k = 1,2, \ldots)$$

where $r_1, r_2, \ldots, r_k$ can be equal to 1 or 2 but at least one element of the sequence $r_1, r_2, \ldots, r_k$ equal to 1.

DEFINITION. The sequence $\xi_1, \xi_2, \ldots$ of random variables is called an *equinormed strongly multiplicative system* (ESMS) if

$$\mathbf{E}(\xi_i) = 0\,, \qquad \mathbf{E}(\xi_i^2) = 1 \qquad (i = 1, 2, \ldots) \tag{0.6.1}$$

$$\mathbf{E}(\xi_{i_1}^{r_1} \xi_{i_2}^{r_2} \ldots \xi_{i_k}^{r_k}) = \mathbf{E}(\xi_{i_1}^{r_1})\, \mathbf{E}(\xi_{i_2}^{r_2}) \ldots \mathbf{E}(\xi_{i_k}^{r_k}) \qquad (k = 1, 2, \ldots) \tag{0.6.2}$$

where $r_1, r_2, \ldots, r_k$ can be equal to 1 or 2.

Clearly, a sequence $\zeta_1, \zeta_2, \ldots$ of independent random variables, with $\mathbf{E}(\zeta_i) = 0$, $\mathbf{E}(\zeta_i^2) = 1$, is an ESMS. Another example is the sequence $\{\sqrt{2} \sin n_k x\}$ on the interval $[0, 2\pi]$ if $n_{k+1}/n_k \geqq 3$ and if the probability measure $\mathbf{P}$ on the Borel measurable subsets of the interval $[0, 2\pi]$ is defined by $\mathbf{P}(A) = \dfrac{\lambda(A)}{2\pi}$, where λ is the ordinary Lebesgue measure.

A common generalization of the ESMS and the symmetrically dependent random variables follows.

DEFINITION. The random variables $\xi_1, \xi_2, \ldots$ are called *quasi-multiplicative system* if the value of the expectation

$$\mathbf{E}(\xi_{i_1}^{t_1} \xi_{i_2}^{t_2} \ldots \xi_{i_n}^{t_n}) \qquad (i_1 < i_2 < \ldots < i_n\,;\ n = 1,2, \ldots)$$

(where t_l $(l = 1, 2, \ldots, n)$ can be equal to 1 or 2) depends only on the number of 1' s in the sequence $t_1, t_2, \ldots, t_n$, i.e.

$$\mathbf{E}(\xi_{i_1}^{t_1} \xi_{i_2}^{t_2} \ldots \xi_{i_n}^{t_n}) = \alpha_{jk}^{(n)} \qquad (j + k = n) \tag{0.6.3}$$

where j (resp. k) is the number of 1's (resp. 2's) in the sequence $t_1, t_2, \ldots, t_n$.

We mention some examples of orthonormal systems.

Example 1. *(Rademacher functions).* The n-th Rademacher function $r_n(x)$, by definition, is equal to $+1$ (resp. -1), if the n-th digit of the dyadic expansion of x $(0 \leq x \leq 1)$ is 0 (resp. 1). It is easy to see that these functions are independent random variables with mean value 0 and variance 1.

An equivalent definition is $r_n(x) = \operatorname{sgn}(\sin 2^n \pi x)$ where $\operatorname{sgn} \alpha = 1$ if $\alpha > 0$, $\operatorname{sgn} \alpha = -1$ if $\alpha < 0$ and $\operatorname{sgn} \alpha = 0$ if $\alpha = 0$.

Example 2 *(Walsh functions).* The definition of the n-th Walsh function $w_n(x)$ is the following: if the binary expansion of the integer n is

$$n = \sum_{k=0}^{p} \varepsilon_k 2^k$$

then

$$w_n(x) = r_1^{\varepsilon_0}(x) r_2^{\varepsilon_1}(x) \ldots r_{p+1}^{\varepsilon_p}(x) \qquad (n = 0, 1, 2, \ldots).$$

Walsh [1] has proved that the sequence $\{w_n(x)\}$ is a complete orthonormal system. (See also Rényi [3].)

Example 3. The system

$$\frac{1}{\sqrt{2\pi}}, \frac{1}{\sqrt{\pi}} \sin x, \frac{1}{\sqrt{\pi}} \cos x, \frac{1}{\sqrt{2\pi}} \sin 2x, \frac{1}{\sqrt{2\pi}} \cos 2x, \ldots$$

is a complete orthonormal system in the interval $[0, 2\pi]$. This system is called the *trigonometric system.*

CHAPTER 1

DEFINITIONS AND GENERALITIES

§ 1.1. The different kinds of the laws of large numbers

In the introduction we have already mentioned that by making use of different modes of convergence, different types of the laws of large numbers can be obtained.

Many different concepts of convergence are used in probability theory. Here only the definitions of those kinds of convergence which are used in this book are given and the relations between them are investigated. Let $\xi_1, \xi_2, \ldots$ be a sequence of random variables. We say that

1. ξ_n converges to ξ with probability 1 (or almost everywhere, or almost surely) if $\xi_n(\omega) \to \xi(\omega)$ except on a set of measure 0. For this kind of convergence the symbol $\xi_n \to \xi$ is used.

2. ξ_n converges to ξ in probability (or in measure) if for all $\varepsilon > 0$

$$\lim_{n\to\infty} \mathbf{P}(|\xi_n - \xi| \geqq \varepsilon) = 0 .$$

We write $\xi_n \Rightarrow \xi$.

3. ξ_n converges to ξ in mean if ξ and $\xi_1, \xi_2, \ldots$ are square integrable and if

$$\lim_{n\to\infty} \mathbf{E}[(\xi_n - \xi)^2] = 0 .$$

We write $\xi_n \xrightarrow{m} \xi$.

4. ξ_n converges to ξ weakly if ξ and $\xi_1, \xi_2, \ldots$ are square integrable and if

$$\lim_{n\to\infty} \mathbf{E}(\xi_n \eta) = \mathbf{E}(\xi\eta)$$

for any square integrable η. We write $\xi_n \rightharpoonup \xi$.

We now give the definitions of the different kinds of laws of large numbers.

Let $\boldsymbol{\xi} = (\xi_1, \xi_2, \ldots)$ be a sequence of random variables and

$$\zeta_n = \frac{\eta_n}{n} = \frac{\xi_1 + \xi_2 + \ldots + \xi_n}{n} .$$

We say that ξ (with the sequence $\{a_n\}$ of real numbers and the random variable η) obeys

1. the weak law of large numbers if

$$\zeta_n - a_n \Rightarrow \eta$$

2. the strong law of large numbers if

$$\zeta_n - a_n \rightarrow \eta$$

3. the mean law of large numbers if

$$\zeta_n - a_n \xrightarrow{m} \eta.$$

The random variable η is called the (weak, strong, resp. mean) limit of $\zeta_n - a_n$.

Without the loss of generality we may assume that the median of η is 0. We will sometimes use this restriction.

To study the relations between these concepts of convergence two classical inequalities are given:

THEOREM 1.1.1 (MARKOV INEQUALITY). *If ξ is a non-negative integrable random variable then*

$$\mathbf{P}(\xi > \varepsilon) \leqq \frac{\mathbf{E}(\xi)}{\varepsilon} \tag{1.1.1}$$

for any $\varepsilon > 0$.

PROOF. We have

$$\mathbf{E}(\xi) = \int_{\Omega} \xi \, d\mathbf{P} \geqq \int_{\{\omega : \xi > \varepsilon\}} \xi \, d\mathbf{P} \geqq \int_{\{\omega : \xi > \varepsilon\}} \varepsilon \, d\mathbf{P} = \varepsilon \, \mathbf{P}(\xi > \varepsilon)$$

what implies (1.1.1).

THEOREM 1.1.2 (CHEBYSHEV INEQUALITY). *If η is a square integrable random variable then*

$$\mathbf{P}(|\eta - \mathbf{E}(\eta)| > \delta) \leqq \frac{\mathbf{D}^2(\eta)}{\delta^2} \tag{1.1.2}$$

for any $\delta > 0$.

PROOF. Replacing in (1.1.1) the random variable ξ by $(\eta - \mathbf{E}(\eta))^2$ and ε by δ^2 the inequality (1.1.2) will be obtained.

By the CHEBYSHEV inequality if $\xi_n \xrightarrow{m} \xi$ then $\xi_n \Rightarrow \xi$. By the Cauchy inequality if $\xi_n \xrightarrow{m} \xi$ then $\xi_n \rightarrow \xi$.

By Theorem 0.1.6 if ξ_n converges to ξ with probability 1 then it also converges in probability.

The connection between the different kinds of convergence is shown by the following diagram:

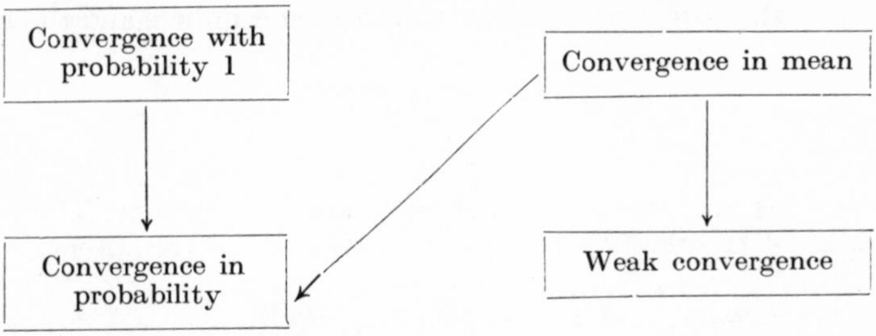

The next theorem gives another connection between the convergence with probability 1 and the convergence in probability.

THEOREM 1.1.3. *The following two conditions are equivalent*

$$\xi_n \to \xi \tag{1.1.3}$$

$$\psi_N = \sup_{n \geqq N} |\xi_n - \xi| \Rightarrow 0 \text{ whenewer } N \to \infty. \tag{1.1.4}$$

PROOF. Clearly (1.1.3) implies that $\psi_N \to 0$, so (1.1.4) holds. The converse statement follows from the fact that ψ_N is monotonically decreasing in N.

The above mentioned facts show the exact connections among the different kinds of the laws of large numbers. Beside this, it is worth while to take a look at the statistical meaning of these theorems, because in general the statisticians do not pay enough attention to the differences of the statements of these laws. We investigate the example of coin tossing. Toss a coin n times independently and define the random variables ξ_i $(i = 1, 2, \ldots, n)$ by

$$\xi_i = \begin{cases} 1 & \text{if the result of the } i\text{-th tossing is head} \\ 0 & \text{if the result of the } i\text{-th tossing is tail.} \end{cases}$$

In this case

$$\zeta_n = \frac{\xi_1 + \xi_2 + \ldots + \xi_n}{n}$$

is the relative frequency of the heads after the n-th tossing. In a concrete sequence of coin tossings the relative frequencies can be given by a diagram. After n tossings, 2^n different curves of relative frequencies, can be obtained depending on the results of tossings. A theorem stating that $\zeta_n \Rightarrow {}^1/_2$ essentially states that almost the whole of most of these 2^n curves are near to ${}^1/_2$ if n is large enough but it can happen that all curves strongly deviate from ${}^1/_2$, infinitely many times, while n tending to infinity.

By Theorem 1.1.3, $\zeta_n \to {}^1/_2$ essentially states that for large enough n these relative frequency curves (except $o(2^n)$) are near to ${}^1/_2$ and do not leave a neighbourhood of ${}^1/_2$.

To make this difference more clear we mention that by Theorem 2.4.2

$$\tau_n^* = \frac{\xi_1+\xi_2+\ldots+\xi_n}{\sqrt{n}\,\omega(n)} \Rightarrow 0$$

where $\omega(n)$ is an increasing function tending to infinity. This means that most of the relative frequency curves are in the interval

$$\left(\frac{1}{2}-\frac{\omega(n)}{\sqrt{n}},\ \frac{1}{2}+\frac{\omega(n)}{\sqrt{n}}\right)$$

if n is large enough. One cannot state that these curves do not leave this interval, for in fact the law of the iterated logarithm (see Theorem 2.8.2) states that almost all relative frequency curves infinitely many times nearly reach the values

$$\frac{1}{2}-\sqrt{\frac{2\log\log n}{n}} \quad\text{and}\quad \frac{1}{2}+\sqrt{\frac{2\log\log n}{n}}$$

but do not leave the interval

$$\left(\frac{1}{2}-\sqrt{\frac{2\log\log n}{n}},\ +\frac{1}{2}\sqrt{\frac{2\log\log n}{n}}\right).$$

§ 1.2. General theorems

The theorems of this paragraph give some general methods which will be applied many times throughout this book.

THEOREM 1.2.1. *Let* $\xi_1, \xi_2, \ldots$ *and* $\eta_1, \eta_2, \ldots$ *be two sequences of random variables defined on the same or different probability spaces. Suppose that the corresponding n-dimensional* $(n = 1, 2, \ldots)$ *distribution functions are equal to each other, i.e.*

$$\mathbf{P}(\xi_{i_1} < x_1, \xi_{i_2} < x_2, \ldots, \xi_{i_n} < x_n) =$$
$$= \mathbf{P}(\eta_{i_1} < x_1, \eta_{i_2} < x_2, \ldots, \eta_{i_n} < x_n) \quad (i_1 < i_2 < \ldots < i_n).$$

Further let ξ^* *and* η^* *be the same Baire functions of* $\xi_1, \xi_2, \ldots$ and $\eta_1, \eta_2, \ldots,$ *resp. i.e.*

$$\xi^* = g(\xi_1, \xi_2, \ldots)$$

$$\eta^* = g(\eta_1, \eta_2, \ldots).$$

Then

$$\mathbf{P}(\xi^* < x) = \mathbf{P}(\eta^* < x)$$

for any real x.

PROOF. This theorem immediately follows from Theorem 0.1.4.

COROLLARY. *Let* $\boldsymbol{\xi} = (\xi_1, \xi_2, \ldots)$ *and* $\boldsymbol{\eta} = (\eta_1, \eta_2, \ldots)$ *be two sequences of random variables with*

$$\mathbf{P}(\xi_{i_1} < x_1, \xi_{i_2} < x_2, \ldots, \xi_{i_n} < x_n) =$$
$$= \mathbf{P}(\eta_{i_1} < x_1, \eta_{i_2} < x_2, \ldots, \eta_{i_n} < x_n) \quad (i_1 < i_2 < \ldots < i_n).$$

Then $\sum_{i=1}^{\infty} \xi_i$ *converges (with probability* 1*) if and only if* $\sum_{i=1}^{\infty} \eta_i$ *converges (with probability* 1*) and* $\boldsymbol{\xi}$ *obeys a law of large numbers if* $\boldsymbol{\eta}$ *does the same.*

The next two theorems (1.2.2 and 1.2.3) concern numerical series but their applications for random variables (1.2.2.a and 1.2.3a) are interesting from the point of view of the laws of large numbers.

THEOREM 1.2.2 (KRONECKER LEMMA). *If* $\lambda_1, \lambda_2, \ldots$ *is a monotonically increasing sequence of positive numbers tending to infinity and* $u_1, u_2, \ldots$ *is an arbitrary sequence of real numbers then the convergence of the series* $\sum_{n=1}^{\infty} \frac{u_n}{\lambda_n}$ *implies* $\frac{s_n}{\lambda_n} \to 0$ *where* $s_n = \sum_{k=1}^{n} u_k$.

PROOF. Set

$$R_n = \sum_{k=n}^{\infty} \frac{u_k}{\lambda_k}.$$

Since $R_n = o(1)$, for $n > m$ we have

$$|s_n - s_m| = \left| \sum_{k=m+1}^{n} \frac{u_k}{\lambda_k} \lambda_k \right| \leq \sum_{k=m+2}^{n} |R_k| (\lambda_k - \lambda_{k-1}) +$$
$$+ |R_{m+1}| \lambda_{m+1} + |R_{n+1}| \lambda_n = o_m(1)(\lambda_n - \lambda_m) +$$
$$+ o_m(1) \lambda_{m+1} + o_n(1) \lambda_n = o_m(1) \lambda_n$$

and since $s_m/\lambda_n = o_n(1)$ we have

$$|s_n| \leq |s_n - s_m| + |s_m| \leq o_m(1) \lambda_n + o_n(1) \lambda_n .$$

Hence our assertion is proved.

THEOREM 1.2.2a. *Let* $\boldsymbol{\xi} = (\xi_1, \xi_2, \ldots)$ *be a sequence of random variables for which the series* $\sum_{k=1}^{\infty} \frac{\xi_k}{k}$ *is convergent with probability* 1. *Then* $\boldsymbol{\xi}$ *obeys the strong law of large numbers, i.e.*

$$\frac{\xi_1 + \xi_2 + \ldots + \xi_n}{n} \to 0$$

THEOREM 1.2.3 (TOEPLITZ LEMMA). *Let*

$$\begin{array}{l} \mu_{11}, \mu_{12}, \mu_{13}, \dots \\ \mu_{21}, \mu_{22}, \mu_{23}, \dots \\ \mu_{31}, \mu_{32}, \mu_{33}, \dots \\ \dots\dots\dots\dots \\ \dots\dots\dots\dots \end{array}$$

be a double-sequence of positive numbers (weights) for which

$$\lim_{n\to\infty} \sum_{k=1}^{\infty} \mu_{nk} = 1 \qquad (n = 1, 2, \dots) \tag{1.2.1}$$

and

$$\lim_{n\to\infty} \mu_{nk} = 0 \qquad (k = 1, 2, \dots). \tag{1.2.2}$$

Further let $s_1, s_2, \dots$ *be a sequence of real numbers for which*

$$s_n \to s. \tag{1.2.3}$$

Then

$$t_n = \sum_{k=1}^{\infty} \mu_{nk}\, s_k \to s \tag{1.2.4}$$

Conversely, if (1.2.4) *holds for any sequence* s_n *(with* (1.2.3)*) then for the weights* $\{\mu_{nk}\}$ (1.2.1) *and* (1.2.2) *hold.*

PROOF. Since

$$t_n = s \sum_{k=1}^{\infty} \mu_{nk} + \sum_{k=1}^{k_0} \mu_{nk}(s_k - s) + \sum_{k=k_0+1}^{\infty} \mu_{nk}(s_k - s)$$

if k_0 is sufficiently large then by (1.2.3) the third member of the right hand side is small. After the choosing of k_0, by (1.2.2) the integer n can be chosen such that the second member of the right hand side would be small, which by (1.2.1) implies (1.2.4).

In order to prove the converse statement apply condition (1.2.4) for $(s_n - s) \to 0$ where s_n is a sequence tending to $s \neq 0$.

Since

$$t_n = s \sum_{k=1}^{\infty} \mu_{nk} + \sum_{k=1}^{\infty} \mu_{nk}(s_k - s) = s \sum_{k=1}^{\infty} \mu_{nk} + o(1)$$

we have (1.2.1).

To see (1.2.2) suppose that $\lim_{n\to\infty} \mu_{nk_0} \neq 0$ and let s_n be a sequence with $s_{k_0} = 0$ and $s_k = s \neq 0$ if $k \neq k_0$. Then

$$\lim_{n\to\infty} t_n = s \lim_{n\to\infty} \left(\sum_{k=1}^{\infty} \mu_{nk} - \mu_{nk_0} \right) = s$$

and so

$$\lim_{n\to\infty}\left(\sum_{k=1}^{\infty}\mu_{nk}-\mu_{nk_0}\right)=1.$$

By (1.2.1) this is a contradiction.

THEOREM 1.2.3a. *If* $\boldsymbol{\xi}=(\xi_1,\xi_2,\dots)$ *is a sequence of random variables then* ξ *obeys the strong law of large numbers, i.e.*

$$\zeta_n=\frac{\eta_n}{n}=\frac{\xi_1+\xi_2+\dots+\xi_n}{n}\to 0$$

if and only if

$$\frac{\xi_{2^n+1}+\xi_{2^n+2}+\dots+\xi_{2^{n+1}}}{2^n}=\frac{\eta_{2^{n+1}}-\eta_{2^n}}{2^n}\to 0\,.$$

We give the following

DEFINITION. The sequences $\{\xi_n\}$ and $\{\xi_n^*\}$ are called *equivalent in the sense of Khinchin if*

$$\sum_{k=1}^{\infty}\mathbf{P}(\xi_k\neq\xi_k^*)<\infty\,.$$

In connection with this concept we have

THEOREM 1.2.4. *Let* $\{\xi_n\}$ *and* $\{\xi_n^*\}$ *be two sequences of random variables equivalent in the sense of Khinchin. If*

$$\zeta_n=\frac{\xi_1+\xi_2+\dots+\xi_n}{n}$$

obeys the (strong or the weak) law of large numbers then

$$\zeta_n^*=\frac{\xi_1^*+\xi_2^*+\dots+\xi_n^*}{n}$$

does the same, with the same $\{a_n\}$ *and the same limit* η.

(This Theorem is false if ζ_n only obeys the mean law of large numbers.)

PROOF. Our statement follows immediately from the Borel–Cantelli lemma (Theorem 0.2.3).

THEOREM 1.2.5. *If* $\boldsymbol{\xi}$ *obeys any law of large numbers with* $\{a_n\}$ *and* η $(m(\eta)=0)$ *then*

$$m(\zeta_n)-a_n\to 0\,.$$

PROOF. It is a trivial consequence of Theorem 0.2.1.

THEOREM 1.2.6. *If* $\boldsymbol{\xi}$ *obeys the weak (resp. the strong) law of large numbers with* a_n *then*

$$\frac{\xi_n}{n}-b_n\Rightarrow 0\qquad(n\to\infty)\tag{1.2.5}$$

resp.

$$\frac{\xi_n}{n} - b_n \to 0 \qquad (n \to \infty) \tag{1.2.6}$$

where

$$b_n = a_n - a_{n-1} + \frac{a_{n-1}}{n}$$

and

$$m\left(\frac{\xi_n}{n}\right) - b_n \to 0. \tag{1.2.7}$$

PROOF of (1.2.5) and (1.2.6) is so simple that we omit it; (1.2.7) follows from Theorem 0.2.1.

CHAPTER 2

INDEPENDENT RANDOM VARIABLES

In this chapter $\boldsymbol{\xi} = (\xi_1, \xi_2, \ldots)$ denotes a sequence of independent random variables

$$\eta_n = \xi_1 + \xi_2 + \ldots + \xi_n$$

and

$$\zeta_n = \frac{\xi_1 + \xi_2 + \ldots + \xi_n}{n} = \frac{\eta_n}{n}.$$

§ 2.1. Inequalities

We first develop some inequalities. Roughly speaking the first two say that the partial sums of a finite sequence of independent random variables cannot be large unless the total sum is. The third one gives an estimation on the moments of the sum of independent random variables.

THEOREM 2.1.1 (KOLMOGOROV INEQUALITY). *Let $\xi_1, \xi_2, \ldots, \xi_n$ be a sequence of independent random variables with*

$$\mathbf{E}(\xi_i) = 0, \ \mathbf{E}(\xi_i^2) = \sigma_i^2 \ (i = 1, 2, \ldots, n)$$

then

$$\mathbf{P}\left\{\sup_{1\leq k\leq n}\left|\sum_{j=1}^{k} \xi_j\right| \geq \varepsilon\right\} \leq \frac{1}{\varepsilon^2}\sum_{j=1}^{n} \sigma_j^2$$

for any $\varepsilon > 0$.

REMARK. This inequality can be considered as a generalization of the Chebyshev inequality. In the case $n = 1$ this is the Chebyshev inequality.

PROOF. Let

$$A = \left\{\omega : \max_{1\leq k\leq n}\left|\sum_{j=1}^{k} \xi_j\right| \geq \varepsilon\right\}$$

$$A_k = \{\omega : |\eta_1| < \varepsilon, |\eta_2| < \varepsilon, \ldots, |\eta_{k-1}| < \varepsilon, |\eta_k| \geq \varepsilon\} \ (k = 1, 2, \ldots. n)$$

where $\eta_k = \xi_1 + \xi_2 + \ldots + \xi_k$. Then

$$\sum_{k=1}^{n} A_k = A \ \text{ and } \ A_i A_j = \emptyset \ \text{ if } i \neq j.$$

Since $\int\limits_{A_k} \xi_i \xi_j \, d\mathbf{P} = 0$ if $j > k, j > i$ we have

$$\int\limits_{A_k} \eta_n^2 \, d\mathbf{P} = \int\limits_{A_k} \eta_k^2 \, d\mathbf{P} + \sum_{l=k+1}^{n} \int\limits_{A_k} \xi_l^2 \, d\mathbf{P} + 2 \sum_{j=1}^{l-1} \sum_{l=k+1}^{n} \int\limits_{A_k} \xi_j \xi_l \, d\mathbf{P} =$$

$$= \int\limits_{A_k} \eta_k^2 \, d\mathbf{P} + \sum_{l=k+1}^{n} \int\limits_{A_k} \xi_l^2 \, d\mathbf{P} \geq \int\limits_{A_k} \eta_k^2 \, d\mathbf{P} \geq \varepsilon^2 \, \mathbf{P}(A_k)$$

and so

$$\sum_{k=1}^{n} \mathbf{E}(\xi_k^2) = \mathbf{E}\left[\left(\sum_{k=1}^{n} \xi_k\right)^2\right] \geq \int\limits_{A} \eta_n^2 \, d\mathbf{P} = \sum_{k=1}^{n} \int\limits_{A_k} \eta_n^2 \, d\mathbf{P} \geq \varepsilon^2 \sum_{k=1}^{n} \mathbf{P}(A_k) = \mathbf{P}(A) \, \varepsilon^2$$

which proves the theorem. (A generalization of this theorem is given by HAJEK–RÉNYI [1].)

THEOREM 2.1.2. *Let $\xi_1, \xi_2, \ldots, \xi_n$ be a sequence of independent, identically distributed random variables with* $\mathbf{E}(\xi_i) = 0$, $\mathbf{D}^2(\xi_i) = 1$. *Then*

$$\mathbf{P}\left\{\max_{i \leq k \leq n} \sum_{j=1}^{k} \xi_j > x\right\} \leq \frac{4}{3} \mathbf{P}\left(\sum_{k=1}^{n} \xi_k > x - 2\sqrt{n}\right).$$

PROOF. Let

$$\eta_j = \xi_1 + \xi_2 + \ldots + \xi_j$$

$$A_k = \{\omega : \eta_1 \leq x, \eta_2 \leq x, \ldots, \eta_{k-1} \leq x, \eta_k > x\}$$

$$B_k = \{\omega : \eta_n - \eta_k \geq -2\sqrt{n}\}$$

and

$$A = \{\omega : \eta_n > x - 2\sqrt{n}\}.$$

Clearly,

$$A_k B_k \subset A \qquad (k = 1, 2, \ldots, n)$$

and

$$A_k A_j = \varnothing \qquad (\text{if } k \neq j).$$

Hence,

$$\sum_{k=1}^{n} \mathbf{P}(A_k) \, \mathbf{P}(B_k) = \sum_{k=1}^{n} \mathbf{P}(A_k B_k) = \mathbf{P}\left(\sum_{k=1}^{n} A_k B_k\right) \leq \mathbf{P}(A) \qquad (2.1.1)$$

and by the Chebyshev inequality

$$1 - \mathbf{P}(B_k) \leq \mathbf{P}\left(|\xi_{k+1} + \xi_{k+2} + \ldots + \xi_n| > 2\sqrt{n}\right) \leq$$

$$\leq \frac{n-k}{4n} \leq \frac{1}{4} \qquad (k = 1, 2, \ldots, n). \qquad (2.1.2)$$

(2.1.1) and (2.1.2) together imply

$$\mathbf{P}\left(\sum_{k=1}^{n} \xi_k > x - 2\sqrt{n}\right) = \mathbf{P}(A) \geq \sum_{k=1}^{n} \mathbf{P}(A_k B_k) \geq \frac{3}{4} \sum_{k=1}^{n} \mathbf{P}(A_k) =$$

$$= \frac{3}{4} \mathbf{P}\left(\sum_{k=1}^{n} A_k\right) = \frac{3}{4} \mathbf{P}\left(\max_{1 \leq k \leq n} \sum_{j=1}^{k} \xi_j > x\right)$$

which is our statement.

THEOREM 2.1.3. (MARCZINKIEWICZ–ZYGMUND [1]). *Let $\xi_1, \xi_2, \ldots, \xi_n$ be a sequence of independent random variables, then*

$$\mathbf{E}\left(\left|\sum_{k=1}^{n} \xi_k\right|^{2r}\right) \leq A n^{r-1} \sum_{k=1}^{n} \mathbf{E}(|\xi_k|^{2r})$$

where r is a positive real number and A is a positive constant depending only on r.

The proof of this theorem is quite simple whenever r is an integer. The general case is more complicated and the details are omitted.

§ 2.2. The three series theorem

It was mentioned in the introduction that a theorem stating the convergence of a series $\sum_{k=1}^{\infty} \xi_k$ cannot be considered as a law of large numbers, but making use of the Kronecker lemma it implies a law of large numbers. This is the reason for the investigation of this type of theorems in this book.

The necessary and sufficient conditions for the convergence of a series $\sum_{k=1}^{\infty} \xi_k$ ($\xi_1, \xi_2, \ldots$ are independent) was found by KOLMOGOROV ([1], [2]).

THEOREM 2.2.1. (THREE SERIES THEOREM). *If $\xi_1, \xi_2, \ldots$ is a sequence of independent random variables and C is a positive constant and if $E_n = \{\omega : |\xi_n(\omega)| \leq C\}$ then a necessary and sufficient condition for the almost everywhere convergence of $\sum_{k=1}^{\infty} \xi_k$ is the convergence of all three series*

$$\sum_{n=1}^{\infty} \mathbf{P}(\bar{E}_n)$$

$$\sum_{n=1}^{\infty} \int_{E_n} \xi_n \, d\mathbf{P}$$

$$\sum_{n=1}^{\infty} \left(\int_{E_n} \xi_n^2 \, d\mathbf{P} - \left(\int_{E_n} \xi_n \, d\mathbf{P}\right)^2\right).$$

The proof of this theorem is based on three lemmas. The first one is interesting in itself.

LEMMA 2.2.1. *If $\xi_1, \xi_2, \ldots$ is a sequence of independent square integrable random variables then the series $\sum_{k=1}^{\infty} \xi_k$ is convergent with probability 1 if the series $\sum_{k=1}^{\infty} \mathbf{E}(\xi_k)$ and $\sum_{k=1}^{\infty} \mathbf{E}(\xi_k^2)$ are convergent.*

PROOF. Let

$$\eta_n = \xi_1 + \xi_2 + \ldots + \xi_n$$

$$\alpha_m = \sup_k |\eta_{m+k} - \eta_m|$$

$$\alpha = \inf_m \alpha_m .$$

In order to prove the convergence almost everywhere of $\sum_{k=1}^{\infty} \xi_k$ it is enough to show that $\mathbf{P}(\alpha = 0) = 1$. By the Kolmogorov inequality, for any $\varepsilon > 0$ and for any integers m and n, we have

$$\mathbf{P}\left(\sup_{1 \leq k \leq n} |\eta_{m+k} - \eta_m| \geq \varepsilon\right) \leq \frac{1}{\varepsilon^2} \sum_{j=m+1}^{n} \mathbf{D}^2(\xi_j) .$$

Hence,

$$\mathbf{P}(\alpha_m \geq \varepsilon) \leq \frac{1}{\varepsilon^2} \sum_{j=m+1}^{\infty} \mathbf{D}^2(\xi_j)$$

and

$$\mathbf{P}(\alpha \geq \varepsilon) \leq \frac{1}{\varepsilon^2} \sum_{j=m+1}^{\infty} \mathbf{D}^2(\xi_j)$$

for any integer m. Therefore, for any $\varepsilon > 0$, $\mathbf{P}(\alpha \geq \varepsilon) = 0$. This concludes the proof.

LEMMA 2.2.2. *If $\xi_1, \xi_2, \ldots$ is a sequence of independent random variables with $\mathbf{E}(\xi_n) = 0$, $|\xi_n| \leq C$ $(n = 1, 2, \ldots)$ (where C is a positive constant) and if the series $\sum_{n=1}^{\infty} \xi_n$ is convergent on a set of positive measure then $\sum_{n=1}^{\infty} \mathbf{E}(\xi_n^2) < \infty$.*

PROOF. Let

$$\eta_0 = 0$$

$$\eta_n = \xi_1 + \xi_2 + \ldots + \xi_n \quad (n = 1, 2, \ldots).$$

Then by the Egorov theorem (Theorem 0.1.6) there exists a real, positive d such that the set

$$E = \prod_{n=0}^{\infty} \{\omega : |\eta_n(\omega)| \leq d\}$$

is of positive measure. Setting

$$E_n = \prod_{i=0}^{n} \{\omega : |\eta_i(\omega)| \leq d\} \quad (n = 0, 1, 2, \ldots),$$

$$F_n = E_{n-1} - E_n \qquad (x = 1,2, \ldots)$$

and

$$\alpha_n = \int_{E_n} \eta_n^2 \, d\mathbf{P} \qquad (n = 0, 1, 2 \ldots)$$

we have

$$E_0 \supset E_1 \supset E_2 \supset \cdots ,$$

$$\prod_{n=0}^{\infty} E_n = E$$

and

$$\alpha_n - \alpha_{n-1} = \int_{E_{n-1}} \eta_n^2 \, d\mathbf{P} - \int_{F_n} \eta_n^2 \, d\mathbf{P} - \int_{E_{n-1}} \eta_{n-1}^2 \, d\mathbf{P} =$$

$$= \int_{E_{n-1}} \xi_n^2 \, d\mathbf{P} + 2 \int_{E_{n-1}} \xi_n \eta_{n-1} \, d\mathbf{P} - \int_{F_n} \eta_n^2 \, d\mathbf{P}.$$

Since

$$\int_{E_{n-1}} \xi_n^2 \, d\mathbf{P} = \mathbf{P}(E_{n-1}) \, \mathbf{E}(\xi_n^2), \qquad \int_{E_{n-1}} \xi_n \eta_{n-1} \, d\mathbf{P} = 0$$

and for any $\omega \in F_n$

$$|\eta_n| \leq c + d,$$

we have

$$\alpha_n - \alpha_{n-1} \geq \mathbf{P}(E) \, \mathbf{E}(\xi_n^2) - (c + d)^2 \, \mathbf{P}(F_n) \qquad (n = 1, 2, \ldots).$$

Summing these inequalities we obtain

$$d^2 \geq \mathbf{P}(E_k) \, d^2 \geq \alpha_k \geq \mathbf{P}(E) \sum_{n=1}^{k} \mathbf{E}(\xi_n^2) - (c + d)^2$$

which proves this assertion.

LEMMA 2.2.3. *If* $\xi_1, \xi_2, \ldots$ *is a sequence of independent random variables with* $|\xi_n| \leq C$ *(*$n = 1, 2, \ldots$ *;* C *is a positive constant) then the series* $\sum_{k=1}^{\infty} \xi_k$ *is convergent with probability* 1 *if and only if the series*

$$\sum_{n=1}^{\infty} \mathbf{E}(\xi_n) \quad \text{and} \quad \sum_{n=1}^{\infty} \mathbf{D}^2(\xi_n) \tag{2.2.1}$$

are convergent.

In this proof the following definition will be needed.

DEFINITION. A random variable ξ is called symmetrically distributed if for every x

$$\mathbf{P}(\xi \leq x) = \mathbf{P}(\xi \geq -x).$$

A *symmetrized random variable* $\xi^{(s)}$, obtained from ξ is $\xi^{(s)} = \xi - \xi'$ where ξ' is independent of ξ and has the same distribution, i.e.

$$\mathbf{P}(\xi < x) = \mathbf{P}(\xi' < x)$$

for every x.

PROOF. By Lemma 2.2.1 the convergence of the series (2.2.1) implies the convergence of $\sum_{k=1}^{\infty} \xi_k$. In order to prove the converse statement let $\xi_k^{(s)}$ $(k = 1, 2, \ldots)$ be the symmetrized random variable obtained from ξ_k. Then $\mathbf{E}(\xi_k^{(s)}) = 0$ $(k = 1, 2, \ldots)$ and $\sum_{k=1}^{\infty} \xi_k^{(s)}$ is convergent with probability 1. Hence by Lemma 2.2.2. we have

$$\sum_{n=1}^{\infty} \mathbf{D}^2(\xi_k^{(s)}) < \infty$$

and since $\mathbf{D}^2(\xi_k^{(s)}) = 2\,\mathbf{D}^2(\xi_k)$, we have also

$$\sum_{n=1}^{\infty} \mathbf{D}^2(\xi_k) < \infty. \tag{2.2.2}$$

This implies the convergence almost everywhere of the series

$$\sum_{k=1}^{\infty} (\xi_k - \mathbf{E}(\xi_k))$$

and so

$$\sum_{k=1}^{\infty} \mathbf{E}(\xi_k) \tag{2.2.3}$$

is also convergent. (2.2.2) and (2.2.3) together imply our lemma.

PROOF OF THEOREM 2.2.1. Let

$$\xi_n^{(m)} = \begin{cases} \xi_n & \text{if } |\xi_n| \leq C \\ -C & \text{if } |\xi_n| > C \end{cases}$$

$$\xi_n^{(p)} = \begin{cases} \xi_n & \text{if } |\xi_n| \leq C \\ +C & \text{if } |\xi_n| > C. \end{cases}$$

The series

$$\sum_{n=1}^{\infty} \xi_n, \qquad \sum_{n=1}^{\infty} \xi_n^{(m)}, \qquad \sum_{n=1}^{\infty} \xi_n^{(p)}$$

are convergent in the same time. By Lemma 2.2.3 this fact implies that the series $\sum_{n=1}^{\infty} \xi_n$ is convergent if and only if the series

$$\sum_{n=1}^{\infty} \Big(\int_{E_n} \xi_n \, d\mathbf{P} \pm C\,\mathbf{P}(\bar{E}_n)\Big)$$

and

$$\sum_{n=1}^{\infty} \Big(\int_{E_n} \xi_n^2 \, d\mathbf{P} - \Big(\int_{E_n} \xi_n \, d\mathbf{P}\Big)^2 + C^2\,\mathbf{P}(E_n)\,\mathbf{P}(\bar{E}_n) \pm 2\,C\,\mathbf{P}(\bar{E}_n) \int_{E_n} \xi_n \, d\mathbf{P}\Big)$$

are convergent.

Since the convergence of these series is equivalent with the convergence of the series of our theorem, the proof is complete.

§ 2.3. What are the possible limits?

The zero-one law (Theorem 0.2.2) evidently implies the following:

THEOREM 2.3.1. *If ζ_n obeys any law of large numbers from the three types considered above then the limit η of $\zeta_n - a_n$ is constant with probability* 1.

A more complicated problem is to characterize the sequence $\{a_n\}$.

By Theorem 1.2.5 we have $m(\zeta_n) - a_n \to 0$ but we would like to characterize the dependence of a_n on $\boldsymbol{\xi}$.

We obtain this characterization in Theorem 2.5.2.

§ 2.4. Convergence in mean

The necessary and sufficient condition of the mean law is very trivial:

THEOREM 2.4.1. *There exists a sequence $\{a_n\}$ of real numbers such that*

$$\zeta_n - a_n \xrightarrow{m} 0$$

if and only if

$$\frac{\mathbf{D}^2(\xi_1) + \mathbf{D}^2(\xi_2) + \ldots + \mathbf{D}^2(\xi_n)}{n^2} \to 0 \quad (n \to \infty). \tag{2.4.1}$$

In this case

$$\lim_{n\to\infty}\left[a_n - \frac{\mathbf{E}(\xi_1) + \mathbf{E}(\xi_2) + \ldots + \mathbf{E}(\xi_n)}{n}\right] = 0$$

PROOF. The sufficiency is obvious. The necessity of the condition (2.4.1) follows from the inequality (0.2.1).

This theorem can be generalized as follows:

THEOREM 2.4.2. *For a sequence $\omega(n)$ of positive numbers we have*

$$\frac{\eta_n - (\mathbf{E}(\xi_1) + \mathbf{E}(\xi_2) + \ldots + \mathbf{E}(\xi_n))}{\sqrt{\mathbf{D}^2(\xi_1) + \mathbf{D}^2(\xi_2) + \ldots + \mathbf{D}^2(\xi_n)}\,\omega(n)} \xrightarrow{m} 0$$

if and only if $\lim\limits_{n\to\infty} \omega(n) = \infty$.

A sufficient condition for the mean law is given in

THEOREM 2.4.3. *If there exists a sequence $\{b_n\}$ of real numbers such that*

$$\zeta_{2^n} - b_n \xrightarrow{m} 0 \tag{2.4.2}$$

then there exists a sequence $\{a_n\}$ of real numbers such that

$$\zeta_n - a_n \xrightarrow{m} 0 \tag{2.4.3}$$

and $a_{2^n} = b_n$.

PROOF. Condition (2.4.2) and the inequality (0.2.1) imply

$$\frac{\mathbf{D}^2(\xi_1)+\mathbf{D}^2(\xi_2)+\ldots+\mathbf{D}^2(\xi_{2^n})}{2^{2n}}\to 0 \qquad (n\to\infty).$$

This fact implies (2.4.1). Hence by Theorem 2.4.1 we have (2.4.3)

§ 2.5. Weak laws

It is very easy to obtain a sufficient condition ensuring the validity of the weak law.

THEOREM 2.5.1. *If there exists a sequence $\{\alpha_k\}$ of real numbers such that*

$$\sum_{k=1}^{\infty}\mathbf{P}(|\xi_k-\alpha_k|\geq k)<\infty \tag{2.5.1}$$

and

$$\frac{1}{n^2}\sum_{k=1}^{n}\int_{|y|\leq k} y^2\,dF_k(y+\alpha_k)\to 0 \qquad (n\to\infty) \tag{2.5.2}$$

where $F_k(x)=P(\xi_k<x)$, then there exists a sequence $\{a_n\}$ of real numbers such that

$$\frac{\xi_1+\xi_2+\ldots+\xi_n}{n}-a_n\Rightarrow 0. \tag{2.5.3}$$

PROOF. Let us define the random variable ξ_k^* by

$$\xi_k^*=\begin{cases}\xi_k-\alpha_k & \text{if } |\xi_k-\alpha_k|\leq k,\\ 0 & \text{otherwise.}\end{cases}$$

Then by condition (2.5.1) the sequences $\{\xi_k^*\}$ and $\{\xi_k-\alpha_k\}$ are equivalent in the sense of Khinchin and by the inequality (0.2.1) we have

$$\mathbf{D}^2(\xi_k^*)\leq\mathbf{E}(\xi_k^{*2})=\int_{|y|\leq k} y^2\,dF_k(y+\alpha_k).$$

Therefore by condition (2.5.2) and Theorem 2.4.1 there exists a sequence $\{a_n^*\}$ of real numbers such that

$$\frac{\xi_1^*+\xi_2^*+\ldots+\xi_n^*}{n}-a_n^*\Rightarrow 0.$$

Now Theorem 1.2.4 implies (2.5.3).

The conditions (2.5.1) and (2.5.2) are not necessary conditions. This fact is shown by the following example: let the distribution of the independent random variables ξ_n be defined by

$$\mathbf{P}\{\xi_n = 2n\} = \mathbf{P}\{\xi_n = -2n\} = \frac{1}{n \log n}$$

$$\mathbf{P}\{\xi_n = 0\} = 1 - \frac{2}{n \log n}.$$

Then there does not exist a sequence $\{\alpha_k\}$ for which (2.5.1) holds, but Theorem 2.4.1 proves the validity of the law in this case.[1]

The following theorem of Kolmogorov gives a necessary and sufficient condition for the weak law of large numbers, and shows that the condition (2.5.2) alone is necessary.

THEOREM 2.5.2 (see GNEDENKO–KOLMOGOROV [1], p. 105). ξ *obeys the weak law of large numbers if and only if*

$$\sum_{k=1}^{n} \mathbf{P}\{|\xi_k - m_k| \geq n\} \to 0 \qquad (n \to \infty),$$

$$\frac{1}{n^2} \sum_{k=1}^{n} \int_{|x| \leq n} x^2 \, dF_k(x + m_k) \to 0. \tag{2.5.2a}$$

We may then take

$$a_n = \frac{1}{n} \sum_{k=1}^{n} \left[\int_{|x| \leq n} x \, dF_k(x + m_k) + m_k \right]$$

where $F_k(x)$ *is the distribution function of* ξ_k *and* m_k *is any median of* $F_k(x)$.

PROOF OF THE SUFFICIENCY. Let us put

$$\xi'_k = \xi_k - m_k,$$

$$\xi^*_k = \xi^*_k(n) = \begin{cases} \xi'_k & \text{if } |\xi'_k| \leq n \\ 0 & \text{otherwise} \end{cases}$$

$$a_n = \frac{\sum_{k=1}^{n} (m_k + \mathbf{E}(\xi^*_k(n)))}{n}$$

and

$$\zeta'_n = \frac{\sum_{k=1}^{n} \xi'_k}{n}, \qquad \zeta^*_n = \frac{\sum_{k=1}^{n} \xi^*_k}{n}.$$

[1] In this example $\frac{\xi_n}{n} \Rightarrow 0$, of course, but $\mathbf{P}\left\{\frac{\xi_n}{n} \to 0\right\} = 0$. (Cf. Theorem 1.2.6).

Furthermore, let B_n be the event that $\zeta'_n = \zeta^*_n$. Then it is clear that

$$\mathbf{P}\{|\zeta_n - a_n| \geq \varepsilon\} = \mathbf{P}(B_n)\,\mathbf{P}(|\zeta_n - a_n| \geq \varepsilon \mid B_n) + \\ + \mathbf{P}(\bar{B})\,\mathbf{P}(|\zeta_n - a_n| \geq \varepsilon \mid \bar{B}_n)\,.$$

We can estimate the first and the second member of the right hand side as follows:

$$\mathbf{P}(\bar{B}_n)\,\mathbf{P}(|\zeta_n - a_n| \geq \varepsilon \mid \bar{B}_n) \leq \mathbf{P}(\bar{B}_n) \leq \sum_{k=1}^{n} \mathbf{P}\{|\xi'_k| > n\}$$

and

$$\mathbf{P}(B_n)\,\mathbf{P}(|\zeta_n - a_n| \geq \varepsilon \mid B_n) \leq \mathbf{P}(|\zeta^*_n - E(\zeta^*_n)| \geq \varepsilon) \geq$$

$$\geq \frac{1}{\varepsilon^2}\,\mathbf{D}^2(\zeta^*_n) \leq \frac{1}{n^2\,\varepsilon^2} \sum_{k=1}^{n} \mathbf{E}(\xi^{*2}_k(n))\,.$$

Thus we have the sufficiency of the conditions of the theorem.

THE PROOF OF THE NECESSITY. First of all, assume that the random variables $\xi_1, \xi_2, \ldots$ are symmetrically distributed (in this case $m(\xi_k) = 0$ $(k = 1, 2, \ldots)$).

If $\boldsymbol{\xi}$ obeys the law of large numbers then for some A_n

$$\zeta_n - A_n \Rightarrow 0 \qquad (n \to \infty)\,,$$

then by Theorem 0.2.4 we have

$$e^{-iA_n t} \prod_{k=1}^{n} \varphi_k\left(\frac{t}{n}\right) \to 1 \qquad (n \to \infty)$$

for all real t, where $\varphi_k(t)$ is the characteristic function of ξ_k. From this we conclude that

$$\prod_{k=1}^{n} \left|\varphi_k\left(\frac{t}{n}\right)\right| \to 1$$

and therefore

$$\sup_{1 \leq k \leq n} \left|1 - \varphi_k\left(\frac{t}{n}\right)\right| \to 0 \qquad (n \to \infty).$$

By the inequality $-\log(1 - a) \geq a$ $(0 \leq a \leq 1)$ we have

$$\int_{-1}^{+1} \sum_{k=1}^{n} \left(1 - \varphi_k\left(\frac{t}{n}\right)\right) dt \to 0. \qquad (2.5.4)$$

Making use of the simple formulas:

$$\varphi(t) = \int_{-\infty}^{+\infty} \cos tx \, dF(x)$$

$$\int_{-1}^{+1} \cos tx \, dt = \frac{2 \sin x}{x}$$

$$\frac{1}{2} \int_{-1}^{+1} (1 - \varphi(t)) \, dt = \int_{-\infty}^{+\infty} \left(1 - \frac{\sin x}{x}\right) dF(x)$$

$$1 - \frac{\sin x}{x} \geqq \frac{1}{10} \quad \text{if} \quad |x| > 1$$

$$1 - \frac{\sin x}{x} \geqq \frac{x^2}{8} \quad \text{if} \quad |x| \leqq 1$$

$$\int_{-1}^{+1} (1 - \varphi(t)) \, dt \geqq \frac{1}{4} \int_{|x| \leqq 1} x^2 \, dF(x) + \frac{1}{5} \int_{|x| > 1} dF(x)$$

(where $\varphi(t)$ is the characteristic function of a symmetrically distributed random variable and $F(x)$ is the corresponding distribution function) we obtain

$$\int_{-1}^{+1} \sum_{k=1}^{n} \left(1 - \varphi_k\left(\frac{t}{n}\right)\right) dt \geqq \frac{1}{4} \sum_{k=1}^{n} \int_{|x| \leqq n} x^2 \, dF_k(x) + \frac{1}{5} \sum_{k=1}^{n} \int_{|x| > n} dF_k(x) \geqq 0 .$$

By (2.5.4) this implies the necessity of our conditions in the case when the random variables $\xi_1, \xi_2, \ldots$ are symmetrically distributed.

In order to prove the general theorem let $\xi_1', \xi_2', \ldots$ be a sequence of independent random variables with the same distributions as the distribution of $\xi_1, \xi_2, \ldots$, i.e. $\mathbf{P}(\xi_k < x) = \mathbf{P}(\xi_k' < x)$ $(k = 1, 2, \ldots)$ and suppose that the systems $\xi_1, \xi_2, \ldots$ and $\xi_1', \xi_2', \ldots$ are also independent. Then $\boldsymbol{\xi}' = (\xi_1', \xi_2', \ldots)$ and $\boldsymbol{\xi}^{(s)} = (\xi_1^{(s)}, \xi_2^{(s)}, \ldots)$ (where $\xi_k^{(s)} = \xi_k - \xi_k'$) obey the law of large numbers. Hence

$$\sum_{k=1}^{n} \mathbf{P}(|\xi_k^{(s)}| \geqq n) \to 0 \tag{2.5.5}$$

and

$$\frac{1}{n^2} \sum_{k=1}^{n} \int_{\{\omega: |\xi_k^{(s)}| \leqq n\}} (\xi_k^{(s)})^2 \, d\mathbf{P} \to 0 . \tag{2.5.6}$$

(2.5.5) immediately implies the first condition of our theorem and (2.5.6) gives the second one by applying the simple inequality

$$\int_{\{\omega:|\xi_k^{(s)}|\leqq n\}} \xi_k^2 \, d\mathbf{P} \geqq \frac{1}{2} \int_{\{\omega:|\xi_k|\leqq n\}} (\xi_k - m(\xi_k))^2 d\mathbf{P} .$$

We note that Theorem 2.5.2 implies Theorem 2.5.1. We presented the latter only to show the method of proof in a very simple case.

Some equivalent forms and consequences of Theorem 2.5.2 are treated in GNEDENKO–KOLMOGOROV [1] (p. 105–109 and p. 133––139). We mention one of these without proof:

THEOREM 2.5.3.[1] *In order that the sequence of independent random variables* $\xi_1, \xi_2, \ldots$ *having finite mathematical expectations* $\mathbf{E}(\xi_k) = b_k$ *obey the weak law of large numbers, i.e. for every* $\varepsilon > 0$

$$\mathbf{P}\left\{\left|\frac{\sum_{k=1}^{n}(\xi_k - b_k)}{n}\right| \geqq \varepsilon\right\} \to 0 \qquad (n \to \infty) \qquad (2.5.7)$$

it is necessary and sufficient that as $n \to +\infty$

$$\sum_{k=1}^{n} \int_{|x|>n} dF_k(x + b_k) \to 0 , \qquad (2.5.8)$$

$$\frac{1}{n} \sum_{k=1}^{n} \int_{|x|<n} x dF_k(x + b_k) \to 0 , \qquad (2.5.9)$$

$$\frac{1}{n^2} \sum_{k=1}^{n} \left\{ \int_{|x|<n} x^2 \, dF_k(x + b_k) - \left(\int_{|x|<n} x \, dF(x + b_k) \right)^2 \right\} \to 0 . \quad (2.5.10)$$

REMARK. (2.5.8), (2.5.9) and (2.5.10) are necessary and sufficient conditions for (2.5.7), but it can happen that there exists a sequence a_n such that

$$\frac{\sum_{k=1}^{n} (\xi_k - b_k)}{n} - a_n \Rightarrow 0 \qquad (\mathbf{E}(\xi_k) = b_k)$$

and in this case our conditions do not hold. This fact is shown by the following example: let the distribution of ξ_n be defined by

$$\mathbf{P}\{\xi_n = n^2\} = \frac{1}{n^2}, \quad \mathbf{P}\left\{\xi_n = -\frac{n^2}{n^2-1}\right\} = 1 - \frac{1}{n^2} \quad (n = 1, 2, \ldots) .$$

[1] In GNEDENKO–KOLMOGOROV [1] this theorem is given in a false form, namely condition (2.5.10) is replaced by a stronger one, which is not necessary. One can find the correction and a counterexample in BREIMAN, L. [1] and ROGERS, H. [1].

In this case

$$\mathbf{E}(\xi_n) = 0 \qquad (n = 1, 2, \ldots)$$

and

$$\sum_{n=1}^{\infty} \mathbf{P}\{\xi_n = n^2\} < \infty .$$

Therefore, by the Borel–Cantelli lemma, $\xi_n = n^2$ only finitely often and so

$$\frac{\xi_1 + \xi_2 + \ldots + \xi_n}{n} \to -1 .$$

In this case it is easy to check that (2.5.9) does not hold.

We can obtain two interesting consequences of Theorem 2.5.2 for identically distributed random variables.

THEOREM 2.5.4 (see KOLMOGOROV [4]). *In order that the independent identically distributed random variables obey the weak law of large numbers it is necessary and sufficient that*

$$n\,\mathbf{P}\{|\xi_i| > n\} \to 0 \qquad (n \to \infty). \tag{2.5.11}$$

Here we may take

$$a_n = \int_{-n}^{+n} x\, dF(x + m) + m \tag{2.5.12}$$

where $F(x) = \mathbf{P}(\xi_i < x)$ $(i = 1, 2, \ldots)$ *and* m *is the median of* $F(x)$.

PROOF. To prove our theorem we show that (2.5.11) implies (2.5.2a). In fact

$$\int_{|x|<n} x^2\, dF(x) = \sum_{k=1}^{n} \int_{k-1 \leqq |x| < k} x^2\, dF(x) < \sum_{k=1}^{n} k^2\, \mathbf{P}(k - 1 \leqq |\xi_j| < k) \leqq$$

$$\leqq 2 \sum_{k=1}^{n} \left(\sum_{i=1}^{k} i \right) \mathbf{P}(k - 1 \leqq |\xi_j| < k) = 2 \sum_{i=1}^{n} i\, \mathbf{P}(i \leqq \xi_j < n) \leqq$$

$$\leqq 2 \sum_{i=1}^{n} (i - 1)\, \mathbf{P}(i \leqq |\xi_j|)$$

therefore, we have

$$\frac{1}{n} \int_{|x|<n} x^2\, dF(x) \to 0 .$$

Condition (2.5.11) is equivalent with $n\mathbf{P}(\,|\,\xi_i - m(\xi_i)\,| > n) \to 0$ which is the analogue of the first condition of Theorem 2.5.2.

Hence we have obtained our theorem as a consequence of Theorem 2.5.2.

REMARK. It is a very strange fact that a_n can also fluctuate in the case of identically distributed random variables. Let us construct a concrete example. Let the distribution of ξ_j be defined by

$$\mathbf{P}(\xi_j = k) = \frac{C}{k^2 \log k} \quad \text{if } n_{2i} \leq k < n_{2i+1}$$

$$\mathbf{P}(\xi_j = -k) = \frac{C}{k^2 \log k} \quad \text{if } n_{2i+1} \leq k < n_{2i+2}$$

$(j = 1, 2, \ldots)$ where

$$C = \frac{1}{\sum_{n=3}^{\infty} \frac{1}{n^2 \log n}}$$

and

$$n_i = 3^{3^i} \qquad (i = 0, 1, 2, \ldots).$$

It is easy to see that (2.5.11) holds in this case and $a_n = \int_{-n}^{+n} x dF(x+m) + m$ fluctuates between $+\log 3$ and $-\log 3$.

The other interesting consequence of Theorem 2.5.2 is

THEOREM 2.5.5 (see EHRENFEUCHT–FISZ [1]). *In order that the independent identically distributed random variables obey the weak law of large numbers with $a_n = a$, i.e. that*

$$\frac{\sum_{k=1}^{n} \xi_k}{n} - a \Rightarrow 0$$

it is necessary and sufficient that $\varphi'(0)$ exists and

$$\varphi'(0) = ia$$

where $\varphi(t)$ is the common characteristic function of ξ_i.

PROOF. This theorem follows from Theorems 0.2.6 nd 2.5.4. In [1] of EHRENFEUCHT–FISZ a direct proof is given.

To complete this § we give the following analogue of Theorem 2.4.3.

THEOREM 2.5.6 (see CHUNG [1]). *If there exists a sequence $\{b_n\}$ of real numbers such that*

$$\zeta_{2^n} - b_n \Rightarrow 0 \qquad \left(\zeta_n = \frac{\xi_1 + \xi_2 + \ldots + \xi_n}{n}\right) \tag{2.5.13}$$

then there exists a sequence $\{a_n\}$ of real numbers such that

$$\zeta_n - a_n \Rightarrow 0 \tag{2.5.14}$$

and

$$a_{2^n} = b_n .$$

PROOF. We shall make use of the method of characteristic functions. Let the characteristic function of ξ_n be $\varphi_n(t)$. Then

$$\lim_{n\to\infty} \prod_{j=1}^{2^n} \left| \varphi_j \left(\frac{t}{2^n} \right) \right| = 1$$

uniformly in any finite interval $|t| \leq T$, i.e. for any $\varepsilon > 0$ and $T > 0$ there exists an integer n_0 such that

$$\prod_{j=1}^{2^n} \left| \varphi_j \left(\frac{t}{2^n} \right) \right| \geq 1 - \varepsilon$$

if $n \geq n_0$ and $|t| \leq T$. This implies

$$\left| \prod_{j=1}^{k} \varphi_j \left(\frac{2^n}{k} \cdot \frac{t}{2^n} \right) \right| \geq 1 - \varepsilon$$

if $2^{n-1} \leq k < 2^n$, $n > n_0$ and $|t| \leq \frac{T}{2}$. So

$$\lim_{k\to\infty} \prod_{j=1}^{k} \left| \varphi_j \left(\frac{t}{k} \right) \right| = 1$$

which implies (2.5.14).

§ 2.6. Estimation of the rate of convergence

In § 2.5 we have proved (under certain conditions) that $P_n(\varepsilon) = \mathbf{P}(|\zeta_n - a_n| \geq \varepsilon)$ converges to 0. In the present paragraph we ask how rapidly does $P_n(\varepsilon)$ tend to 0?

In this § it will be assumed that

$$\mathbf{E}(\xi_i) = 0 \qquad (i = 1, 2, \ldots) .$$

The following estimations are generally based on the Markov or on the Chebyshev inequalities. The simplest result is

THEOREM 2.6.1. *If the variances of the ξ_k's are finite then*

$$\mathbf{P}\left(\left| \frac{\xi_1 + \xi_2 + \ldots + \xi_n}{n} \right| \geq \varepsilon \right) \leq \frac{\mathbf{D}^2(\xi_1) + \mathbf{D}^2(\xi_2) + \ldots + \mathbf{D}^2(\xi_n)}{\varepsilon^2 n} .$$

In particular, if $\mathbf{D}^2(\xi_i) = 1$ $(i = 1, 2, \ldots)$, *then*

$$\mathbf{P}\left(\left| \frac{\xi_1 + \xi_2 + \ldots + \xi_n}{n} \right| \geq \varepsilon \right) = O\left(\frac{1}{n} \right) .$$

PROOF. It is a trivial consequence of the Chebyshev inequality.

This theorem is "almost" the best possible. This fact is shown by the following theorem of ERDŐS [1]:

THEOREM 2.6.2. *Let* $\xi_1, \xi_2, \ldots$ *be a sequence of independent identically distributed random variables. Then* $\mathbf{E}(\xi_k^2) < \infty$ *if and only if*

$$\sum_{n=1}^{\infty} \mathbf{P}\left(\left|\frac{\xi_1 + \xi_2 + \ldots + \xi_n}{n}\right| \geq \varepsilon\right) < \infty$$

for any $\varepsilon > 0$.

The proof of this theorem is omitted.

To obtain a result analogous to that of Theorem 2.6.1 for the case where the higher moments of the random variables exist is not very easy. The following theorem presents such a result:

THEOREM 2.6.3. *If the t-th* $(t = 3, 4, \ldots)$ *moments of the random variables* $\xi_1, \xi_2, \ldots$ *exist and are uniformly bounded, i.e.*

$$\mathbf{E}(|\xi_k|^t) \leq C \qquad (k = 1, 2, \ldots)$$

(where C is a positive constant) then

$$\mathbf{P}\left(\left|\frac{\xi_1 + \xi_2 + \ldots + \xi_n}{n}\right| \geq \varepsilon\right) = O\left(\frac{1}{n^{t-1}}\right). \tag{2.6.1}$$

PROOF. Set

$$\xi_k^*(n) = \begin{cases} \xi_k & \text{whenever } |\xi_k| \leq n \\ 0 & \text{whenever } |\xi_k| > n \end{cases}$$

and

$$\zeta_n^* = \frac{\xi_1^*(n) + \xi_2^*(n) + \ldots + \xi_n^*(n)}{n} - a_n$$

where

$$a_n = \frac{\alpha_1(n) + \alpha_2(n) + \ldots + \alpha_n(n)}{n}$$

and

$$\alpha_k(n) = \mathbf{E}(\xi_k^*(n)).$$

For the moments of the random variables $\xi_k^*(n)$ one obtains:

$$|\mathbf{E}(\xi_k^*(n))| = |\mathbf{E}(\xi_k^*(n) - \xi_k)| \leq \mathbf{E}(|\xi_k^*(n) - \xi_k|) \leq$$

$$\leq \sum_{j=1}^{\infty} (n + j)\,\mathbf{P}(n + j - 1 < |\xi_k| \leq n + j) \leq$$

$$\leq \sum_{j=1}^{\infty} (n + j)\,\mathbf{P}(|\xi_k| > n + j - 1) = \sum_{j=1}^{\infty} (n+j)\,\mathbf{P}(|\xi_k|^t > (n+j-1)^t) \leq$$

$$\leq \sum_{j=1}^{\infty} (n + j) \frac{C}{(n + j - 1)^t} \leq \frac{C}{(n + 1)^{t-2}} \tag{2.6.2}$$

and if $l > t$ then

$$\mathbf{E}(|\xi_k^*(n) - \alpha_k(n)|^l) \leq \mathbf{E}(|\xi_k^*(n)|^l) = \int_{-n}^{+n} |x|^l \, dF_k(x) \leq$$

$$\leq n^{l-t} \int_{-n}^{+n} |x|^t \, dF_k(x) \leq C n^{l-t} \tag{2.6.3}$$

where $F_k(x)$ is the distribution function of ξ_k.

Now (2.6.1) can be proved as follows: let $n > \frac{C}{\varepsilon}$ then

$$\mathbf{P}(|\zeta_n| \geq \varepsilon) \leq \mathbf{P}(|\zeta_n^*| \geq 2\varepsilon) + \mathbf{P}(|\xi_k| \geq n \text{ at least for one } k \leq n) \leq$$

$$\leq \mathbf{P}(|\zeta_n^*|^{2t-2} \geq (2\varepsilon)^{2t-2}) + \sum_{k=1}^{n} \mathbf{P}(|\xi_k| \geq n) \leq \frac{\mathbf{E}(|\zeta_n^*|^{2t-2})}{(2\varepsilon)^{2t-2}} +$$

$$+ \sum_{k=1}^{n} \mathbf{P}(|\xi_k|^t \geq n^t) \leq \frac{\mathbf{E}(\zeta_n^{*2t-2})}{(2\varepsilon)^{2t-2}} + \frac{C}{n^{t-1}} \,. \tag{2.6.4}$$

After a simple calculation we get from (2.6.3)

$$\mathbf{E}(\zeta_n^{*2t-2}) = O\left(\frac{1}{n^{t-1}}\right).$$

This and (2.6.4) imply (2.6.1).

A generalization of Theorem 2.6.2 for random variables having finite t-th ($t \geq 1$) moments was obtained by Katz and Baum–Katz [1]. The following theorem is due to Katz:

Theorem 2.6.4. *Let $\xi_1, \xi_2, \ldots$ be a sequence of independent, identically distributed random variables. Then $\mathbf{E}(|\xi_k|^t) < \infty$ if and only if*

$$\sum_{n=1}^{\infty} n^{t-2} \mathbf{P}\left(\left|\frac{\xi_1 + \xi_2 + \ldots + \xi_n}{n}\right| > \varepsilon\right) < \infty.$$

The proof of this theorem is omitted.[1]

Applying the method of the paper of Baum–Katz–Read [1] the following converse result of Theorem 2.6.3 can be obtained.

Theorem 2.6.5. *If*

$$\mathbf{P}\left(\left|\frac{\xi_1 + \xi_2 + \ldots + \xi_n}{n}\right| \geq \varepsilon\right) \leq \frac{C}{n^t} (n = 1, 2 \ldots ; t = 3,4, \ldots) \tag{2.6.5}$$

then $\mathbf{E}(\xi_i^{t-2})$ is finite for each i.

[1] An estimation of the rate of convergence in the case of non-identically distributed random variables was obtained recently by Franck–Hanson [1]. The special case $t = 1$ of Theorem 2.6.4 was treated by Spitzer [1].

PROOF. By condition (2.6.5) we have

$$\frac{C}{n^t} \geq \mathbf{P}\left(\sum_{j=1}^{n} \xi_j \geq n\varepsilon\right) \geq \mathbf{P}(\xi_{j_0} \geq 4n\varepsilon) - \mathbf{P}\left(\sum_{j \neq j_0} \xi_j \leq -2n\varepsilon\right) \quad (2.6.6)$$

and

$$\mathbf{P}\left(\sum_{j \neq j_0} \xi_j \leq -2n\varepsilon\right) \mathbf{P}(\xi_{j_0} \leq n\varepsilon) \leq \mathbf{P}\left(\sum_{j=1}^{n} \xi_j \leq -n\varepsilon\right) \leq \frac{C}{n^t}. \quad (2.6.7)$$

If n is great enough (say $n \geq n_0 = n(j_0)$) then $\mathbf{P}(\xi_{j_0} \leq n\varepsilon) \geq \frac{1}{2}$.
Thus from (2.6.6) and (2.6.7) we obtain

$$\mathbf{P}(\xi_{j_0} \geq 4n\varepsilon) \leq \frac{3C}{n^t}$$

and[2]

$$\begin{aligned}\mathbf{E}\big((\xi_{j_0}^+)^{t-2}\big) &\leq \sum_{\nu=0}^{\infty} \big(4(\nu+1)\varepsilon\big)^{t-2} \mathbf{P}\big(4\nu\varepsilon \leq \xi_{j_0} < 4(\nu+1)\varepsilon\big) \leq \\ &\leq \sum_{\nu=0}^{n_0-1} \big(4(\nu+1)\varepsilon\big)^{t-2} + \sum_{\nu=n_0}^{\infty} \big(4(\nu+1)\varepsilon\big)^{t-2} \mathbf{P}(\xi_{j_0} \geq 4\nu\varepsilon) \leq \\ &\leq \sum_{\nu=0}^{n_0-1} \big(4(\nu+1)\varepsilon\big)^{t-2} + \sum_{\nu=n_0}^{\infty} \big(4(\nu+1)\varepsilon\big)^{t-2} \frac{3C}{\nu^t}\end{aligned}$$

which is finite. Similarly, we can see that

$$\mathbf{E}(\xi_{j_0}^-)^{t-2} < \infty .$$

This proves the theorem.

In connection with the rate of convergence an important problem is to find conditions ensuring exponential convergence rates, i.e. ensuring the validity of the inequality

$$\mathbf{P}\left(\left|\frac{\xi_1 + \xi_2 + \ldots + \xi_n}{n}\right| \geq \varepsilon\right) \leq A\varrho^n$$

where A is a positive constant and $0 < \varrho < 1$.

Before solving this problem we mention that generally the probability

$$\mathbf{P}\left(\left|\frac{\xi_1 + \xi_2 + \ldots + \xi_n}{n}\right| \geq \varepsilon\right)$$

cannot tend to 0 more rapidly than the exponent.

This kind of theorem can be proven by using the theory of large deviations (see, for instance, LINNIK [1]). We mention an example

[2] ξ_j^{*+} is the positive part of ξ_j.

demonstrating this fact. Let $\xi_1, \xi_2, \ldots$ be a sequence of independent, identically distributed random variables with

$$\mathbf{P}(\xi_i < x) = \frac{1}{\sqrt{2\pi}} \int_{-\infty}^{x} e^{-\frac{t^2}{2}} dt .$$

In this case

$$\mathbf{P}\left(\left|\frac{\xi_1 + \xi_2 + \ldots + \xi_n}{n}\right| \geqq \varepsilon\right) = \frac{2}{\sqrt{2\pi}} \int_{\sqrt{n}\,\varepsilon}^{\infty} e^{-\frac{t^2}{2}} dt \geqq \frac{2}{\sqrt{2\pi}} e^{-\frac{n+1}{2}\varepsilon^2} .$$

A necessary and sufficient condition for exponential convergence rates is given in BAUM–KATZ–READ [1].

THEOREM 2.6.6. *The probability*

$$P_n(\varepsilon) = \mathbf{P}\left(\left|\frac{\xi_1 + \xi_2 + \ldots + \xi_n}{n}\right| \geqq \varepsilon\right)$$

converges exponentially to 0 *for any* $\varepsilon > 0$, *i.e. there exist an* $A > 0$ *and a* $0 < \varrho < 1$ *such that*

$$P_n(\varepsilon) \leqq A\,\varrho^n \tag{2.6.8}$$

if and only if for all $\varepsilon > 0$ *there exist a constant* $E_\varepsilon > 0$ *and a* $t_\varepsilon > 0$ *such that*

$$\prod_{k=1}^{n} \mathbf{E}(e^{t\xi_k}) \leqq \mathbf{E}_\varepsilon\, e^{|t|\varepsilon n} \qquad \textit{whenever} \quad -t_\varepsilon \leqq t \leqq t_\varepsilon . \tag{2.6.9}$$

PROOF OF NECESSITY. From (2.6.8) and the assumption of independence we have

$$\mathbf{P}\left\{\eta_{jn} \geqq jn\frac{\delta}{2}\right\} \leqq A\,\varrho^{jn} \quad \text{and} \quad \mathbf{P}\left(\eta_{jn} \leqq -jn\frac{\delta}{2}\right) \leqq A\varrho^{jn}$$

$$(j = 1, 2, \ldots ; \ n = 1, 2, \ldots), \tag{2.6.10}$$

$$\mathbf{P}\left\{\eta_n \leqq n\frac{\delta}{2}\right\} \mathbf{P}\left\{\eta_{jn} - \eta_n \leqq -(j+1)\,n\frac{\delta}{2}\right\} \leqq \mathbf{P}\left\{\eta_{jn} \leqq -jn\frac{\delta}{2}\right\} \tag{2.6.11}$$

and

$$\mathbf{P}(\eta_n \geqq (j+1)\,n\,\delta) \leqq \mathbf{P}\left(\eta_n \geqq \left(j + \frac{1}{2}\right) n\delta\right) \leqq$$

$$\leqq \mathbf{P}\left(\eta_{jn} \geqq jn\frac{\delta}{2}\right) + \mathbf{P}\left(\eta_{jn} - \eta_n \leqq -(j+1)\,n\frac{\delta}{2}\right) . \tag{2.6.12}$$

If n is sufficiently large (say $n \geqq n_0$) then

$$\mathbf{P}\left\{\eta_n \leqq n\frac{\delta}{2}\right\} > \frac{1}{2}. \tag{2.6.13}$$

(2.6.10), (2.6.11) and (2.6.13) imply

$$\mathbf{P}\left\{\eta_{jn} - \eta_n \leqq -(j+1)\,n\frac{\delta}{2}\right\} \leqq 2\,A\,\varrho^{jn}\ (n \geqq n_0;\ j = 1, 2, \ldots). \tag{2.6.14}$$

(2.6.12) and (2.6.14) imply

$$\mathbf{P}\left\{\eta_n \geqq (j+1)\,n\,\delta\right\} \leqq 3\,A\,\varrho^{jn} \qquad (n \geqq n_0\,;\ j = 1,\ 2,\ \ldots).$$

Now we can estimate $\mathbf{E}(e^{t\eta_n^+})$ as follows:

$$\mathbf{E}(e^{t\eta_n^+}) \leqq \mathbf{P}(\eta_n < 0) + \sum_{k=0}^{\infty} e^{t(k+1)\delta}\,\mathbf{P}(k\,\delta \leqq \eta_n < (k+1)\,\delta) \leqq$$

$$\leqq 1 + \sum_{k=0}^{\infty} e^{t(k+1)\delta}\,\mathbf{P}(\eta_n \geqq k\,\delta) = 1 + \sum_{j=0}^{\infty}\sum_{k=jn}^{(j+1)n-1} e^{t(k+1)\delta}\,\mathbf{P}(\eta_n \geqq k\delta) \leqq$$

$$\leqq 1 + n\sum_{j=0}^{\infty} e^{t\delta(j+1)n}\,\mathbf{P}(\eta_n \geqq jn\,\delta) \leqq 1 + n\left[e^{t\delta n} + \sum_{j=0}^{\infty} e^{t\delta(j+2)n} \times\right.$$

$$\left.\times\,\mathbf{P}\big(\eta_n \geqq (j+1)^{n\delta}\big)\right] \leqq 1 + n\left[e^{t\delta n} + \sum_{j=0}^{\infty} e^{t\delta(j+2)n}\,3\,A\,\varrho^{jn}\right].$$

Hence if n is sufficiently large ($n \geqq n_0$) and t is small enough ($\varrho e^{t\delta} < 1$) then

$$\mathbf{E}(e^{t\eta_n^+}) \leqq C\,n\,e^{2|t|n\delta}$$

is finite, where δ is an arbitrary positive number and C is a constant depending only on δ. Similarly, the same bound can be obtained for $\mathbf{E}(e^{t\eta_n^-})$.

Thus it follows that there exists $E_\varepsilon > 0$ and $t_\varepsilon > 0$ such that (2.6.6) holds.

Proof of sufficiency. By the Markov inequality for $t > 0$ we have

$$\mathbf{P}(\eta_n \geqq n\,\varepsilon) = \mathbf{P}\big(t(\eta_n - n\,\varepsilon) \geqq 0\big) = \mathbf{P}(e^{t(\eta_n - n\varepsilon)} \geqq 1) = \mathbf{E}(e^{t(\eta_n - n\varepsilon)}).$$

Choosing $\delta < \varepsilon$, we obtain

$$\mathbf{P}(\eta_n \geqq n\,\varepsilon) \leqq e^{-t\delta n\varepsilon}\,E_\delta\,e^{t\delta n\delta} = E_\delta\,e^{t\delta(\delta-\varepsilon)n}.$$

Similar arguments show that $\mathbf{P}(\eta_n \leqq -n\varepsilon)$ converges to 0 exponentially fast and this completes the proof.

Remark. Baum–Katz–Read [1] calls attention to the really strange fact that the exponential converge rate implies the existence of $\mathbf{E}(e^{t\xi_j})$ for each j. Similarly, (2.6.5) implies the existence of $\mathbf{E}(\xi_j^{t-2})$

for each j, but, of course, this result is not that exact. We can find a large unknown area between the condition of Theorem 2.6.5 and the statement of Theorem 2.6.3.

§ 2.7. Strong laws

To obtain a satisfactory necessary and sufficient condition for the weak law was not too difficult (see Theorem 2.5.2). In the case of the strong law a good necessary and sufficient condition is unknown. In this § we give the most important strong laws.

The main results (such as Theorems 2.7.2, 2.7.3, 2.7.4, 2.7.5, 2.7.8, 2.7.9, 2.7.10 and 2.7.11) of this section are due to CHUNG [1] and PROKHOROV [1], [2].

First of all we give two proofs of a very simple strong law. Roughly speaking the proof of any other strong law is a combination of these two methods.

THEOREM 2.7.1. *Let $\xi_1, \xi_2, \ldots$ be a sequence of independent, uniformly bounded random variables with*

$$|\xi_i| \leq K, \quad \mathbf{E}(\xi_i) = 0 \qquad (i = 1,2, \ldots).$$

Then

$$\zeta_n = \frac{\xi_1 + \xi_2 + \ldots + \xi_n}{n} \to 0.$$

PROOF. I. (Gap method). Clearly

$$\mathbf{E}(\zeta_n^2) \leq \frac{K^2}{n}$$

and

$$\sum_{n=1}^{\infty} \mathbf{E}(\zeta_{n^2}^2) \leq \sum_{n=1}^{\infty} \frac{K^2}{n^2} < \infty.$$

Hence, by Theorem 0.1.2

$$\zeta_{n^2} \to 0.$$

Now we have to estimate the values of ζ_ν for the ν's in the gap between n^2 and $(n+1)^2$. If $n^2 \leq \nu < (n+1)^2$ then

$$|\zeta_\nu| = \left|\zeta_{n^2}\frac{n^2}{\nu} + \frac{\xi_{n^2+1} + \xi_{n^2+2} + \ldots + \xi_\nu}{\nu}\right| \leq |\zeta_{n^2}| + \frac{(2n+1)K}{\nu}.$$

Since both members of the right hand side tend to 0, the proof is complete.

PROOF II. (Method of high moments). Clearly

$$\mathbf{E}(\zeta_n^4) \leq \frac{1}{n^4} K^4 + 6K^4 \binom{n}{2} \leq \frac{4K^4}{n^2}.$$

Hence,

$$\sum_{n=1}^{\infty} \mathbf{E}(\zeta_n^4) < \infty .$$

By Theorem 0.1.2 this fact proves our statement.

As we have already mentioned in general the proofs of the strong laws are based on these two methods. To this remark we have to add some further notes:

1. In the gap method the main problem is the estimation of ζ_ν for the ν's in the gap. In these estimations different inequalities (like the Kolmogorov inequality (Theorem 2.1.1)) will be applied.

2. In connection with the second method the exponential moments, i.e. $\mathbf{E}(e^{\zeta_n})$, will (occasionally) be evaluated.

3. At times these two methods will be applied to truncated random variables. The method of truncation was applied in the proofs of Three Series Theorem and Theorem 2.5.2.

Now we can turn to the investigation of more general results.

First of all we prove a very weak necessary condition.

THEOREM 2.7.2 *If* $\boldsymbol{\xi}$ *obeys the strong law of large numbers, then*

$$\frac{\xi_n - m(\xi_n)}{n} \to 0 \tag{2.7.1}$$

and

$$\sum_{n=1}^{\infty} \mathbf{P}\{ | \xi_n - m(\xi_n) | \geqq \varepsilon n\} < \infty \tag{2.7.2}$$

for any $\varepsilon > 0$.

PROOF. (2.7.1) and (2.7.2) are equivalent by the Borel–Cantelli lemma. The necessity of (2.7.1) follows from Theorem 1.2.6.

This theorem and Theorem 1.2.4 show that $\boldsymbol{\xi} = \{\xi_k\}$ obeys the strong law of large numbers if and only if $\boldsymbol{\xi}^* = \{\xi_k^*\}$ does, where

$$\xi_k^* = \begin{cases} \xi_k - m(\xi_k) \text{ if } | \xi_k - m(\xi_k) | \leqq \dfrac{k}{2} \\ 0 \text{ otherwise.} \end{cases} \tag{2.7.3}$$

Since $m(\xi_k^*) = 0$ $(k = 1, 2, \ldots)$ if $\boldsymbol{\xi}^*$ obeys the strong law then Theorem 2.5.2 implies that

$$\frac{\xi_1^* + \xi_2^* + \ldots + \xi_n^*}{n} - \frac{\mathbf{E}(\xi_1^*) + \mathbf{E}(\xi_2^*) + \ldots + \mathbf{E}(\xi_n^*)}{n} \to 0 .$$

Hence it would be enough to obtain necessary and sufficient conditions for random variables having the form

$$\tilde{\xi}_k = \xi_k^* - \mathbf{E}(\xi_k^*) \tag{2.7.4}$$

where ξ_k^* is defined by (2.7.3). (Clearly $|\widetilde{\xi}_k| \leqq k$, but in general $m(\widetilde{\xi}_k) \neq 0$.)

So, without the loss of generality we can assume that

$$|\xi_k| \leqq k, \quad \mathbf{E}(\xi_k) = 0 \quad (k = 1, 2, \ldots) \tag{2.7.5}$$

but we do not use this restriction in all cases.

Our next theorem gives a necessary and sufficient condition which is an analogue of Theorem 2.4.3 and Theorem 2.5.6.

THEOREM 2.7.3.

$$\zeta_n = \frac{\eta_n}{n} \to 0 \tag{2.7.6}$$

if and only if

$$\zeta_{2^n} \to 0. \tag{2.7.7}$$

PROOF. The necessity of (2.7.7) is trivial. To prove the sufficiency let k be an integer between $2^{n(k)-1}$ and $2^{n(k)}$, i.e. $2^{n-1} \leqq k < 2^n$ $(n = n(k))$. Then we have

$$\mathbf{P}\left\{|\eta_{2^n} - \eta_k| \leqq 2^n \varepsilon\right\} = 1 - \mathbf{P}\left\{|\eta_{2^n} - \eta_k| > 2^n \varepsilon\right\} \geqq$$
$$\geqq 1 - \mathbf{P}\left\{|\eta_{2^n}| > 2^{n-1}\varepsilon\right\} - \mathbf{P}\left\{|\eta_k| > 2^{n-1}\varepsilon\right\}.$$

By (2.7.7) and Theorem 2.5.6 the second and third members of the right hand side are very small if k is sufficiently large, and therefore

$$\mathbf{P}\left\{|\eta_{2^n} - \eta_k| \leqq 2^n\varepsilon\right\} \geqq \frac{1}{2}$$

if k is great enough (say $k \geqq k_0$). Let us denote the events

$$|\eta_k| > 2^{n+1}\varepsilon, \quad |\eta_{2^n} - \eta_k| \leqq 2^n\varepsilon, \quad |\eta_{2^{n(k)}}| \geqq 2^{n(k)}\varepsilon$$

by A_k, B_k, C_k, respectively. Then evidently, $A_k B_k \subset C_k$ and

$$\mathbf{P}\{|\eta_{2^{n(k)}}| \geqq 2^{n(k)}\varepsilon \quad \text{for some} \quad k \geqq k_0\} = \mathbf{P}\Big(\sum_{k=k_0}^{\infty} C_k\Big) \geqq$$

$$\geqq \mathbf{P}\left(\sum_{k=k_0}^{\infty} A_k B_k\right) = \mathbf{P}(A_{k_0} B_{k_0}) + \mathbf{P}(A_{k_0+1} B_{k_0+1} \overline{A_{k_0} B_{k_0}}) +$$

$$+ \mathbf{P}(A_{k_0+2} B_{k_0+2} \overline{A_{k_0+1} B_{k_0+1}}\, \overline{A_{k_0} B_{k_0}}) + \ldots \geqq \mathbf{P}(A_{k_0} B_{k_0}) +$$
$$+ \mathbf{P}(A_{k_0+1} B_{k_0+1} \bar{A}_{k_0}) + \mathbf{P}(A_{k_0+2} B_{k_0+2} \bar{A}_{k_0+1} \bar{A}_{k_0}) + \ldots =$$
$$= \mathbf{P}(B_{k_0})\,\mathbf{P}(A_{k_0}) + \mathbf{P}(B_{k_0+1})\,\mathbf{P}(A_{k_0+1} \bar{A}_{k_0}) +$$
$$+ \mathbf{P}(B_{k_0+2})\,\mathbf{P}(A_{k_0+2} \bar{A}_{k_0+1} \bar{A}_{k_0}) + \ldots \geqq$$

$$\geq \frac{1}{2}\,[\mathbf{P}(A_{k_0}) + \mathbf{P}(A_{k_0+1}\bar{A}_{k_0}) + \mathbf{P}(A_{k_0+2}\bar{A}_{k_0+1}\bar{A}_{k_0}) + \ldots] =$$

$$= \frac{1}{2}\,\mathbf{P}\left(\sum_{k=k_0}^{\infty} A_k\right) = \frac{1}{2}\,\mathbf{P}\left\{|\eta_k| \geq 2^{n(k)+1}\varepsilon \quad \text{for some} \quad k \geq k_0\right\}.$$

Letting $k_0 \to \infty$, we obtain

$$\mathbf{P}\{|\eta_k| \geq 4k\varepsilon \text{ infinitely often}\} \leq$$
$$\leq \mathbf{P}\{|\eta_{2^n}| \geq 2^n\varepsilon \text{ infinitely often}\} = 0$$

for any $\varepsilon > 0$. So the theorem is proved.

If we want to apply this theorem to obtain satisfactory sufficient conditions then we have to give another (equivalent) form of (2.7.7).

THEOREM 2.7.4. *The conditions*

$$\zeta_{2^n} \to 0, \tag{2.7.7}$$

$$\frac{\eta_{2^{n+1}} - \eta_{2^n}}{2^n} \to 0 \tag{2.7.8}$$

and

$$\sum_{n=1}^{\infty} \mathbf{P}\{|\eta_{2^{n+1}} - \eta_{2^n}| > 2^n\varepsilon\} < \infty \quad (\textit{for any } \varepsilon > 0) \tag{2.7.9}$$

are equivalent.

PROOF. By the Borel–Cantelli lemma (2.7.8) and (2.7.9) are equivalent. (2.7.7) and (2.7.8) are equivalent by Theorem 1.2.3a.

Using this theorem it is easy to obtain some sufficient conditions.

THEOREM 2.7.5.

$$\zeta_n \to 0 \tag{2.7.10}$$

if $\mathbf{E}(\xi_n) = 0$ $(n = 1, 2, \ldots)$ *and for some real numbers* $r \geq 1$

$$\mathbf{E}(|\xi_n|^{2r}) < \infty$$

and

$$\sum_{n=1}^{\infty} \frac{\mathbf{E}(|\xi_n|^{2r})}{n^{r+1}} < \infty. \tag{2.7.11}$$

PROOF. We have to show that (2.7.11) implies (2.7.9). By Theorem 2.1.3.

$$\mathbf{P}(|\eta_{2^{n+1}} - \eta_{2^n}| > 2^n\varepsilon) \leq \frac{\mathbf{E}(|\eta_{2^{n+1}} - \eta_{2^n}|^{2r})}{(2^n\varepsilon)^{2r}} \leq$$

$$\leq \frac{A}{(2^n\varepsilon)^{2r}}\,(2^n)^{r-1}\sum_{k=2^n+1}^{2^{n+1}} \mathbf{E}(|\xi_k|^{2r}) \leq \frac{A}{\varepsilon^{2r}}\,2^{r+1}\sum_{k=2^n+1}^{2^{n+1}} \frac{\mathbf{E}(|\xi_k|^{2r})}{k^{r+1}}$$

so we have (2.7.9).

A very important special case of this theorem is

THEOREM 2.7.5a. ξ *obeys the strong law of large numbers with*

$$a_n = \frac{\mathbf{E}(\xi_1) + \mathbf{E}(\xi_2) + \ldots + \mathbf{E}(\xi_n)}{n}$$

if

$$\sum_{k=1}^{\infty} \frac{\mathbf{D}^2(\xi_k)}{k^2} < \infty . \tag{2.7.12}$$

This theorem is due to KOLMOGOROV. The simplest way to prove this theorem is to obtain it as a consequence of the Three Series Theorem (more precisely Lemma 2.2.1) and Theorem 1.2.2a.

The special case of Theorem 2.7.5 when r is an integer is due to BRUNK [1].

A somewhat sharper version of Theorem 2.7.5a was obtained by OBRETENOV [1]:

THEOREM 2.7.6. ξ *obeys the strong law of large numbers with*

$$a_n = m(\zeta_n)$$

if

$$\sum_{k=1}^{\infty} \mathbf{E}\left(\frac{\xi_k^{*2}}{k^2 + \xi_k^{*2}}\right) < \infty$$

where $\xi_k^* = \xi_k - \mathbf{E}(\xi_k)$.

The proof of this theorem is omitted.

Since condition (2.7.12) is the most suitable in practice, it is important to know how far is it from the necessity. In connection with this question we can mention that condition (2.7.12) is the best possible in the following sense:

if we have a sequence $\{\sigma_k^2\}$ *of positive real numbers for which*

$$\sum_{k=1}^{\infty} \frac{\sigma_k^2}{k^2} = \infty$$

then we can construct a sequence ξ *not obeying the strong law such that* $\mathbf{E}(\xi_k) = 0$ *and* $\mathbf{D}^2(\xi_k) = \sigma_k^2$.

This fact is shown by the following example: let the distribution of ξ_n be defined by

$$\mathbf{P}(\xi_n = n) = \mathbf{P}(\xi_n = -n) = \frac{\sigma_n^2}{2n^2}$$

$$\mathbf{P}(\xi_n = 0) = 1 - \frac{\sigma_n^2}{n^2}$$

if $\sigma_n^2 \leqq n^2$ and

$$\mathbf{P}(\xi_n = \sigma_n) = \mathbf{P}(\xi_n = -\sigma_n) = \frac{1}{2}$$

if $\sigma_n^2 > n^2$.

Then evidently $\mathbf{E}(\xi_n) = 0$, $\mathbf{D}^2(\xi_n) = \sigma_n^2$ and Theorem 2.7.2 shows that $\boldsymbol{\xi}$ does not obey the strong law.

We have seen that condition (2.7.12) is the best possible in the mentioned sense, but it is not necessary at all. Actually, the existence of the variance is unnecessary, but (2.7.12) is also not necessary if the variances are finite. This fact is shown by the following example.

Let the distribution of ξ_n be defined by

$$\mathbf{P}\left\{\xi_n = n^2\right\} = \mathbf{P}\left\{\xi_n = -n^2\right\} = \frac{1}{n^2},$$

$$\mathbf{P}\left\{\xi_n = 0\right\} = 1 - \frac{2}{n^2}.$$

In this case (2.7.12) does not hold but the Borel–Cantelli lemma shows that $\xi_n \neq 0$ only for finitely many n with probability 1. Therefore (2.7.10)

$$\zeta_n = \frac{\xi_1 + \xi_2 + \ldots + \xi_n}{n} \to 0.$$

In this case (2.7.12) holds for the truncated random variables

$$\xi_k^* = \begin{cases} \xi_k & \text{if } \quad |\xi_k| \leqq k, \\ 0 & \text{otherwise} \end{cases}$$

and the sequences $\{\xi_k^*\}$ and $\{\xi_k\}$ are equivalent. So (2.7.10) follows from Theorems 2.7.5a and 1.2.4.

Knowing this example and Theorem 2.7.2 one might think that the validity of (2.7.12) is necessary for the truncated random variables

$$\xi_k^* = \begin{cases} \xi_k - m(\xi_k) & \text{if } \ |\xi_k - m(\xi_k)| \leqq \dfrac{k}{2}, \\ 0 & \text{otherwise.} \end{cases} \tag{2.7.3}$$

(If $\boldsymbol{\xi}$ obeys the strong law then $\{\xi_k\}$ and $\{\xi_k^*\}$ are equivalent by Theorem 2.7.2.)

Unfortunately this conjecture is false. To see this fact let us consider the random variables ξ_n with the distribution

$$\mathbf{P}\left\{\xi_n = \sqrt{\frac{n}{\log n}}\right\} = \mathbf{P}\left\{\xi_n = -\sqrt{\frac{n}{\log n}}\right\} = \frac{1}{2}.$$

In this case (2.7.12) does not hold but Theorem 2.7.5 (in the case $r = 2$) proves (2.7.10).

The next theorem is also simple. It shows that (2.7.12) is not really far from necessary under the condition (2.7.5).

THEOREM 2.7.7. *If*

$$|\xi_n| \leq n, \qquad \mathbf{E}(\xi_n) = 0 \tag{2.7.5}$$

and

$$\zeta_n \to 0 \tag{2.7.10}$$

then

$$\lim_{n\to\infty} \frac{1}{\log n} \sum_{k=1}^{n} \frac{\mathbf{E}(\xi_k^2)}{k^2} = 0. \tag{2.7.13}$$

Moreover, for any $\varepsilon > 0$ *there exists a sequence* $\{\xi_k\}$ *with properties* (2.7.5) *and* (2.7.10) *such that*

$$\sum_{k=1}^{n} \frac{\mathbf{E}(\xi_k^2)}{k^2} \geq (\log n)^{1-\varepsilon}.$$

It is easier to compare (2.7.12) and (2.7.13) if we mention that (2.7.13) evidently implies

$$\sum_{k=1}^{\infty} \frac{\mathbf{E}(\xi_k^2)}{k^2(\log k)^{1+\varepsilon}} < \infty$$

for any $\varepsilon > 0$.

PROOF OF THEOREM 2.7.7. By Theorem 2.5.2 conditions (2.7.5) and (2.7.10) imply

$$\frac{1}{n^2} \sum_{k=1}^{n} \mathbf{E}(\xi_k^2) \to 0 \qquad (n \to \infty) \tag{2.7.14}$$

and this evidently implies (2.7.13).

To prove the other part of this theorem we have to consider the sequence $\{\xi_n\}$ defined by

$$\mathbf{P}\left(\xi_n = \frac{\sqrt{n}}{(\log n)^{\varepsilon/2}}\right) = \mathbf{P}\left(\xi_n = -\frac{\sqrt{n}}{(\log n)^{\varepsilon/2}}\right) = \frac{1}{2}.$$

In this case

$$\sum_{k=1}^{n} \frac{\mathbf{E}(\xi_k^2)}{k^2} \geq \sum_{k=2}^{n} \frac{1}{k(\log k)^{\varepsilon}} \geq (\log n)^{1-\varepsilon}.$$

The validity of (2.7.10) follows from Theorem 2.7.5 if we apply it for a sufficiently large r. Our proof is complete.

We have seen from Theorem 2.7.7 that condition (2.7.12) is not necessary but it is almost so.

Actually it is impossible to obtain a necessary and sufficient condition expressed only by the second moments even in the case (2.7.5). This fact was shown by FISZ [2]. He constructed two sequences of random variables obeying (2.7.5) and having the same variances but such that one of these sequences obeys the strong law and the other one does not. He proved at the same time that it is impossible to obtain a necessary and sufficient condition expressed by the (at most) r-th moments, although he could not prove the same under the condition (2.7.5).

Let us return to the further discussion of Theorem 2.7.3. In our next theorem we obtain a generalization of it.

THEOREM 2.7.8. *If there exists a sequence $\{b_n\}$ of real numbers such that*

$$\zeta_{2^n} - b_n \to 0 \tag{2.7.15}$$

then there exists a sequence $\{a_n\}$ of real numbers such that

$$\zeta_n - a_n \to 0$$

and

$$a_{2^n} = b_n \,.$$

PROOF. By Theorem 0.2.1 b_n can be replaced by $m(\zeta_{2^n})$ and by Theorem 2.5.6. (2.7.15) implies

$$\zeta_n - m(\zeta_n) \Rightarrow 0 \,. \tag{2.7.16}$$

Hence, we can obtain the proof of our theorem by making use of the method of Theorem 2.7.3 and the obvious fact that (2.7.16) implies

$$\frac{m(\eta_{2^{n+1}} - \eta_{2^n}) - [m(\eta_{2^{n+1}}) - m(\eta_{2^n})]}{2^n} \to 0 \cdot$$

We can prove the following analogue of Theorem 2.7.4 without any new concepts:

THEOREM 2.7.9. *The conditions*

$$\zeta_{2^n} - m(\zeta_{2^n}) \to 0 \,, \tag{2.7.7'}$$

$$\frac{\eta_{2^{n+1}} - \eta_{2^n} - m(\eta_{2^{n+1}} - \eta_{2^n})}{2^n} \to 0 \tag{2.7.8'}$$

and

$$\sum_{n=1}^{\infty} \mathbf{P}\{|\eta_{2^{n+1}} - \eta_{2^n} - m(\eta_{2^{n+1}} - \eta_{2^n})| \geq 2^n \varepsilon\} < \infty \tag{2.7.9'}$$

are equivalent.

To complete this section we give two further results without proofs. The first one is a consequence of Theorem 2.7.8 and a central limit theorem of FELLER [1]. It gives a satisfactory necessary and sufficient condition in the case where

$$\sup |\xi_n| = o\left(\frac{n}{\log\log n}\right). \tag{2.7.17}$$

THEOREM 2.7.10. *Under the conditions* (2.7.17) *and* $\mathbf{E}(\xi_n) = 0$ $(n = 1, 2, \ldots)$ *one has* (2.7.10)

$$\zeta_n \to 0$$

if and only if

$$\sum_{r=1}^{\infty} e^{-\frac{\varepsilon}{H_r}} < \infty \tag{2.7.18}$$

for any $\varepsilon > 0$ *where*

$$H_r = \mathbf{D}^2\left(\frac{\eta_{2^{r+1}} - \eta_{2^r}}{2^r}\right).$$

THEOREM 2.7.11. *One has*

$$\zeta_n \to 0$$

if for each $\varepsilon > 0$

$$\sum_{r=0}^{\infty} \mathbf{P}(\tau_r \geqq \varepsilon) < \infty$$

where τ_r *is a random variable with characteristic function*

$$f_r(t) = \exp\int \left(e^{\frac{itu}{2r}} - 1\right) d\left(\sum_{k=2^r+1}^{2^{r+1}} \mathbf{P}(\xi_k < u)\right).$$

§ 2.8. The law of the iterated logarithm

Let $\boldsymbol{\xi} = (\xi_1, \xi_2, \ldots)$ be a sequence of independent random variables for which

$$\zeta_n - a_n = \frac{\xi_1 + \xi_2 + \ldots + \xi_n}{n} - a_n \to 0.$$

In this § we want to characterize the rate of convergence by the class of functions $f(n)$ for which

$$f(n)(\zeta_n - a_n) \to 0. \tag{2.8.1}$$

The first authors working in this direction were interested in number theory. HAUSDORFF [1] proved that[1]

$$\frac{r_1(x) + r_2(x) + \ldots + r_n(x)}{n^{1/2+\varepsilon}} \to 0$$

[1] The number theoretical meaning of this result is treated in Chapter XI.

where $\varepsilon > 0$ and $r_k(x)$ is the k-th Rademacher function.

We give a proof of this simple fact in a more general form.

THEOREM 2.8.1. *Let $\xi_1, \xi_2, \ldots$ be a sequence of independent uniformly bounded random variables with*

$$\mathbf{E}(\xi_n) = 0\,, \quad |\xi_n| \leqq K \quad (n = 1, 2, \ldots)\,.$$

Then

$$n^{1/2-\varepsilon}\,\zeta_n = \frac{\xi_1 + \xi_2 + \ldots + \xi_n}{n^{1/2+\varepsilon}} \to 0 \tag{2.8.2}$$

for any $\varepsilon > 0$.

PROOF. This result can be proved by the method of high-order moments. Let r be an integer, larger than $1/2\varepsilon$. Then it is easy to see that

$$\mathbf{E}[(\xi_1 + \xi_2 + \ldots + \xi_n)^{2r}] = O(n^r)\,.$$

Hence

$$\mathbf{E}\left[\left(\frac{\xi_1 + \xi_2 + \ldots + \xi_n}{n^{1/2+\varepsilon}}\right)^{2r}\right] = O\left(\frac{1}{n^{2\varepsilon r}}\right)$$

and

$$\sum_{n=1}^{\infty} \mathbf{E}\left[\left(\frac{\xi_1 + \xi_2 + \ldots + \xi_n}{n^{1/2+\varepsilon}}\right)^{2r}\right] < \infty\,.$$

By Theorem 0.1.2, this implies (2.8.2).

Other authors also investigated the Rademacher functions. The most important steps in this direction are due to[1] KHINCHIN [1], ERDŐS [2], KOLMOGOROV [5] and LÉVY [1].

The best results for general random variables were obtained by FELLER [2] and HARTMAN–WINTNER [1]. A very interesting generalization of these theorems in another direction is due to STRASSEN [1], [2] but we will not investigate it here, since this would divert us from the purposes of this book.

Here only the most important results will be given.

TREOREM 2.8.2 (see HARTMAN–WINTNER [1]). *Let $\xi_1, \xi_2, \ldots$ be a sequence of independent, identically distributed random variables such that*

$$\mathbf{E}(\xi_n) = 0\,, \quad \mathbf{E}(\xi_n^2) = 1\,.$$

Then

$$\mathbf{P}\left(\overline{\lim_{n\to\infty}} \frac{\xi_1 + \xi_2 + \ldots + \xi_n}{\sqrt{2\,n \log \log n}} = 1\right) = 1\,.$$

THEOREM 2.8.3 (see FELLER [2]). *Let $\xi_1, \xi_2, \ldots$ be a sequence of independent random variables with*

$$\mathbf{E}(\xi_k) = 0\,, \qquad \mathbf{E}(\xi_k^2) = \sigma_k^2\,.$$

[1] For a detailed history of the question see FELLER [2].

Assume that

$$\lim_{n\to\infty} s_n = \infty$$

and

$$\mathbf{P}\left(|\xi_n| \leq \frac{s_n}{(\log\log s_n)^{3/2}} \right) = 1$$

where $s_n^2 = \sigma_1 + \sigma_2^2 + \ldots + \sigma_n^2$. *Then*

$$\mathbf{P}\left(\overline{\lim_{n\to\infty}} \frac{\xi_1 + \xi_2 + \ldots + \xi_n}{s_n \sqrt{2\log\log s_n^2}} = 1 \right) = 1 .$$

THEOREM 2.8.4 (see FELLER [2]). *Let* $\xi_1, \xi_2, \ldots$ *be a sequence of independent random variables with*

$$\mathbf{E}(\xi_k) = 0, \quad \mathbf{E}(\xi_k^2) = \sigma_k^2, \quad \mathbf{P}(\xi_k < x) = F_k(x) \qquad (k = 1, 2, \ldots).$$

Suppose that there exist two constants $\delta > 0$ *and* $A > 0$ *such that*

$$\int_{-\infty}^{+\infty} x^2 \left|\log|x|\right|^{1+\delta} dF_k(x) < A\,\sigma_k^2 .$$

Then

$$\mathbf{P}\left(\overline{\lim_{n\to\infty}} \frac{\xi_1 + \xi_2 + \ldots + \xi_n}{s_n f(n)} \leq 1 \right) = 1$$

if and only if

$$\sum_{n=1}^{\infty} \frac{\sigma_n^2}{s_n^2} f(n)\, e^{-\frac{f^2(n)}{n}} < \infty$$

where $s_n^2 = \sigma_1^2 + \sigma_2^2 + \ldots + \sigma_n^2$.

Here we give the proof for a very simple case. Namely, we prove the following:

Let $\xi_1, \xi_2, \ldots$ *be a sequence of independent, identically distributed random variables with*

$$\mathbf{E}(\xi_n) = 0, \qquad \mathbf{E}(\xi_n^2) = 1 ,$$

$$|\xi_n| \leq K .$$

Then

$$P\left(\overline{\lim_{n\to\infty}} \frac{\xi_1 + \xi_2 + \ldots + \xi_n}{\sqrt{2n\log\log n}} \leq 1 \right) 1 .$$

REMARK. The inequality

$$\overline{\lim_{n\to\infty}} \frac{\xi_1 + \xi_2 + \ldots + \xi_n}{\sqrt{2n\log\log n}} \leq 1$$

(with probability 1) means that when

$$f(n) = o\left(\sqrt{\frac{n}{\log \log n}}\right)$$

then (2.8.1) holds. The other part (which will not be proved here) of Theorem 2.8.2 and 2.8.3 means that these results are the best possible.

PROOF. First estimate the expectation

$$\mathbf{E}(e^{\lambda_N \eta_N})$$

where

$$\lambda_N = \sqrt{\frac{2 \log \log N}{N}}$$

and

$$\eta_N = \xi_1 + \xi_2 + \ldots + \xi_N .$$

The following simple fact will be used: for any $\varepsilon > 0$ there exists a $\delta > 0$ such that

$$e^x \leqq 1 + x + \frac{x^2}{2 - \varepsilon} \quad \text{whenever } |x| \leqq \delta .$$

Hence, if N is sufficiently large then

$$\mathbf{E}(e^{\lambda_N \eta_N}) \leqq \prod_{k=1}^{n} \mathbf{E}\left(1 + \lambda_N \xi_k + \frac{\lambda_N^2 \xi_k^2}{2 - \varepsilon}\right) = \left(1 + \frac{\lambda_N^2}{2 - \varepsilon}\right)^N =$$

$$= \left[\left(1 + \frac{2 \log \log N}{(2 - \varepsilon) N}\right)^{\frac{N(2-\varepsilon)}{2 \log \log N}}\right]^{\frac{2 \log \log N}{2 - \varepsilon}} \leqq e^{\frac{2 \log \log N}{2 - 2\varepsilon}}$$

and so

$$\mathbf{E}(e^{\lambda_N \eta_N - T_N}) \leqq e^{-(2+3\varepsilon) \log \log N + \frac{2}{2 - 2\varepsilon} \log \log N} =$$

$$= \frac{1}{(\log N)^{1 + 3\varepsilon - \frac{\varepsilon}{1 - \varepsilon}}} \leqq \frac{1}{(\log N)^{1+\varepsilon}}$$

where $T_N = (2 + 3\varepsilon) \log \log N$ and $0 < \varepsilon < \frac{1}{2}$. Making use of the Markov inequality we have

$$\mathbf{P}\left(\frac{\eta_N}{\sqrt{\frac{(2 + 3\varepsilon)^2}{2} N \log \log N}} \geqq 1\right) = \mathbf{P}(e^{\lambda_N \eta_N - T_N} \geqq 1) \leqq \frac{1}{(\log N)^{1+\varepsilon}}$$

and by Theorem 2.1.2 for sufficiently large ν we have

$$\mathbf{P}\left(\sup_{\Theta^\nu \leqq k < \Theta^{\nu+1}} \frac{\eta_k}{\sqrt{\frac{(2+4\varepsilon)^2}{2} k \log\log k}} \geqq 1\right) \leqq$$

$$\leqq \mathbf{P}\left(\sup_{1 \leqq k < \Theta^{\nu+1}} \frac{\eta_k}{\sqrt{\frac{(2+4\varepsilon)^2}{2} \Theta^\nu \log\log \Theta^\nu}} \geqq 1\right) \leqq$$

$$\leqq \frac{4}{3} \mathbf{P}\left(\eta_{[\Theta^{\nu+1}]} \geqq \sqrt{\frac{(2+4\varepsilon)^2}{2} \Theta^\nu \log\log\Theta^\nu} - 2\sqrt{\Theta^{\nu+1}}\right) \leqq$$

$$\leqq \frac{4}{3} \mathbf{P}\left(\eta_{[\Theta^{\nu+1}]} \geqq \sqrt{\frac{(2+3\varepsilon)^2}{2} \Theta^{\nu+1} \log\log\Theta^{\nu+1}}\right) \leqq$$

$$\leqq \frac{4}{3} \frac{1}{(\nu+1)^{1+\varepsilon} (\log\Theta)^{1+\varepsilon}}$$

where Θ is a real number larger than 1, but sufficiently near to it. This inequality and the Borel–Cantelli lemma prove the statement.

Very recently Petrov [1] proved the following:

Theorem 2.8.5. *Let $\xi_1, \xi_2, \ldots$ be a sequence of independent random variables with $\mathbf{E}(\xi_n) = 0$ and $\mathbf{E}(\xi_n^2) = \sigma_n^2$. Suppose that*

$$\lim_{n\to\infty} \frac{B_n}{n} > 0$$

and

$$\overline{\lim_{n\to\infty}} \frac{1}{n} \sum_{j=1}^{n} \mathbf{E}(\xi_j^2 |\log|\xi_j||^{1+\delta}) < \infty$$

for a $\delta > 0$, where $B_n = \sigma_1^2 + \sigma_2^2 + \ldots + \sigma_n^2$. Then

$$\mathbf{P}\left(\overline{\lim_{n\to\infty}} \frac{\xi_1 + \xi_2 + \ldots + \xi_n}{\sqrt{2 B_n \log\log B_n}} = 1\right) = 1.$$

Among the other generalizations of the law of the iterated logarithm for independent random variables we mention the very recent paper of Chover [1].

§ 2.9. Identically distributed random variables

The fundamental law on identically distributed random variables is due to KOLMOGOROV. It states that

$$\zeta_n = \frac{\xi_1 + \xi_2 + \ldots + \xi_n}{n}$$

tends to a constant m if and only if the expectation of ξ_i exists. (Throughout this §, the random variables ξ_i will be assumed to be independent and identically distributed.)

Here we study the laws of identically distributed variables in a more general form. Let $\xi_1, \xi_2, \ldots$ be a sequence of independent and identically distributed variables and $c_1, c_2, \ldots$ be a sequence of real numbers; we ask, under what conditions does the sequence

$$\tilde{\zeta}_n = \frac{c_1 \xi_1 + c_2 \xi_2 + \ldots + c_n \xi_n}{n}$$

tend strongly to a limit a?

First of all let us mention a simple consequence of Theorem 2.8.3 which shows the interest of this question.

THEOREM 2.9.1. *If $\xi_1, \xi_2, \ldots$ is a sequence of independent random variables with common distribution function $F(x)$ and $\{c_n\}$ is a sequence of real numbers, such that*

$$\int_{-\infty}^{+\infty} x^2 \left| \log |x| \right|^{1+\delta} dF(x) < \infty, \qquad \mathbf{E}(\xi_i) = 0 \tag{2.9.1}$$

for some $\delta > 0$ and

$$s_n = \sqrt{c_1^2 + c_2^2 + \ldots + c_n^2} = o(n)$$

then we have

$$\tilde{\zeta}_n = \frac{c_1 \xi_1 + c_2 \xi_2 + \ldots + c_n \xi_n}{n} \to 0 \tag{2.9.2}$$

if

$$\sum_{k=1}^{\infty} \frac{c_k^2}{s_k^3} k e^{-\frac{k^2}{2s_k^2}} < \infty. \tag{2.9.3}$$

For instance if $c_n = \dfrac{\sqrt{n}}{K\sqrt{\log\log n}}$ (where K is a sufficiently large constant), then (2.9.3) holds. So (2.9.2) holds (if (2.9.1) is true) but this does not follow directly from the theorems of § 2.7.

The aim of this § is to obtain the analogous form of the previous theorem without the condition (2.9.1). Our first result is a simple generalization of the mentioned classical result of KOLMOGOROV.

THEOREM 2.9.2. *The sequence* $c_1\xi_1, c_2\xi_2, \ldots$ *obeys the strong law of large numbers (i.e.* (2.9.2) *holds) if*

$$\mathbf{E}(\xi_k) = 0, \quad \mathbf{E}(|\xi_k|^p) < \infty \quad (1 \leq p < 2) \tag{2.9.4}$$

and

$$k^{2-p} \sum_{n=[k^p]}^{\infty} \frac{|c_n^2|}{n^2} \leq K \tag{2.9.5}$$

where K is a positive constant.

(2.9.5) holds for example if $|c_n| \leq n^{\frac{p-1}{p}}$.

Define the sequence ξ_n^* as follows:

$$\xi_n^* = \begin{cases} \xi_n \text{ if } |\xi_n| \leq n^{\frac{1}{p}}, \\ 0 \text{ otherwise.} \end{cases}$$

The first step of our proof is to show that ξ_n^* and ξ_n are equivalent in the sense of Khinchin. This can be seen by the following inequalities:

$$\sum_{n=1}^{\infty} \mathbf{P}(\xi_n \neq \xi_n^*) = \sum_{n=1}^{\infty} \mathbf{P}(|\xi_n| > n^{\frac{1}{p}}) = \sum_{n=1}^{\infty} [1 - F(n^{\frac{1}{p}}) + F(-n^{\frac{1}{p}})] \leq$$

$$\leq \int_{-\infty}^{+\infty} |x|^p \, dF(x) < \infty$$

where $F(x)$ is the common distribution function of the random variables ξ_n.

Since, $\mathbf{E}(\xi_n^*) \to 0$ (as $n \to \infty$) (see Theorem 0.1.1) our theorem follows from Theorems 1.2.4, 2.7.5a and the following inequalities:

$$\sum_{n=1}^{\infty} \frac{c_n^2 \mathbf{E}(\xi_n^{*2})}{n^2} = 2 \sum_{n=1}^{\infty} \frac{c_n^2}{n^2} \int_0^{n^{1/p}} x^2 \, dF(x) \leq$$

$$\leq 2 \sum_{n=1}^{\infty} \frac{c_n^2}{n^2} \sum_{k=1}^{[n^{1/p}]+1} k^2 [F(k) - F(k-1)] =$$

$$= O(1) + 2 \sum_{k=2}^{\infty} [F(k) - F(k-1)] k^2 \sum_{n=[(k-1)^p]}^{\infty} \frac{c_n^2}{n^2} \leq$$

$$\leq O(1) + 8K \sum_{k=2}^{\infty} [F(k) - F(k-1)] k^p < \infty .$$

We can give the following converse form of our previous theorem.

THEOREM 2.9.3. *If* ξ_n *obeys the strong law of large numbers (i.e.* (2.9.2) *holds) with* $c_n \geq A n^{\frac{p-1}{p}}$ $(1 \leq p < 2)$ *(A is a positive constant) then* $\mathbf{E}(\xi_n) = 0$ *and* $\mathbf{E}(|\xi_n|^p) < \infty$.

PROOF. (2.9.2) implies that

$$\frac{c_n \xi_n}{n} \to 0\,,$$

i.e. by the Borel–Cantelli lemma:

$$\sum_{n=1}^{\infty} \mathbf{P}\left(\left|\frac{c_n \xi_n}{n}\right| \geq \varepsilon\right) \leq \sum_{n=1}^{\infty}\left[1 - F\left(\frac{\varepsilon n}{c_n}\right)\right] + \sum_{n=1}^{\infty} F\left(-\frac{\varepsilon n}{c_n}\right) < \infty$$

for any $\varepsilon > 0$. Therefore we have

$$\int_{-\infty}^{+\infty} |x|^p\, dF(x) \leq \sum_{n=0}^{\infty} [1 - F(n^{1/p})] + \sum_{n=0}^{\infty} F(-n^{1/p}) \leq$$

$$\leq \sum_{n=1}^{\infty}\left[1 - F\left(\frac{An}{c_n}\right)\right] + \sum_{n=0}^{\infty} F\left(-\frac{An}{c_n}\right)$$

which implies our theorem.

To finish this § we make the following

REMARK. In § 2.3 we saw the following strange result: $\xi_1, \xi_2, \ldots$ is a sequence of identically distributed random variables and

$$\frac{\xi_1 + \xi_2 + \ldots + \xi_n}{n} - a_n \Rightarrow 0 \tag{2.9.6}$$

where $\{a_n\}$ is a sequence of real numbers oscillating between $-\log 3$ and $+\log 3$. It is easy to see (using Theorem 1.2.6) that this cannot happen if we replace the strong convergence for the stochastic convergence in (2.9.6).

§ 2.10. Weighted averages

Let $\xi_1, \xi_2, \ldots$ be a sequence of independent random variables with $\mathbf{E}(\xi_n) = 0$ and $c_1, c_2, \ldots$ a sequence of non-negative real numbers. Here we are interested in the asymptotical properties of the ratio

$$\psi_n = \frac{c_1 \xi_1 + c_2 \xi_2 + \ldots + c_n \xi_n}{c_1 + c_2 + \ldots + c_n}.$$

More exactly we study two questions.

1. What is the "best" sequence $\{c_n\}$ of weights? (What sequence will ensure the convergence of ψ_n when the weights $c_n = 1$ do not.) This question will be treated for random variables with finite variances.

2. What weights are "good enough"? (What weights are able to ensure the convergence of ψ_n in general.) This question will be treated in the case of identically distributed random variables.

The first question is discussed in KOMLÓS–RÉVÉSZ [1], and the second one in BENTON–OREY–PRUIT [1].

An answer to the first question is given in the following two theorems.

THEOREM 2.10.1. *Let* $\xi_1, \xi_2, \ldots$ *be a seuqence of independent random variables with* $\mathbf{E}(\xi_n) = m$, $\mathbf{D}^2(\xi_n) = \sigma_n^2$ $(n = 1, 2, \ldots)$. *Then*

$$\frac{\sum_{k=1}^{n} \frac{\xi_k}{\sigma_k{}^2}}{\sum_{k=1}^{n} \frac{1}{\sigma_k{}^2}} \tag{2.10.1}$$

converges to m *with probability* 1, *provided that*

$$\sum_{k=1}^{\infty} \frac{1}{\sigma_k^2} = \infty . \tag{2.10.2}$$

We mention that condition (2.10.2) holds if the sequence $\frac{1}{n^2} \sum_{k=1}^{n} \sigma_k^2$ is bounded, or at least $\frac{1}{n^2} \sum_{k=1}^{n} \sigma_k^2 = O(\log n)$ or $\sum_{n=1}^{\infty} \frac{n}{\sum_{k=1}^{n} \sigma_k^2} = \infty$.

THEOREM 2.10.2. *If* $\{\sigma_k^2\}$ *is any sequence of positive real numbers for which* $\sum_{k=1}^{\infty} \frac{1}{\sigma_k^2} < \infty$, *then there exists a sequence* $\xi_1, \xi_2, \ldots$ *of independent random variables such that*

$$\mathbf{E}(\xi_i) = 0 \qquad (i = 1, 2, \ldots)$$

$$\mathbf{D}^2(\xi_i) = \sigma_i^2 \qquad (i = 1, 2, \ldots)$$

and such that the weighted average

$$a_1^{(n)} \xi_1 + a_2^{(n)} \xi^2 + \ldots + a_n^{(n)} \xi_n \qquad \left(\sum_{k=1}^{n} a_k^{(n)} = 1 \,;\; n = 1, 2, \ldots \right) \tag{2.10.3}$$

does not converge to any real number m *in probability for any choice of the weights* $a_k^{(n)}$.

Summarizing Theorems 2.10.1 and 2.10.2 we can say that if $\xi_1, \xi_2, \ldots$ is a sequence of independent random variables with $\mathbf{E}(\xi_i) = m$ and $\mathbf{D}^2(\xi_i) = \sigma_i^2$ then the weighted average (2.10.1) of $\xi_1, \xi_2, \ldots$ converges to m with probability 1 provided that $\sum_{k=1}^{\infty} \frac{1}{\sigma_k^2} = \infty$. But if $\sum_{k=1}^{\infty} \frac{1}{\sigma_k^2} < \infty$ then in general there does not exist a weighted average of these random variables which converges to a real number m even in probability.

The proof of Theorem 2.10.1 is based on the following:

LEMMA 2.10.1. *Let $\xi_1, \xi_2, \ldots$ be a sequence of independent random variables with $\mathbf{E}(\xi_i) = m$, $\mathbf{D}^2(\xi_i) = \sigma_i^2$ $(i = 1, 2, \ldots)$. Then*

$$\mathbf{D}^2(x_1 \xi_1 + x_2 \xi_2 + \ldots + x_n \xi_n) \geq \frac{1}{\sum_{k=1}^{n} \frac{1}{\sigma_k^2}}$$

where $x_1, x_2, \ldots, x_n$ are arbitrary real numbers for which $x_1 + x_2 + \ldots + x_n = 1$. The equality holds if and only if

$$x_k = \frac{1}{\sigma_k^2 \sum_{k=1}^{n} \frac{1}{\sigma_k^2}} \qquad (k = 1, 2, \ldots, n).$$

PROOF OF THE LEMMA. It follows from the Cauchy inequality that

$$1 = \left(\sum_{k=1}^{n} x_k\right)^2 = \left(\sum_{k=1}^{n} x_k \sigma_k \frac{1}{\sigma_k}\right)^2 \leq \sum_{k=1}^{n} x_k^2 \sigma_k^2 \sum_{k=1}^{n} \frac{1}{\sigma_k^2}$$

so that

$$\mathbf{D}^2(x_1 \xi_1 + x_2 \xi_2 + \ldots + x_n \xi_n) = \sum_{k=1}^{n} x_k^2 \sigma_k^2 \geq \frac{1}{\sum_{k=1}^{n} \frac{1}{\sigma_k^2}}.$$

The equality holds if and only if $x_k \sigma_k = \frac{\lambda}{\sigma_k}$ and since $\sum_{k=1}^{n} x_k = 1$,

$$\lambda = \frac{1}{\sum_{k=1}^{n} \frac{1}{\sigma_k^2}}.$$

PROOF OF THEOREM 2.10.1. Put

$$\eta_k = \frac{\xi_k - m}{\sigma_k^2 \sum_{j=1}^{k} \frac{1}{\sigma_j}} \qquad (k = 1, 2, \ldots).$$

Then

$$\mathbf{D}^2(\eta_k) = \frac{1}{\sigma_k^2 \left(\sum_{j=1}^{k} \frac{1}{\sigma_j^2}\right)^2} \leq \frac{1}{\sum_{j=1}^{k-1} \frac{1}{\sigma_j^2}} - \frac{1}{\sum_{j=1}^{k} \frac{1}{\sigma_j^2}} \qquad (k = 1, 2, \ldots)$$

and therefore

$$\sum_{k=1}^{\infty} \mathbf{D}^2(\eta_k) < \infty.$$

By Kolmogorov's theorem (Lemma 2.2.1),

$$\sum_{k=1}^{\infty} \eta_k = \sum_{k=1}^{\infty} \frac{\xi_k - m}{\sigma_k^2 \sum_{j=1}^{k} \frac{1}{\sigma_j^2}}$$

converges with probability 1, and by Kronecker's theorem (Theorem 1.2.2) we have our theorem.

Proof of Theorem 2.10.2. To prove this theorem we have to construct a sequence $\xi_1, \xi_2, \ldots$ of random variables with the desired properties. Let $\xi_1, \xi_2, \ldots$ be independent random variables, having a normal distribution with mean value 0 and variance σ_i^2 ($\mathbf{E}(\xi_i) = 0$, $\mathbf{D}^2(\xi_i) = \sigma_i^2$; $i = 1, 2, \ldots$). Then by Lemma 2.10.1 the variance of the weighted average (2.10.3) does not converge to 0 and this fact proves our theorem.

We note that it is very easy to construct a sequence $\xi_1, \xi_2, \ldots$ of independent random variables such that

$$\mathbf{E}(\xi_i) = 0\,,$$

$$\sum_{i=1}^{\infty} \frac{1}{\mathbf{D}^2(\xi_i)} < \infty$$

and the sequence

$$\frac{\xi_1 + \xi_2 + \ldots + \xi_n}{n}$$

converges to 0 (or another number) with probability 1. However, in this case

$$\sum_{n=1}^{\infty} \mathbf{P}\{\xi_n > n\} = \infty$$

and

$$\frac{\sum_{k=1}^{n} \mathbf{D}^2(\xi_n^*)}{n^2} \to 0$$

where

$$\xi_n^* = \begin{cases} \xi_n & \text{if } |\xi_n| \leq n \\ 0 & \text{otherwise}. \end{cases}$$

We turn now to the investigation of the second question. As an answer of this question we obtain

Theorem 2.10.3. *Let $\xi_1, \xi_2, \ldots$ be a sequence of independent, identically distributed random variables with $\mathbf{E}(\xi_i) = 0$ $(i = 1, 2, \ldots)$ and let $\{c_k\}$ be a sequence of positive numbers. Let $G_k = c_1 + c_2 + \ldots + c_k$.*

We define for each $x > 0$ $N(x)$ as the number of those n for which $G_n/c_n \leqq x$. Then we have

$$\psi_n = \frac{c_1 \xi_1 + c_2 \xi_2 + \ldots + c_n \xi_n}{G_n} \to 0 \tag{2.10.4}$$

if

$$\overline{\lim_{x\to\infty}} \frac{N(x)}{x} < \infty \tag{2.10.5}$$

and

$$\lim_{k\to\infty} G_k = \infty . \tag{2.10.6}$$

This relation holds, e.g. if $c_n = n^t$ $(t > 0)$.

PROOF. Define the random variables ξ_k^* as follows:

$$\xi_k^* = \begin{cases} \xi_k \text{ if } |\xi_k| < \dfrac{G_k}{c_k} \\ 0 \text{ otherwise} . \end{cases}$$

The sequence: $\{\xi_k\}$ and $\{\xi_k^*\}$ are equivalent in the sense of Khinchin:

$$\sum_{k=1}^{\infty} \mathbf{P}(\xi_k \neq \xi_k^*) = \sum_{k=1}^{\infty} \mathbf{P}\left(|\xi_k| \geqq \frac{G_k}{c_k}\right) = \sum_{k=1}^{\infty} \int_{|x| \geqq \frac{G_k}{c_k}} dF(x) =$$

$$= \int N(|x|)\, dF(x) < \infty$$

where $F(x)$ is the distribution function of ξ_i.

In our next step we will use the following estimation:

$$\sum_{k:\, \frac{G_k}{c_k} > |x|} \frac{c_k^2}{G_k^2} = \lim_{z\to\infty} \sum_{k:\, |x| < \frac{G_k}{c_k} \leqq z} \frac{c_k^2}{G_k^2} = \lim_{z\to\infty} \int_{|x| < y \leqq z} \frac{dN(y)}{y^2} = \lim_{z\to\infty} \frac{N(z)}{z^2} -$$

$$- \frac{N(|x|)}{x^2} + \lim_{z\to\infty} 2 \int_{|x| < y \leqq z} \frac{N(y)}{y^3}\, dy \leqq 2K \int_{|x|}^{\infty} \frac{dy}{y^2} = \frac{2K}{|x|}$$

provided that $\lim_{x\to\infty} \dfrac{N(x)}{x} \leqq K$.

Since, $\sum_{k=1}^{\infty} \mathbf{E}\left|\dfrac{c_k}{G_k} \xi_k^*\right| < \infty$ is convergent we obtain our theorem using Theorem 1.2.4, the Three Series Theorem, the Kronecker lemma and the following inequalities:

$$\sum_{k=1}^{\infty} \mathbf{E}\left(\frac{c_k^2}{G_k^2}\xi_k^{*2}\right) = \sum_{k=1}^{\infty} \frac{c_k^2}{G_k^2} \int\limits_{|x|<\frac{G_k}{c_k}} x^2\,dF(x) = \int x^2 \sum_{k:\frac{G_k}{c_k}<|x|} \frac{c_k^2}{G_k^2}\,dF(x) \leq$$

$$\leq 2K \int |x|\,dF(x).$$

As a partial converse of this result we have

THEOREM 2.10.4. *If* $\{c_k\}$ *is a sequence of positive real numbers such that* $\overline{\lim\limits_{x\to\infty}} \frac{N(x)}{x} = \infty$ *(where* $N(x)$ *is the number of those* n *for which* $G_n/c_n \leq x$ *and* $G_n = c_1 + c_2 + \ldots + c_n$*) then there exists a sequence* $\xi_1, \xi_2, \ldots$ *of independent, identically distributed random variables such that*

$$\mathbf{E}(\xi_i) = 0 \qquad (i = 1, 2, \ldots)$$

and

$$\frac{c_1\xi_1 + c_2\xi_2 + \ldots + c_n\xi_n}{G_n}$$

does not converge to 0 *with probability* 1.

PROOF. If

$$\overline{\lim_{x\to\infty}} \frac{N(x)}{x} = \infty$$

then there exists a sequence $\{x_k\}$ of real numbers teding to infinity such that $\frac{N(x_k)}{x_k}$ is a monotone sequence tending to infinity. We can construct a sequence $\{p_k\}$ of positive real numbers such that

$$\sum_{k=1}^{\infty} p_k = 1,$$

$$M = \sum_{k=1}^{\infty} p_k x_k < \infty$$

and

$$\sum_{k=1}^{\infty} p_k N(x_k) = \infty.$$

The sequence $\xi_1, \xi_2, \ldots$ of independent random variables with the distribution

$$\mathbf{P}\{\xi_j = x_k - M\} = p_k$$

obeys the requirements of the theorem. To see this, it is enough to prove that

$$\sum_{j=k}^{\infty} \mathbf{P}\left\{\left|\frac{c_j}{G_j}\xi_j\right| \geq \varepsilon\right\} = \infty$$

for any $\varepsilon > 0$. In fact

$$\sum_{j=1}^{\infty} \mathbf{P}\left\{\left|\frac{c_j}{G_j}\xi_j\right| \geq \varepsilon\right\} = \sum_{j=1}^{\infty} \int\limits_{|x| \geq \varepsilon \frac{G_j}{c_j}} dF(x) = \int N\left(\frac{|x|}{\varepsilon}\right) dF(x) = \infty .$$

By similar methods it can be proved that (2.10.4) holds for any divergent sequence of weights $\left(\sum_{k=1}^{\infty} c_k = \infty\right)$ if $\mathbf{E}(|\xi_i| \log^+ |\xi_i|) < \infty$ (see BENTON–OREY–PRUIT [1]).

§ 2.11. Convergence to $+\infty$

Let $\xi_1, \xi_2, \ldots$ be a sequence of independent, identically distributed random variables. Obviously by Theorem 2.9.2 the conditions

$$\mathbf{E}(\xi_i^+) = \infty , \qquad \mathbf{E}(\xi_i^-) < \infty$$

imply that

$$\mathbf{P}\left(\lim_{n\to\infty} \frac{\xi_1 + \xi_2 + \ldots + \xi_n}{n} = \infty\right) = 1. \tag{2.11.1}$$

Here,

$$\xi^+ = \begin{cases} \xi \text{ if } \xi \geq 0 \\ 0 \text{ if } \xi < 0 \end{cases} \qquad \text{and } \xi^- = \begin{cases} -\xi \text{ if } \xi < 0 \\ 0 \text{ if } \xi \geq 0. \end{cases}$$

Our problem is to find more general conditions implying (2.11.1) or at least

$$\lim_{n\to\infty} \mathbf{P}\left(\frac{\xi_1 + \xi_2 + \ldots + \xi_n}{n} \geq K\right) = 1 \text{ for any } K > 0. \tag{2.11.2}$$

Is (2.11.1) true if $\mathbf{E}(\xi_i^-)$ is also infinite but $\mathbf{E}(\xi_i^+)$ is "more infinite"? One possible way of defining the expression "more infinite" is that

$$\lim_{n\to\infty} \int_{-n}^{+n} x\, dF(x) = \infty \tag{2.11.3}$$

where $F(x) = \mathbf{P}(\xi_i < x) \quad (i = 1, 2, \ldots)$.

However, (2.11.3) does not imply (2.11.1) or (2.11.2). This can be seen by the following example:

Let $\xi_1, \xi_2, \ldots$ and $\eta_1, \eta_2, \ldots$ be two sequences of mutually independent random variables. (We assume that the random variables

ξ_i's and the random variables η_i's are also indèpendent on each other.) Define the distribution of these random variables by

$$\varphi_{\xi_i}(t) = e^{-|t|^{1/2}} \qquad (i = 1,\ 2, \ldots) \tag{2.11.4}$$

$$\mathbf{P}(\eta_i = k) = \frac{C}{k^2 \log k} \quad (k = 2,\ 3, \ldots;\ i = 1,\ 2, \ldots)$$

where

$$C = \frac{1}{\sum_{k=2}^{\infty} \frac{1}{k^2 \log k}}$$

Condition (2.11.4) means that the distribution of ξ_i is a stable distribution with parameters $\alpha = 1/2$, $\beta = 0$. (See GNEDENKO–KOLMOGOROV [1].)

Then by Theorem 2.5.4 we have

$$\frac{\eta_1 + \eta_2 + \ldots + \eta_n}{n} - O(\log \log n) \Rightarrow 0\,. \tag{2.11.5}$$

On the other hand the characteristic function of the random variables

$$\bar{\zeta}_n = \frac{1}{n} \zeta_n = \frac{\xi_1 + \xi_2 + \ldots + \xi_n}{n^2}$$

is

$$\varphi_{\bar{\zeta}_n}(t) = e^{-|t|^{1/2}} \qquad (n = 1,\ 2, \ldots).$$

This fact implies that

$$\mathbf{P}\left(\frac{\xi_1 + \xi_2 + \ldots + \xi_n}{n} < -n\right) \geq c > 0 \tag{2.11.6}$$

where c is a fixed constant, not depending on n.

(2.11.5) and (2.11.6) together imply that

$$\frac{\vartheta_1 + \vartheta_2 + \ldots + \vartheta_n}{n}$$

does not tend to infinity (even in probability) where

$$\vartheta_i = \xi_i + \eta_i \qquad (i = 1,\ 2, \ldots).$$

It is easy to check that (2.11.3) holds when

$$F(x) = \mathbf{P}(\vartheta_i < x)\,.$$

The problem to find conditions ensuring (2.11.1) and (2.11.2) is considered by DERMAN–ROBBINS [1] and BAUM [1].

DERMAN and ROBBINS proved the following.

THEOREM 2.11.1. *Let $\xi_1, \xi_2, \ldots$ be a sequence of independent identically distributed random variables with distribution function $F(x)$. Suppose that for some constants $0 < \alpha < \beta < 1$ and $C > 0$*

$$F(x) \leqq 1 - \frac{C}{x^\alpha} \tag{2.11.7}$$

for large positive C and

$$\int_{-\infty}^{0} |x|^\beta \, dF(x) < \infty . \tag{2.11.8}$$

Then (2.11.1) *holds.*

The proof is omitted. Clearly, condition (2.11.7) implies

$$\int_{0}^{\infty} x^\alpha \, dF(x) = \infty . \tag{2.11.9}$$

BAUM [1] has shown by a counterexample that (2.11.8) and (2.11.9) do not imply (2.11.1) or (2.11.2). At the same time a sufficient condition for (2.11.2) is given in BAUM [1].

CHAPTER 3

ORTHOGONAL RANDOM VARIABLES

In the practical and theoretical applications of probability theory it is very difficult to check whether our random variables are independent. It is much easier to check the orthogonality of the random variables. Hence it is very important to find the analogues of the theorems of Chapter 2 for the case in which the random variables are not independent but orthogonal.

It is very easy to see that Theorems 2.4.1, 2.4.2, 2.4.3 and 2.6.1 remain valid for orthogonal random variables.

However, Theorem 2.1.1 is no longer valid. Conversely, the limit of ζ_n (if ξ_k's are orthogonal) can be any random variable η. More exactly, if we have a distribution function $G(x)$ then we can construct a probability space $\{\Omega, \mathscr{S}, \mathbf{P}\}$ and a sequence $\{\xi_k\}$ of orthogonal random variables on Ω such that $\zeta_n \to \eta$ where $\mathbf{P}(\eta < x) = G(x)$. We omit the proof of this simple fact.

Throughout this chapter we assume that the expectations of the random variables ξ_k's are 0 and that the random variables are orthogonal.

§ 3.1. Inequalities

A fundamental inequality of the theory of orthogonal series which plays a role similar to that of the Kolmogorov inequality in the theory of independent random variables is the following:

THEOREM 3.1.1 (RADEMACHER–MENSOV INEQUALITY). *Let $\xi_1, \xi_2, \ldots, \xi_n$ be a sequence of orthonormal random variables and $c_1, c_2, \ldots, c_n$ be a sequence of real numbers. Then*[1]

$$\mathbf{E}\left[\max_{1\leq k\leq n}\left(\sum_{j=1}^{k} c_j\,\xi_j\right)^2\right] \leq (\log^2 4\,n)\sum_{j=1}^{n} c_j^2 .$$

PROOF. First of all, assume that $n = 2^\nu$ (ν is an integer) and introduce the following notations

[1] In this chapter $\log x$ means the logarithm with the base 2.

$$\eta_j = c_1\xi_1 + c_2\xi_2 + \ldots + c_j\xi_j$$

$$\psi_{\alpha\beta} = c_{\alpha+1}\xi_{\alpha+1} + c_{\alpha+2}\xi_{\alpha+2} + \ldots + c_\beta\xi_\beta$$

where $\alpha = \mu\, 2^k$; $\beta = \beta(\alpha) = (\mu+1)2^k$; $\mu = 0, 1, 2, \ldots, \quad 2^{\nu-k} - 1$; $k = 0, 1, 2, \ldots, \nu$. Consider the random variable η_j as the sum of some $\psi_{\alpha\beta}$ and put

$$\eta_j = \sum_i \psi_{\alpha_i\beta_i}$$

where $\beta_1 - \alpha_1 > \beta_2 - \alpha_2 > \ldots$. Clearly, the number of the members of the sum $\sum_i \psi_{\alpha_i\beta_i}$ is less than ν. Therefore, by the Cauchy inequality we have

$$\mathbf{E}(\eta_j^2) \leqq \nu \sum_i \mathbf{E}(\psi^2_{\alpha_i\beta_i}) \leqq \nu \sum_{\alpha,\beta} \mathbf{E}(\psi^2_{\alpha\beta})$$

for any j which implies

$$\mathbf{E}\left(\max_{1\leqq j\leqq n} \eta_j^2\right) \leqq \nu \sum_{\alpha,\beta} \mathbf{E}(\psi^2_{\alpha\beta})$$

where α and $\beta = \beta(\alpha)$ run through all their possible values. Clearly,

$$\sum_{\alpha,\beta} \mathbf{E}\,(\psi^2_{\alpha\beta}) = (\nu+1) \sum_{j=1}^{n} c_j^2\,.$$

So in the case $n = 2^\nu$ we obtained

$$\mathbf{E}\left(\max_{1\leqq j\leqq n}\left(\sum_{k=1}^{j} c_k\xi_k\right)^2\right) \leqq \nu(\nu+1)\sum_{j=1}^{n} c_j^2 = (\log^2 2\,n)\sum_{j=1}^{n} c_j^2$$

Our inequality in the case $2^\nu \leqq n < 2^{\nu+1}$ follows immediately from this fact, by setting

$$c_{n+1} = c_{n+2} = \ldots = c_{2^{\nu+1}} = 0.$$

Among the different investigations in connection with this inequality we mention the papers: Rényi–Zergényi [1], and Tandori [2].

Our next inequality is very similar to the above inequality:

Theorem 3.1.2 (Révész [8])[1]. *Let $\xi_1, \xi_2, \ldots, \xi_n$ be a sequence of random variables such that*

$$\mathbf{E}(\xi_i^6) \leqq K \qquad (i = 1, 2, \ldots, n) \tag{3.1.1}$$

and

$$\mathbf{E}(\xi_i^2\,\xi_j\,\xi_k) = \mathbf{E}(\xi_i^2\,\xi_j) = \mathbf{E}(\xi_i\,\xi_j\,\xi_k\,\xi_l) = \mathbf{E}(\xi_i\,\xi_j\,\xi_k) = \mathbf{E}(\xi_i\,\xi_j) = \mathbf{E}(\xi_i) = 0 \tag{3.1.2}$$

[1] In this paper the proof is not quite correct, now the corrected proof is given.

where the indices i, j, k, l are different and K is a positive constant greater than 1. *Further let $c_1, c_2, \ldots, c_n$ be a sequence of real numbers. Then*

$$\mathbf{E}\left(\max_{1\leq k\leq n}\left(\sum_{j=1}^{k} c_j\,\xi_j\right)^4\right) \leq 7K(\log 4n)^4\left(\sum_{j=1}^{n} c_j^2\right)^2 .$$

REMARK. This lemma is not the best possible. It can be proved (see RÉVÉSZ [7]) that in the case $c_1 = c_2 = \ldots = c_n = 1$, $\log^4 n$ can be replaced by $O(1)\log^3 n$. That method can be applied in this more general case to obtain a stronger inequality. In the last mentioned paper (in the case $c_1 = c_2 = \ldots = c_n = 1$) the condition (3.1.1.) was replaced by the weaker condition $\mathbf{E}\,(\xi_i^4 \leq K$, it seems to be probably that this weaker condition is enough in this general case.

PROOF. First of all we assume that $n = 2^\nu$ $(\nu = 1, 2, \ldots)$ and introduce the following notations

$$\sigma_j = c_1\,\xi_1 + c_2\,\xi_2 + \ldots + c_j\,\xi_j \qquad (j = 1, 2, \ldots)$$

$$\psi_{\alpha\beta} = c_{\alpha+1}\,\xi_{\alpha+1} + c_{\alpha+2}\,\xi_{\alpha+2} + \ldots + c_\beta\,\xi_\beta$$

$$\vartheta_{\alpha\beta} = c_{\alpha+1}^3\,\xi_{\alpha+1}^3 + c_{\alpha+2}^3\,\xi_{\alpha+2}^3 + \ldots + c_\beta^3\,\xi_\beta^3$$

$$\int_\Omega \vartheta_{\alpha\beta}\,\xi_i\,d\mathbf{P} = d_i(\alpha,\beta) = d_i$$

where $\alpha = \mu 2^k$; $\beta = \beta(\alpha) = (\mu + 1)2^k$; $\mu = 0, 1, 2, \ldots, 2^{\nu-k} - 1$; $k = 0,1,2,\ldots,\nu$. Consider the random variable σ_j as the sum of some $\psi_{\alpha\beta}$. Let

$$\sigma_j = \sum_i \psi_{\alpha_i\beta_i}$$

where $\beta_1 - \alpha_1 > \beta_2 - \alpha_2 > \ldots.$ Clearly, the number of the members of the sum $\sum_i \psi_{\alpha_i\beta_i}$ is less than ν. Therefore by the Cauchy inequality we have

$$\sigma_j^4 = \left(\sum_i \psi_{\alpha_i\beta_i}\right)^4 \leq \nu^2\left(\sum_i \psi_{\alpha_i\beta_i}^2\right) \leq \nu^3 \sum_i \psi_{\alpha_i\beta_i}^4$$

what implies

$$\int_\Omega \max_{1\leq j\leq 2^\nu} \sigma_j^4\,d\mathbf{P} \leq \nu^3 \sum_{\alpha,\beta}\int_\Omega \psi_{\alpha\beta}^4\,d\mathbf{P} = \nu^3 \sum_{k=0}^{\nu}\sum_{\mu=0}^{2^{\nu-k}-1}\int_\Omega\left|\sum_{i=\mu 2^k+1}^{(\mu+1)2^k} c_i\,\xi_i\right|^4 d\mathbf{P} \qquad (3.1.3)$$

where α and β run through all their possible values.

To obtain an estimation of the right hand side of (3.1.3) we will use the following inequalities

$$\int_\Omega \psi_{\alpha\beta}^4 d\mathbf{P} = 6\sum_{\alpha<i<j\leq\beta} c_i^2\,c_j^2 \int_\Omega \xi_i^2\,\xi_j^2\,d\mathbf{P} + 4\sum_{i=\alpha+1}^{\beta}\int_\Omega \vartheta_{\alpha\beta}\,c_i\,\xi_i\,d\mathbf{P} -$$

$$-3\sum_{i=\alpha+1}\int_\Omega c_i^4\xi_i^4\,d\mathbf{P}\leq 6\sum_{\alpha<i<j\leq\beta}c_i^2c_j^2\int_\Omega\xi_i^2\xi_j^2\,d\mathbf{P}+4\sum_{i=\alpha+1}^{\beta}c_i\,d_i\,,$$

$$\int_\Omega \xi_i^4\,d\mathbf{P}\leq\Big(\int_\Omega(\xi_i^4)^{3/2}\,d\mathbf{P}\Big)^{2/3}\leq K,$$

$$\int_\Omega\xi_i^2\xi_j^2\,d\mathbf{P}\leq K,\qquad \int_\Omega\xi_i^3\xi_j^3\,d\mathbf{P}\leq K,$$

$$\sum_{i=\alpha+1}^{\beta}d_i^2\leq K\int_\Omega\vartheta_{\alpha\beta}^2\,d\mathbf{P}\leq K^2\big(|c_{\alpha+1}|^3+|c_{\alpha+2}|^3+\dots+|c_\beta|^3\big)^2\leq$$

$$\leq K^2\left(\sum_{i=\alpha+1}^{\beta}c_i^2\right)^3.$$

These inequalities imply

$$\int_\Omega\psi_{\alpha\beta}^4\,d\mathbf{P}\leq 6K\sum_{\alpha<i<j\leq\beta}c_i^2c_j^2+4\sqrt{\sum_{i=\alpha+1}^{\beta}c_i^2\sum_{i=\alpha+1}^{\beta}d_i^2}\leq$$

$$\leq 7K\left(\sum_{i=\alpha+1}^{\beta}c_i^2\right)^2 \tag{3.1.4}$$

(3.1.3.) and (3.1.4.) imply

$$\int_\Omega\max_{1\leq j\leq 2^\nu}\sigma_j^4\,d\mathbf{P}\leq\nu^3\sum_{k=0}^{\nu}\sum_{\mu=0}^{2^{\nu-k}-1}7K\left(\sum_{i=\mu 2^k+1}^{(\mu+1)2^k}c_i^2\right)^2\leq 7K(\nu+1)^4\left(\sum_{i=1}^{2^\nu}c_i^2\right)^2.$$

This inequality proves our statement in the case $n=2^\nu$. If $2^\nu\leq n<2^{\nu+1}$ then.

$$\int_\Omega\max_{1\leq j\leq n}\sigma_j^4\,d\mathbf{P}\leq 7K(\nu+2)^4\left(\sum_{j=1}^{n}c_j^2\right)^2\leq 7K(\log 4n)^4\left(\sum_{j=1}^{n}c_j^2\right)^2$$

what completes our proof.

§ 3.2. Convergence of series and a strong law of large numbers

As an analogue of Theorem 2.2.1 (more precisely of Lemma 2.2.1) we can present the following result of RADEMACHER and MENSOV.

THEOREM[1] 3.2.1. *Let $\xi_1,\xi_2,\dots$ be a sequence of orthonormal random variables and let $c_1,c_2,\dots$ be a sequence of real numbers for which*

$$\sum_{k=1}^{\infty}c_k^2\log^2 k<\infty\,. \tag{3.2.1}$$

Then the series

$$\sum_{k=1}^{\infty}c_k\,\xi_k \tag{3.2.2}$$

is convergent with probability 1.

PROOF. Set

$$\vartheta_n=\sum_{k=n}^{\infty}c_k\,\xi_k\,.$$

[1] This theorem was proved independently by RADEMACHER [1] and MENSOV [1].

Then $$\mathbf{E}(\vartheta_n^2) = \sum_{k=n}^{\infty} c_k^2 \leq \frac{A}{\log^2 n} \qquad \left(\text{where } A = \sum_{k=1}^{\infty} c_k^2 \log^2 k\right)$$

and $$\sum_{n=1}^{\infty} \mathbf{E}(\vartheta_{2^n}^2) \leq \sum_{n=1}^{\infty} \frac{A}{n^2} < \infty .$$

By Theorem 0.1.2 this implies
$$\vartheta_{2^n} \to 0 . \tag{3.2.3}$$

By Theorem 3.1.1 we have
$$\mathbf{E}\left(\max_{2^n \leq k < 2^{n+1}} \left(\sum_{j=2^n}^{\infty} c_j \xi_j\right)^2\right) \leq 4 n^2 \sum_{j=2^n}^{2^{n+1}-1} c_j^2 \leq 4 \sum_{j=2^n}^{2^{n+1}-1} c_j^2 \log^2 j .$$

Hence by our condition (3.2.1) we have
$$\sum_{n=1}^{\infty} \mathbf{E}\left[\max_{2^n \leq k < 2^{n+1}} \left(\sum_{j=2^n}^{k} c_j \xi_j\right)^2\right] < \infty$$

and again applying Theorem 0.1.2 we obtain
$$\max_{2^n \leq k < 2^{n+1}} \left|\sum_{j=2^n}^{k} c_j \xi_j\right| \to 0 . \tag{3.2.4}$$

(3.2.3) and (3.2.4) together imply
$$\vartheta_n \to 0$$

which proves the almost everywhere convergence of the series (3.2.2).

Making use of Theorem 1.2.2a, the following two theorems can be obtained as a simple consequence of the above theorem.

THEOREM 3.2.2. *Let $\xi_1, \xi_2, \ldots$ be a sequence of square integrable random variables such that*
$$\mathbf{E}(\xi_i) = \mathbf{E}(\xi_i \xi_j) = 0 \qquad (i < j;\ i, j = 1, 2, \ldots)$$
$$\sum_{i=1}^{\infty} \frac{\mathbf{E}(\xi_i^2)}{i^2} \log^2 i < \infty .$$

Then
$$\zeta_n = \frac{\xi_1 + \xi_2 + \ldots + \xi_n}{n} \to 0 .$$

THEOREM 3.2.3. *Let $\xi_1, \xi_2, \ldots$ be a sequence of orthonormal random variables. Then*
$$\frac{\xi_1 + \xi_2 + \ldots + \xi_n}{\sqrt{n}\, \psi(n)} \to 0$$

where $\psi(n)$ is a sequence of real numbers for which
$$\sum_{n=1}^{\infty} \frac{n^2}{(\psi(2^n))^2} < \infty . \tag{3.2.5}$$

For example (3.2.5) holds if $\psi(n) = (\log n)^{3/2} \log\log n$.

In the case of independent random variables it is easy to see that Theorem 2.7.5a is the best possible in a certain sense. The Three Series Theorem (in particular Lemma 2.2.2) shows that the condition $\sum_{k=1}^{\infty} c_k^2 < \infty$ is the best possible sufficient condition for the convergence of the series $\sum_{k=1}^{\infty} c_k \xi_k$ (more precisely it is necessary if the random variables ξ_k are uniformly bounded). In the case of orthogonal random variables the analogous questions are very difficult. The best result in this direction is due to TANDORI [1]:

THEOREM 3.2.4. *If $c_1, c_2, \ldots$ is a monotonically decreasing sequence of real numbers for which $\sum_{k=1}^{\infty} c_k^2 \log^2 k = \infty$ then there exists an orthonormal system $\xi_1, \xi_2, \ldots$ such that the series $\sum_{k=1}^{\infty} c_k \xi_k$ is nowhere convergent.*

Similar results can be obtained in connection with Theorems 3.2.2 and 3.2.3.

§ 3.3. Multiplicative systems

The aim of this paragraph is to show that an ESMS has similar properties as an independent system has. The first results in this direction were due to ALEXITS (see ALEXITS [1] and ALEXITS–TANDORI [1]).

THEOREM 3.3.1. *Let $\xi_1, \xi_2, \ldots$ be a uniformly bounded* ESMS *and let $c_1, c_2, \ldots$ be a sequence of real numbers for which*

$$\sum_{k=1}^{\infty} c_k^2 < \infty .$$

Then

$$\sum_{k=1}^{\infty} c_k \xi_k$$

is convergent with probability 1.

PROOF. Suppose that the random variables $\xi_1, \xi_2, \ldots$ are defined on the probability space $\{\Omega, \mathscr{S}, \mathbf{P}\}$. Define the probability space $\{\bar{\Omega}, \bar{\mathscr{S}}, \bar{\mathbf{P}}\}$ as the product of $\{\Omega, \mathscr{S}, \mathbf{P}\}$ by itself, i.e.

$$\bar{\Omega} = \Omega_1 \times \Omega_2 \qquad (\Omega_1 = \Omega_2 = \Omega),$$

$$\bar{\mathscr{S}} = \mathscr{S}_1 \times \mathscr{S}_2 \qquad (\mathscr{S}_1 = \mathscr{S}_2 = \mathscr{S})$$

and

$$\bar{\mathbf{P}} = \mathbf{P}_1 \times \mathbf{P}_2 \qquad (\mathbf{P}_1 = \mathbf{P}_2 = \mathbf{P}).$$

Further define the orthonormal system $\psi_n(\omega)$ as

$$\psi_n = \xi_{\nu_1+1}\, \xi_{\nu_2+1} \ldots \xi_{\nu_m+1}$$

if the dyadic expansion of n is

$$n = 2^{\nu_1} + 2^{\nu_2} + \ldots + 2^{\nu_m} \qquad (0 \leqq \nu_1 < \nu_2 < \ldots < \nu_m).$$

Put

$$\sigma_n(\omega) = \sum_{k=1}^{n} c_k\, \xi_k(\omega)$$

and

$$\hat{\sigma}_{n(\omega)}(\omega) = \max_{1 \leqq k \leqq n} \sigma_k(\omega).$$

Then we have

$$|\mathbf{E}(\hat{\sigma}_{n(\omega)}(\omega))| = \left| \int_{\Omega} \sigma_n(\omega_1) \sum_{k=1}^{n(\omega_2)} \xi_k(\omega_1)\, \xi_k(\omega_2)\, d\,\overline{\mathbf{P}} \right| =$$

$$= \left| \int_{\Omega} \sigma_n(\omega_1) \sum_{k=1}^{2^{n(\omega_2)}-1} \psi_k(\omega_1)\, \psi_k(\omega_2)\, d\,\overline{\mathbf{P}} \right| \leqq$$

$$\leqq \left(\sum_{k=1}^{n} c_k^2 \right)^{1/2} \left[\int_{\Omega_1} \left(\int_{\Omega_2} \sum_{k=1}^{2^{n(\omega_2)}-1} \psi_k(\omega_1)\, \psi_k(\omega_2)\, d\,\mathbf{P}_2 \right) d\,\mathbf{P}_1 \right]^{1/2}.$$

Considering the square of the integral as a double integral on a product space $\Omega_2 \times \Omega_2^*$ ($\Omega_2^* = \Omega_2$) we obtain

$$\mathbf{E}(\hat{\sigma}_{n(\omega)}(\omega)) \leqq \left(\sum_{k=1}^{n} c_k^2 \right)^{1/2} \left[\int_{\Omega_1} \int_{\Omega_2 \times \Omega_2^*} \left(\sum_{k=1}^{2^{n(\omega_2)}-1} \psi_k(\omega_1)\, \psi_k(\omega_2) \right) \times \right.$$

$$\times \left(\sum_{k=1}^{2^{n(\omega_2^*)}-1} \psi_k(\omega_1)\, \psi_k(\omega_2^*) \right) d\,(\mathbf{P}_2 \times \mathbf{P}_2^*)\, d\mathbf{P}_1 =$$

$$= \left(\sum_{k=1}^{n} c_k^2 \right)^{1/2} \int_{\Omega_2 \times \Omega_2^*} \int_{\Omega_1} \sum_{k=1}^{2^{n(\omega_2)}-1} \psi_k(\omega_1)\, \psi_k(\omega_2) \times$$

$$\times \sum_{k=1}^{2^{n(\omega_2^*)}-1} \psi_k(\omega_1)\, \psi_k(\omega_2^*)\, d\mathbf{P}_1\, d(\mathbf{P}_2 \times \mathbf{P}_2^*) =$$

$$= \left(\sum_{k=1}^{n} c_k^2 \right)^{1/2} \int_{\Omega_2 \times \Omega_2^*} \sum_{k=1}^{2^{\nu(\omega_2,\, \omega_2^*)}-1} \psi_k(\omega_2)\, \psi_k(\omega_2^*)\, d(\mathbf{P}_2 \times \mathbf{P}_2^*) \leqq$$

$$\leqq 2 \left(\sum_{k=1}^{n} c_k^2 \right)^{1/2} \int_{\Omega_2 \times \Omega^*} \sum_{k=1}^{2^{n(\omega_2)}-1} \psi_k(\omega_2)\, \psi_k(\omega_2^*)\, d(\mathbf{P}_2 \times \mathbf{P}_2^*)$$

where $\mathbf{P}_2^* = \mathbf{P}_2$ (defined on Ω_2^*) and $\nu(\omega_2, \omega_2^*) = \min\big(n(\omega_2), n(\omega_2^*)\big)$.
This relation holds because

$$\sum_{k=1}^{2^{n(\omega_2)}-1} \psi_k(\omega_2)\,\psi_k(\omega_2^*) = \prod_{k=1}^{n(\omega_2)} \big(1 + \xi_k(\omega_2)\,\xi_k(\omega_2^*)\big) \geqq 0\,.$$

A lower estimate for $\mathbf{E}\big(\hat{\sigma}_{n(\omega)}(\omega)\big)$ can be obtained similarly. This completes our proof.

This theorem clearly implies:

THEOREM 3.3.2. *If* $\{\xi_i\}$ *is a uniformly bounded* ESMS *and* $\{c_k\}$ *is a sequence of real numbers for which* $\sum_{k=1}^{\infty} \frac{c_k^2}{k^2} < \infty$ *then*

$$\frac{c_1\xi_1 + c_2\xi_2 + \ldots + c_n\xi_n}{n} \to 0\,.$$

A law of the iterated logarithm for ESMS was proved by RÉVÉSZ [7].

THEOREM 3.3.3. *If* $\xi_1, \xi_2, \ldots$ *is a uniformly bounded* ESMS *then*

$$\mathbf{P}\left\{\overline{\lim_{n\to\infty}} \frac{\xi_1 + \xi_2 + \ldots + \xi_n}{\sqrt{n \log\log n}} \leqq 7\right\} = 1\,.$$

The constant 7 is surely not the best possible. In Révész's paper this theorem was proved with the better constant 6. Since we cannot obtain the best possible constant, we do not intend to get a little better constant instead of 7. We cannot give any positive lower limit of

$$\overline{\lim_{n\to\infty}} \frac{\xi_1 + \xi_2 + \ldots + \xi_n}{\sqrt{n \log\log n}}\,.$$

PROOF OF THEOREM 3.3.3. Let us try to estimate the expectation of $e^{\lambda_n\eta_n - \mu_n}$ where

$$\eta_n = \xi_1 + \xi_2 + \ldots + \xi_n$$

$$\lambda_n = \sqrt{\frac{\log\log n}{n}}$$

$$\mu_n = (7 + \varepsilon)\log\log n \qquad (0 < \varepsilon < 1)\,.$$

Then (by the inequality $e^x \leqq 1 + x + x^2$ (if $|x| \leqq 1$)) for sufficiently large n we have

$$\mathbf{E}\big(e^{\lambda_n\eta_n - \mu_n}\big) = e^{-\mu_n}\,\mathbf{E}\left(\prod_{k=1}^{n} e^{\lambda_n\xi_k}\right) \leqq e^{-\mu_n}\,\mathbf{E}\left(\prod_{k=1}^{n} (1 + \lambda_n\xi_k + \lambda_n^2\xi_k^2)\right) =$$

$$= e^{-\mu_n}(1 + \lambda_n^2)^n \leqq e^{-\mu_n} e^{\left(1 + \frac{\varepsilon}{2}\right)\log\log n} = \frac{1}{(\log n)^{6+\varepsilon/2}}\,.$$

Therefore,

$$\mathbf{E}(e^{\lambda_{n_k}\eta_{n_k}-\mu_{n_k}}) \leqq \frac{1}{k^{1+\varepsilon/25}}$$

and

$$\sum_{k=1}^{\infty} \mathbf{E}(e^{\lambda_{n_k}\eta_{n_k}-\mu_{n_k}}) < \infty \tag{3.3.1}$$

where $n_k = \left[\exp\left(k^{\frac{1}{6}-\frac{\varepsilon}{100}}\right)\right]$.

By the Beppo–Levi theorem, (3.3.1) implies the convergence of the series

$$\sum_{k=1}^{\infty} e^{\lambda_{n_k}\eta_{n_k}-\mu_{n_k}}.$$

Therefore

$$e^{\lambda_{n_k}\eta_{n_k}-\mu_{n_k}} \leqq 1,$$

i.e.

$$\lambda_{n_k}\eta_{n_k} - \mu_{n_k} \leqq 0$$

and

$$\frac{\lambda_{n_k}}{\mu_{n_k}}\eta_{n_k} = \frac{\eta_{n_k}}{\sqrt{n_k \log\log n_k}} \frac{1}{7+\varepsilon} \leqq 1$$

with probability 1, if n_k is great enough. More exactly for almost all $\omega \in \Omega$ there exists a $k(\omega)$ such that

$$\frac{\eta_{n_k}}{\sqrt{n_k \log\log n_k}} \leqq 7 + \varepsilon$$

if $k \geqq k(\omega)$. Or, in other words,

$$\mathbf{P}\left\{\overline{\lim_{k\to\infty}} \frac{\eta_{n_k}}{\sqrt{n_k \log\log n_k}} \leqq 7 + \varepsilon\right\} = 1. \tag{3.3.2}$$

Since ε is an arbitrary number $(0 < \varepsilon < 1)$ we have

$$\mathbf{P}\left\{\overline{\lim_{k\to\infty}} \frac{\eta_{n_k}}{\sqrt{n_k \log\log n_k}} \leqq 7\right\} = 1.$$

To prove the theorem we have to estimate

$$\frac{\eta_n - \eta_{n_k}}{\sqrt{n \log\log n}}$$

where n is between n_k and n_{k+1}. The interval $(n_k, n_{k+1}]$ contains $O\left(\frac{\exp\left(\frac{1}{6}-\frac{\varepsilon}{100}\right)}{k^{\frac{5}{6}+\frac{\varepsilon}{100}}}\right)$ integers, and hence by Theorem 3.1.2 we have

$$\mathbf{E}\left\{\max_{n_k<n\leqq n_{k+1}} \left(\frac{\eta_n - \eta_{n_k}}{\sqrt{n \log\log n}}\right)^4\right\} = O\left(\frac{1}{k^{1+\frac{\varepsilon}{50}}}\right).$$

The theorem is proved by the Beppo–Levi theorem.

The aim of the next theorem is to investigate fourwise multiplicative systems. More precisely a system $\xi_1, \xi_2, \ldots$ of orthonormal random variables will be called K-wise equinormed strongly multiplicative systems if the relations (0.6.1) and (0.6.2) hold for $k = 2, 3, \ldots, K$ (and not for all integers k).

Unfortunately, we cannot give any law of the iterated logarithm for K-wise equinormed strongly multiplicative systems but a good analogue of Theorem 3.3.1 can be given for fourwise equinormed strongly multiplicative systems.

THEOREM 3.3.4 (RÉVÉSZ [8]). *Let $\xi_1, \xi_2, \ldots$ be a sequence of random variables. Suppose that*

$$\mathbf{E}(\xi_i^6) \leq K \qquad (i = 1, 2, \ldots) \tag{3.3.3}$$

and

$$\mathbf{E}(\xi_i^2 \xi_j \xi_k) = \mathbf{E}(\xi_j^2 \xi_j) = \mathbf{E}(\xi_i \xi_j \xi_k \xi_l) = \mathbf{E}(\xi_i \xi_j \xi_k) = \mathbf{E}(\xi_i \xi_j) = \mathbf{E}(\xi_i) = 0 \tag{3.3.4}$$

where the indices i, j, k, l are different, and K is a positive constant. Further let $c_1, c_2, \ldots$ be a sequence of real numbers and suppose that there exists an integer r (depending on $\{c_k\}$) such that

$$\sum_{k=1}^{\infty} c_k^2 l_r^2(k) < \infty. \tag{3.3.5}$$

where

$$l(x) = l_1(x) = \begin{cases} \log x \text{ if } x \geq 2 \\ 1 \text{ if } 0 < x < 2 \end{cases}$$

and $l_r(x)$ is the r-th iterated of $l(x)$, i.e. $l_r(x) = l(l_{r-1}(x))$. Then the series

$$\sum_{k=1}^{\infty} c_k \xi_k$$

is convergent with probability 1.

The proof of this theorem is based on Theorem 3.1.2 and the following two lemmas.

LEMMA 3.3.1. *If $c_1, c_2, \ldots$ is a sequence of real numbers for which*

$$\sum_{k=1}^{\infty} c_k^2 l_r^2(k) < \infty$$

then there exists a sequence $n_1, n_2, \ldots$ of integers for which

$$\sum_{k=1}^{\infty} \left(\sum_{j=n_k+1}^{n_{k+1}} c_j^2 \right) l_{r-1}^2(k) < \infty \tag{3.3.6}$$

$$\sum_{k=1}^{\infty} \left(\sum_{j=n_k+1}^{n_{k-1}} c_j^2 \right) l^4(n_{k+1} - n_k) < \infty. \tag{3.3.7}$$

LEMMA 3.3.2. *If* $\{\xi_k\}$ *is a sequence of random variables for which* (3.3.3) *and* (3.3.4) *hold and* $m_1 < m_2 < \ldots$ *is a sequence of integers then for the sequence*

$$\psi_k = \begin{cases} \frac{1}{\alpha_k} \sum_{j=m_k+1}^{m_{k+1}} c_j \xi_j & \text{if } \alpha_k > 0 \\ 0 & \text{if } \alpha_k = 0 \end{cases} \tag{3.3.8}$$

where $\alpha_k = \left[\sum_{j=m_k+1}^{m_{k+1}} c_j^2 \right]^{1/2}$, *we have*

$$\mathbf{E}(\psi_k^4) = O(K)$$

and (3.3.4).

PROOF OF LEMMA 3.3.1. Set

$$A = \sum_{k=1}^{\infty} c_k^2 l_r^2(k)$$

then

$$A \geq \sum_{k=n}^{\infty} c_k^2 l_r^2(k) \geq l_r^2(n) \sum_{k=n}^{\infty} c_k^2$$

and

$$\sum_{k=n}^{\infty} c_k^2 \leq \frac{A}{l_r^2(n)} .$$

Therefore we have

$$\sum_{k=2^\nu+1}^{2^{\nu+1}} c_k^2 \leq \frac{A}{l_{r-1}^2(\nu)} . \tag{3.3.9}$$

Now we can find between $2^\nu + 1$ and $2^{\nu+1}$ a sequence of integers

$$2^\nu + 1 = \tau_0^{(\nu)} \leq \tau_1^{(\nu)} \leq \ \ldots \ \leq \tau_{s_\nu - 1}^{(\nu)} \leq \tau_{s_\nu}^{(\nu)} = 2^{\nu+1}$$

as follows: Let $\tau_2^{(\nu)}$ be the smallest integer for which

$$\sum_{j=2^\nu+1}^{\tau_2^{(\nu)}} c_j^2 \geq \frac{A}{\nu^6 \, l_{r-1}^2(\nu)}$$

and let $\tau_1^{(\nu)} = \tau_2^{(\nu)} - 1$. Similarly, let $\tau_4^{(\nu)}$ be the smallest integer for which

$$\sum_{j=\tau_2^{(\nu)}+1}^{\tau_4^{(\nu)}} c_j^2 \geq \frac{A}{\nu^6 \, l_{r-1}^2(\nu)}$$

and let $\tau_3^{(\nu)} = \tau_4^{(\nu)} - 1$. In general, if $\tau_{2l}^{(\nu)}$ is defined, then we define $\tau_{2(l+1)}^{(\nu)}$ as the smallest integer for which

$$\sum_{j=\tau_{2l}^{(\nu)}+1}^{\tau_{2(l+1)}^{(\nu)}} c_j^2 \geq \frac{A}{\nu^6 \, l_{r-1}^2(\nu)}$$

and let $\tau_{2l+1}^{(\nu)} = \tau_{2(l+1)}^{(\nu)} - 1$. Now let

$$2^\nu + 1 = t_0^{(\nu)} < t_1^{(\nu)} < \ldots < t_{p_\nu}^{(\nu)} = 2^{\nu+1}$$

be the different elements of the sequence $\tau_0^{(\nu)}, \tau_1^{(\nu)}, \ldots, \tau_{s_\nu}^{(\nu)}$. Clearly,

$$p_\nu \leq 2\,\nu^6 .$$

Define now the sequence $\{n_k\}$ as the union of the sequences $t_0^{(\nu)}, t_1^{(\nu)}, \ldots, t_{p_\nu}^{(\nu)}$, i.e. the sequence $n_1, n_2, \ldots$ is the same as the sequence

$$t_0^{(1)}, t_1^{(1)}, t_0^{(2)}, t_1^{(2)}, t_2^{(2)}, t_0^{(3)}, t_1^{(3)}, \ldots, t_{p_3}^{(3)}, t_0^{(4)}, t_1^{(4)}, \ldots, t_{p_4}^{(4)}, t_0^{(5)}, t_1^{(5)}, \ldots, t_{p_5}^{(5)}, \ldots .$$

Clearly, if $n_k \in (2^\nu, 2^{\nu+1}]$ then $k \leq 2 \sum_{j=1}^{\nu+1} j^6 \leq 2(\nu+1)^7$. We prove that (3.3.6) and (3.3.7) hold for this sequence $\{n_k\}$. We have

$$A = \sum_{j=1}^{\infty} c_j^2\, l_r^2(j) = \sum_{\nu=1}^{\infty} \sum_{j=2^\nu+1}^{2^{\nu+1}} c_j^2\, l_r^2(j) \geq \frac{1}{2} \sum_{\nu=1}^{\infty} \sum_{j=2^\nu+1}^{2^{\nu+1}} c_j^2\, l_{r-1}^2(\nu+1) =$$

$$= \frac{1}{2} \sum_{\nu=1}^{\infty} \sum_{n_k \in (2^\nu, 2^{\nu+1}]} \sum_{j=n_k+1}^{n_{k+1}} c_j^2\, l_{r-1}^2(\nu+1) \geq$$

$$\geq \frac{1}{4} \sum_{\nu=1}^{\infty} \sum_{n_k \in (2^\nu, 2^{\nu+1}]} \sum_{j=n_k+1}^{n_{k+1}} c_j^2\, l_{r-1}^2\big(2(\nu+1)^7\big) \geq$$

$$\geq \frac{1}{4} \sum_{k=1}^{\infty} \sum_{j=n_k+1}^{n_{k+1}} c_j^2\, l_{r-1}^2(k) .$$

This proves (3.3.6).

If $n_k \in (2^\nu, 2^{\nu+1}]$ then by the definition of $\{n_k\}$ we have

$$n_{k+1} - n_k \leq 2^{\nu+1}$$

and either

$$\sum_{j=n_k+1}^{n_{k+1}} c_j^2 \leq \frac{1}{\nu^6\, l_{r-1}^2(\nu)}$$

or

$$n_{k+1} - n_k = 1$$

which gives (3.3.7).

Proof of Lemma 3.3.2 is so simple that we can omit it.

Proof of Theorem 3.3.4. First of all we prove that the series $\sum_{k=1}^{\infty} c_k\, \xi_k$ is convergent with probability 1 if

$$\sum_{k=1}^{\infty} c_k^2\, l_2^2(k) < \infty . \tag{3.3.10}$$

Let $\{n_k\}$ be a sequence of integers for which

$$\sum_{k=1}^{\infty} \left(\sum_{j=n_k+1}^{n_{k+1}} c_j^2 \right) l^2(k) < \infty \tag{3.3.11}$$

and (3.3.7) hold. Set

$$\psi_k = \begin{cases} \dfrac{1}{\alpha_k} \sum\limits_{j=n_k+1}^{n_{k+1}} c_j \xi_j & \text{if } \alpha_k > 0 \\ 0 & \text{if } \alpha_k = 0 \end{cases}$$

where $\alpha_k = \left[\sum\limits_{j=n_k+1}^{n_{k+1}} c_j^2 \right]^{1/2}$ and put

$$\sigma_N = \sum_{j=1}^{N} c_j \xi_j .$$

Clearly, we have

$$\sigma_{n_K} = \sum_{j=1}^{K-1} \alpha_j \psi_j . \tag{3.3.12}$$

By Lemma 3.3.2, Theorem 3.2.1 and (3.3.10), the sequence $\{\sigma_{n_K}\}$ is convergent with probability 1. By Theorem 3.1.2 and (3.3.7)

$$\sum_{k=1}^{\infty} \mathbf{E} \left(\max_{n_k < j \leq n_{k+1}} \left(\sum_{l=n_k+1}^{j} c_l \xi_l \right)^4 \right) < \infty . \tag{3.3.13}$$

Hence by the Beppo–Levi theorem we have

$$\sum_{k=1}^{\infty} \max_{n_k < j \leq n_{k+1}} \left(\sum_{l=n_k+1}^{j} c_l \xi_l \right)^4 < \infty$$

and so

$$\max_{n_k < j \leq n_{k+1}} \left| \sum_{l=n_k+1}^{j} c_l \xi_l \right| \to 0 .$$

This fact and the almost everywhere convergence of the sequence (3.3.12) prove our theorem in the case when (3.3.9) holds.

Now Theorem 3.3.4 can be proved by induction. Suppose that we already proved that for every sequence $\{a_k\}$ and for every system $\{\chi_k\}$ having the properties (3.3.3) and (3.3.4) the condition

$$\sum_{k=1}^{\infty} a_k^2 l_{r-1}^2(k) < \infty \tag{3.3.14}$$

implies the almost everywhere convergence of the series

$$\sum_{k=1}^{\infty} a_k \chi_k .$$

Let $\{c_k\}$ be a sequence of real numbers for which (3.3.5) holds. Now we can construct a sequence $\{n_k\}$ for which (3.3.6) and (3.3.7) hold. Then we can obtain in the same way the result that σ_{n_k} (defined by (3.3.12)) is convergent almost everywhere (we replace the reference to Theorem 3.2.1 by a reference to the condition of our induction). (3.3.13) follows from (3.3.11).

§ 3.4. Special orthogonal sequences

The statistical properties of the well-known orthogonal sequences are not very interesting. This can be shown, for example, by the following simple inequality

$$\left|\sum_{k=1}^{n} \sin kx\right| \leq \frac{1}{\left|\sin \frac{x}{2}\right|}.$$

Actually, this inequality shows that the central limit theorem or the law of the iterated logarithm cannot hold for this sequence.

Similar inequalities are valid for other complete orthogonal sequences (e.g. Walsh series, the classical orthogonal polynomials), and therefore the following question is raised.

PROBLEM. Let $\xi_1, \xi_2, \ldots$ be a complete orthonormal sequence of uniformly bounded random variables. Does there exist a reordering $\xi_{n_1}, \xi_{n_2}, \ldots$ of this sequence and a random variable η $(\mathbf{P}(0 < \eta < K) = 1)$ such that

$$|\xi_{n_1} + \xi_{n_2} + \ldots + \xi_{n_k}| \leq \eta \qquad (k = 1, 2, \ldots)?$$

It can be happen that from the point of view of statistics the study of a sequence $\{\xi_k\}$ is not interesting, but the study of the sequence $\{c_k \xi_k\}$ has some interest for certain sequences $\{c_k\}$ of real numbers. The case when $\{c_k\}$ is a sequence of 0's and 1's has some special interest. This case will be treated in Chapter VI.

In connection with the study of the known orthonormal sequences we can mention that for these systems, in general, much stronger results can be obtained than Theorem 3.2.1. Roughly speaking, the $\log^2 k$ in the condition of Theorem 3.2.1 can be replaced by $\log k$ in the commonly used orthonormal systems. This fact is true, e.g. for Walsh functions. For the sequence $\{\sin kx\}$ CARLESON [1] has very recently proved the following:

THEOREM 3.4.1. *The series*

$$\sum_{k=1}^{\infty} c_k \sin kx$$

is convergent almost everywhere if

$$\sum_{k=1}^{\infty} c_k^2 < \infty.$$

CHAPTER 4

STATIONARY SEQUENCES

It is very easy to obtain laws of large numbers for stationary sequences by making use of the results of § 0.5. So we present the most fundamental laws without any proof as consequences of the ergodic theorems and of the results on the representation of stationary sequences by measure preserving transformations. The difficulties from the special point of view of probability theory lie in the investigation of the condition of ergodicity. This investigation seems to be very difficult and not quite solved.[1]

§ 4.1. Stationary sequences in the strong sense

Theorem 0.5.1 and our statement (in § 0.5) about the representation of strongly stationary sequences by measure preserving transformations imply:

THEOREM 4.1.1. *A strongly stationary sequence* $\xi_1, \xi_2, \ldots$ *obeys the strong law of large numbers, i.e.*

$$\zeta_n = \frac{\xi_1 + \xi_2 + \ldots + \xi_n}{n}$$

converges with probability 1 *to an integrable random variable* ξ^* *if* $\mathbf{E}(|\xi_i|) < \infty$.

Without loss of generality we can assume the existence of a measurable and measure preserving transformation T, defined on the same probability space $\{\Omega, \mathscr{S}, \mathbf{P}\}$ as that on which the sequence $\xi_1, \xi_2, \ldots$ is defined, for which $\xi_i(T\omega) = \xi_{i+1}(\omega)$ $(i = 1, 2, \ldots)$. Denote the smallest σ-algebra which contains the T-invariant measurable sets (i.e. those elements of $\mathscr{S}$ for which $T^{-1}A = A$) by $\mathscr{T}$. Then we can give the following characterization of the random variable ξ^* introduced in Theorem 4.1.1.

THEOREM 4.1.1a

$$\xi^* = \mathbf{E}(\xi_i \mid \mathscr{T}) .$$

[1] For the solution see SHIRYAEV [1].

PROOF. By Theorem 0.5.1

$$\int_A \xi^* \, d\mathbf{P} = \int_A \xi_i \, d\mathbf{P}$$

for any $A \in \mathcal{F}$. (Consider the set A as the basic space!) Obviously ξ^* is measurable with respect to $\mathcal{F}$. So the definition of the conditional expectation implies our statement.

In particular, if T, the transformation generating the sequence $\xi_1, \xi_2, \ldots$, is ergodic then ξ^* is constant with probability 1.

A strongly stationary sequence $\xi_1, \xi_2, \ldots$ will be called an *ergodic sequence (or metrically transitive sequence)* if it can be represented by an ergodic transformation, or more precisely, if there can be found a probability space $\{\tilde{\Omega}, \tilde{\mathcal{S}}, \tilde{\mathbf{P}}\}$, an ergodic, measurable and measure preserving transformation $\tilde{\mathcal{T}}$ (defined on $\tilde{\Omega}$) and a random variable $\tilde{\xi}(\tilde{\omega})$ $(\tilde{\omega} \in \tilde{\Omega})$ such that

$$\mathbf{P}(\xi_1 < x_1, \xi_2 < x_2 \ldots, \xi_n < x_n) = \tilde{\mathbf{P}}(\tilde{\xi}_1 < x_1 \tilde{\xi}_2 < x_2, \ldots, \tilde{\xi}_n < x_n)$$

for any integer n and for any real $x_1, x_2, \ldots, x_n$, where $\tilde{\xi}_{i+1}(\tilde{\omega}) = \tilde{\xi}(\tilde{T}^i\tilde{\omega})$ $(i = 0, 1, 2, \ldots)$. It must be emphasized that an ergodic sequence can be always represented by a non-ergodic transformation, too. So $\xi_1, \xi_2, \ldots$ is called an ergodic sequence if there is a *possibility* of representing it by an ergodic transformation, even if it was originally defined by a non-ergodic transformation.

According to Theorem 2.9.3 if $\xi_1, \xi_2, \ldots$ is a stationary sequence of independent random variables then the condition $\mathbf{E}(|\xi_i|) < \infty$ is not only sufficient for the validity of the strong law of large numbers but it is also necessary. In the general case the situation is much more complicated. As a converse of Theorem 4.1.1 we can state:

THEOREM 4.1.2. *If $\xi_1, \xi_2, \ldots$ is a non-negative stationary sequence in the strong sense (i.e. $\mathbf{P}(\xi_i \geq 0) = 1$) and the sequence*

$$\zeta_n = \frac{\xi_1 + \xi_2 + \ldots + \xi_n}{n}$$

converges with probability 1 *to an integrable random variable ξ^*, then ξ_i is integrable.*

PROOF. Let

$$\xi_i^{(K)} = \begin{cases} \xi_i & \text{if } |\xi_i| \leq K \\ 0 & \text{otherwise.} \end{cases}$$

Then the sequence

$$\zeta_n(K) = \frac{\xi_1^{(K)} + \xi_2^{(K)} + \ldots + \xi_n^{(K)}}{n}$$

converges with probability 1 to a bounded random variable $\xi^*(K)$ for which $\mathbf{E}(\xi^*(K)) = \mathbf{E}(\xi_1^{(K)}) \leq \mathbf{E}(\xi^*)$. By Theorem 0.1.1 $\mathbf{E}(\xi_1^{(K)}) \to \mathbf{E}(\xi_1)$ as $K \to \infty$ which proves our theorem.

Clearly, it can happen that ζ_n converges to a non-integrable random variable but in this case ξ_i is also non-integrable provided that $\mathbf{P}(\xi_i \geq 0) = 1$.

It can be shown that our last theorem is false if ξ_i can take negative values, i.e. if $\mathbf{P}(\xi_1 \geq 0) < 1$ (see HALMOS [2] p. 32) even if $\xi_1, \xi_2, \ldots$ is an ergodic sequence.

In the first paragraph of this chapter we have mentioned that it seems to be very difficult to check the ergodicity of a stationary sequence. Obviously if we have only one realization of $\xi_1, \xi_2, \ldots$, i.e. if we only know the values of the random variables $\xi_1, \xi_2, \ldots$ at a fixed point $\omega_1 \in \Omega$ then it is impossible to know anything about the ergodicity of the sequence. If we can start this process once again independently from the first realization, i.e. if we know the values of the random variables $\xi_1, \xi_2, \ldots$ at another point $\omega_2 \in \Omega$, chosen independently of ω_1, then we can say more. Namely we can decide, at least theoretically, whether the points ω_1, ω_2 belong to different invariant classes. This fact can be stated in a more precise form in the following way:

Let the stationary sequence $\xi_1, \xi_2, \ldots$ be defined on a probability space $\{\Omega, \mathscr{S}, \mathbf{P}\}$. Define the product space $\{\tilde{\Omega}, \tilde{\mathscr{S}}, \tilde{\mathbf{P}}\}$ and the stationary sequences $\xi_1^{(1)}(\omega_1, \omega_2)$, $\xi_2^{(1)}(\omega_1, \omega_2)$, $\ldots$, $\xi_1^{(2)}(\omega_1, \omega_2)$, $\xi_2^{(2)}(\omega_1, \omega_2), \ldots$ by

$$\tilde{\Omega} = \Omega_1 \times \Omega_2, \quad \tilde{\mathscr{S}} = \mathscr{S}_1 \times \mathscr{S}_2, \quad \tilde{\mathbf{P}} = \mathbf{P}_1 \times \mathbf{P}_2$$

where

$$\{\Omega_1, \mathscr{S}_1, \mathbf{P}_1\} = \{\Omega_2, \mathscr{S}_2, \mathbf{P}_2\} = \{\Omega, \mathscr{S}, \mathbf{P}\}$$

and

$$\xi_i^{(1)}(\omega_1, \omega_2) = \xi_i(\omega) \quad \text{if} \quad \omega_1 = \omega$$

$$\xi_i^{(2)}(\omega_1, \omega_2) = \xi_i(\omega) \quad \text{if} \quad \omega_2 = \omega\,.$$

Then the processes $\xi^{(1)} = (\xi_1^{(1)}, \xi_2^{(1)}, \ldots)$ and $\xi^{(2)} = (\xi_1^{(2)}, \xi_2^{(2)}, \ldots)$ are independent. Further if we have one realization of $\xi^{(1)}$ and one of $\xi^{(2)}$, i.e. if we know the values of $\xi_1^{(1)}, \xi_2^{(1)}, \ldots$ and the values of $\xi_1^{(2)}$, $\xi_2^{(2)}, \ldots$ at a fixed point $(\omega_1, \omega_2) \in \tilde{\Omega}$ then we can decide whether ω_1 and ω_2 belong to different invariant sets of Ω. So if we start our process twice independently then it can happen that we can prove that our sequence is non-ergodic, but we surely cannot prove its ergodicity.

Obviously, if we want to be sure that our sequence is ergodic then we have to start the sequence independently infinitely many times, i.e. we have to choose independently an infinite sequence $\omega_1, \omega_2, \ldots$. If there are not two points ω_i and ω_j in this sequence belonging to different invariant sets then we can state (and the probability of a false decision is 0) that the sequence is ergodic.

The properties of the weighted averages of strongly stationary sequences, under some strong conditions on the weights, are studied in the papers [1] and [2] of BAXTER. We will not present these results here.

§ 4.2. Strong and weak laws for stationary sequences in the weak sense

Theorem 0.5.3 and our statement (in § 0.5) about the representation of weakly stationary sequences by the isometries of a Hilbert space imply

THEOREM 4.2.1. *A weakly stationary sequence* $\xi_1, \xi_2, \ldots$ *obeys the mean law of large numbers, i.e.*

$$\zeta_n = \frac{\xi_1 + \xi_2 + \ldots + \xi_n}{n}$$

converges in mean to a square integrable random variable ξ^*.

It is not difficult to characterize the random variable ξ^* by the properties of the isometry U generating the sequence $\xi_1, \xi_2, \ldots$. However, from the point of view of probability theory the following simple theorem seems to be more useful.

THEOREM 4.2.2.

$$\zeta_n \xrightarrow{\text{m}} 0$$

if

$$\mathbf{E}(\xi_i) = 0$$

and

$$\frac{K(0) + K(1) + \ldots + K(n)}{n+1} \to 0$$

where $K(i)$ *is a non-negative function for which*

$$R(i) = \mathbf{E}(\xi_1 \xi_{1+i}) \leq K(i). \tag{4.2.1.}$$

The proof is so simple that we omit it.

A much more complicated question is to find strong laws for sequences stationary in the weak sense. A very simple result is the following.

THEOREM 4.3.2. *If*

$$|\xi_i| \leq C, \quad \mathbf{E}(\xi_i) = 0$$

and

$$\sum_{i=0}^{\infty} K(i) < \infty \tag{4.2.2.}$$

where C *is a positive constant and* $K(i)$ *is defined by* (4.2.1), *then*

$$\zeta_n \to 0.$$

REMARK. In the last two theorems it is assumed that $R(k)$ is not a large positive number (if k is large) but there is not any restriction on the lower bound of $R(k)$.

The proof will show that the condition (4.2.2) is far from the best possible.

PROOF. Clearly

$$\mathbf{E}(\zeta_n^2) \leqq \frac{n\,K(0) + (n-1)\,K(1) + \ldots + K(n-1)}{n^2} \leqq$$

$$\leqq \frac{K(0) + K(1) + \ldots + K(n-1)}{n} = O\left(\frac{1}{n}\right).$$

Hence

$$\sum_{N=1}^{\infty} \mathbf{E}(\zeta_{N^2}^2) < \infty$$

and therefore by the Beppo–Levi theorem we have

$$\zeta_{N^2} \to 0.$$

Now if $N^2 \leqq n < (N+1)^2$

$$\zeta_n = \zeta_{N^2}\frac{N^2}{n} + \frac{\xi_{N^2+1} + \xi_{N^2+2} + \ldots + \xi_n}{n}. \tag{4.2.3}$$

The first member of the right-hand side of (4.2.3) tends to 0 and for the second one we have

$$\left|\frac{\xi_{N^2+1} + \xi_{N^2+2} + \ldots + \xi_n}{n}\right| \leqq \frac{2\,NK}{n} \to 0 \quad \text{if} \quad n \to \infty$$

which proves our theorem.

One can obtain other types of conditions implying the convergence of ζ_n with probability 1 by making use of some results of ergodic theory (see DUNFORD). Here we do not give the details because the conditions of these results refer to the structure of the operator generating the process and not to the statistical structure of the process.

§ 4.3. The estimation of the covariance function

Let $\xi_1, \xi_2, \ldots$ be a stationary sequence (in the strong or in the weak sense). Suppose ξ_i is square integrable and denote the covariance function of this sequence by

$$R(\nu) = \mathbf{E}(\xi_n\,\xi_{n+\nu}) \quad (n = 0, 1, 2, \ldots; \nu = 0, 1, 2, \ldots).$$

It is natural to take as an estimate of $R(\nu)$ the average

$$\frac{1}{n}\sum_{j=1}^{n} \xi_j\,\xi_{j+\nu}.$$

As a consequence of Theorems 4.1.1 and 4.1.1a we have

THEOREM 4.3.1. *If $\xi_1, \xi_2, \ldots$ is a stationary sequence in the strong sense with $\mathbf{E}(\xi_i^2) < \infty$ then the sequence*

$$\zeta_n(\nu) = \frac{1}{n} \sum_{j=1}^{n} \xi_j \xi_{j+\nu}$$

converges with probability 1 *to a limit $\xi^*(\nu)$ as $n \to \infty$. In particular if $\xi_1, \xi_2, \ldots$ is an ergodic sequence then*

$$\mathbf{P}\big(\xi^*(\nu) = R(\nu)\big) = 1 .$$

PROOF. The sequence $\xi_1 \xi_{1+\nu}, \xi_2\xi_{2+\nu}, \ldots$ is stationary in the strong sense with finite expectation and is generated by the same transformation T.

If $\xi_1, \xi_2, \ldots$ is a stationary sequence in the weak sense then in general the sequence $\xi_1\xi_{1+\nu}, \xi_2\xi_{2+\nu}, \ldots$ is not stationary even in the weak sense. Therefore it is very difficult in this case to say anything about the limit $\zeta_n(\nu)$. If we assume that the sequence $\xi_1\xi_{1+\nu}, \xi_2\xi_{2+\nu}, \ldots$ is also stationary then as a consequence of Theorem 4.2.1 we obtain

THEOREM 4.3.2. *If $\xi_1, \xi_2, \ldots$ is a stationary sequence in the weak sense and $\xi_1\xi_{1+\nu}, \xi_2\xi_{2+\nu}, \ldots$ is also stationary in the weak sense then the sequence*

$$\frac{1}{n} \sum_{j=1}^{n} \xi_j \xi_{j+\nu}$$

converges in mean to a square integrable random variable $\xi^*(\nu)$. In particular if $\xi_1\xi_{1+\nu}, \xi_2\xi_{2+\nu}, \ldots$ is an ergodic sequence then

$$\mathbf{P}\big(\xi^*(\nu) = R(\nu)\big) = 1 .$$

CHAPTER 5

SUBSEQUENCES OF SEQUENCES OF RANDOM VARIABLES

Let $\boldsymbol{\xi} = (\xi_1, \xi_2, \ldots)$ be a sequence of random variables generally not satisfying any law oflarge numbers. The problem of this chapter is: under what conditions can we find a subsequence of $\boldsymbol{\xi}$ obeying a law of large numbers?

§ 5.1. A conjecture of H. Steinhaus

H. Steinhaus [1] raised the following problem:

"Does there exist a family F of measurable functions such that

1. $|f(t)| = 1$ for $f \in F$,
2. For each sequence $\{f_n(t)\}$ where $f_n(t) \in F$ the sequence

$$\frac{1}{n}\sum_{k=1}^{n} f_k(t)$$

is divergent for almost all t?"

In this § we prove that the answer is no. More exactly the following much more general result will be proved:

Theorem 5.1.1 (see Révész [2]). *Let $\xi_1, \xi_2, \ldots$ be a sequence of random variables for which $\mathbf{E}(\xi_i^2) \leq K$ $(i = 1, 2, \ldots)$. Then there exists a subsequence $n_1, n_2, \ldots$ of integers and a random variable η such that the series*

$$\sum_{k=1}^{\infty} c_k(\xi_{n_k} - \eta)$$

is convergent with probability 1, *for every rearrangement of terms, where $c_1, c_2, \ldots$ is an arbitrary sequence of real numbers for which $\sum_{k=1}^{\infty} c_k^2 < \infty$.*

This theorem and Theorem 1.2.2a imply

Theorem 5.1.2. *Let $\xi_1, \xi_2, \ldots$ be a sequence of random variables for which $\mathbf{E}(\xi_i^2) \leq K$ $(i = 1, 2, \ldots)$. Then there exists a subsequence $n_1, n_2, \ldots$ of integers and a random variable η such that*

$$\mathbf{P}\left\{\frac{c_1(\xi_{n_1} - \eta) + c_2(\xi_{n_2} - \eta) + \ldots + c_k(\xi_{n_k} - \eta)}{k} \to 0\right\} = 1$$

where $c_1, c_2, \ldots$ *is an arbitrary sequence of real numbers for which* $\sum_{k=1}^{\infty} \frac{c_k^2}{k^2} < \infty$.

In the case of uniformly bounded random variables we can prove that the condition $\sum_{k=1}^{\infty} c_k^2 < \infty$ of Theorem 5.1.1 is necessary. More exactly

THEOREM 5.1.3. *Let* $\xi_1, \xi_2, \ldots$ *be a sequence of uniformly bounded random variables* $|\xi_i| \leq K_1$ $(i = 1, 2, \ldots)$. *Then there exists a subsequence* $n_1, n_2, \ldots$ *of the integers such that if there exists a random variable* η^* *and a bounded sequence of real numbers* $(|c_k| \leq K_2)$ *for which*

$$\sum_{k=1}^{\infty} c_k(\xi_{n_k} - \eta^*) \tag{5.1.1}$$

is convergent with probability 1 *then*

$$\sum_{k=1}^{\infty} c_k^2 \, \mathbf{E}[(\xi_{n_k} - \eta^*)^2] < \infty .$$

PROOF OF THEOREM 5.1.1. The condition

$$\mathbf{E}(\xi_i^2) \leq K \qquad (i = 1, \ 2, \ldots) \tag{5.1.2}$$

implies that the sequence $\xi_1, \xi_2, \ldots$ is weakly compact in the Hilbert space of the square integrable random variables, i.e. there exists a subsequence $\xi_{n_1}, \xi_{n_2}, \ldots$ of the given sequence $\xi_1, \xi_2, \ldots$ and a square integrable random variable η with $\mathbf{E}(\eta^2) \leq K$, such that

$$\lim_{k\to\infty} \mathbf{E}(\xi_{n_k} \psi) = \mathbf{E}(\eta\psi)$$

where ψ is any square integrable random variable. Let

$$\delta_k = \xi_{n_k} - \eta . \tag{5.1.3}$$

Let b_k be a sequence of positive integers for which

$$\sum_{k=1}^{\infty} \mathbf{P}(|\delta_k| \geq b_k) < \infty \tag{5.1.4}$$

and

$$\lim_{k\to\infty} \int_{D_k} \delta_k^2 \, d\mathbf{P} = 0 \tag{5.1.5}$$

where

$$D_k = \{\omega : |\delta_k| \geq b_k\} .$$

(The existence of a sequence $\{b_k\}$ with these properties is obvious.)

Let

$$\delta_k^* = \begin{cases} \delta_k & \text{if } |\delta_k| \leq b_k \\ 0 & \text{otherwise} \end{cases}$$

By (5.1.4) the sequences $\{\delta_k\}$ and $\{\delta_k^*\}$ are equivalent in the sense of Khinchin.

By (5.1.5) δ_k^* converges to 0 weakly, and therefore we can construct a subsequence $\{\delta_{\nu_k}^*\}$ of the sequence $\{\delta_k^*\}$ as follows:

$$\delta_{\nu_1}^* = \delta_1^* .$$

ν_2 is an integer for which

$$|\mathbf{E}(\delta_{\nu_2}^*\,\delta_{\nu_1}^*)| \leq \frac{1}{2} \quad \text{and} \quad |\int_{A_1} \delta_{\nu_2}^*\,\delta_{\nu_1}^*\,d\mathbf{P}| \leq \frac{1}{2}$$

where

$$A_1 = A_1(i_1) = \left\{\omega : |\, i_1\,\delta_{\nu_1}^*(\omega)| \geq \frac{1}{2}\right\}$$

and

$$i_1 = 0\,,\pm\frac{1}{2\,b_{\nu_1}}\,,\pm\frac{2}{2\,b_{\nu_1}}\,,\,\ldots\,,\pm\frac{2\,b_{\nu_1}-1}{2\,b_{\nu_1}}\,,\pm 1 .$$

The integer $\nu_3 > \nu_2$ is defined by the following inequalities:

$$|\mathbf{E}(\delta_{\nu_3}^*\,\delta_{\nu_1}^*)| \leq \frac{1}{4}, \qquad |\mathbf{E}(\delta_{\nu_3}^*\,\delta_{\nu_2}^*)| \leq \frac{1}{4},$$

$$|\int_{A_2} \delta_{\nu_3}^*\,\delta_{\nu_1}^*\,d\mathbf{P}| \leq \frac{1}{4}, \qquad |\int_{A_2} \delta_{\nu_3}^*\,\delta_{\nu_2}^*\,d\mathbf{P}| \leq \frac{1}{4},$$

and

$$|\int_{A_1} \delta_{\nu_3}^*\,\delta_{\nu_1}^*\,d\mathbf{P}| \leq \frac{1}{4}\,, \qquad |\int_{A_1} \delta_{\nu_3}^*\,\delta_{\nu_2}^*\,d\mathbf{P}| \leq \frac{1}{4}$$

where

$$A_2 = A_2^{(j_2)}(i_1, i_2) = \left\{\omega: |\, i_2\,\delta_{\nu_2}^* + i_1\,\delta_{\nu_1}^*| \geq \frac{1}{2^{j_2}}\,|\, i_1\,\delta_{\nu_1}^*| < \frac{1}{2^{j_2}}\right\}$$

and

$$i_2 = 0, \pm\frac{1}{4\,b_{\nu_2}}, \pm\frac{2}{4\,b_{\nu_2}}, \ldots, \pm\frac{4\,b_{\nu_2}-1}{4\,b_{\nu_2}}, \pm 1; \quad j_2 = 1, 2.$$

If the sequence $\nu_1, \nu_2, \ldots, \nu_k$ is already defined, then we can define the integer $\nu_{k+1} > \nu_k$ as the smallest number for which the following inequalities hold:

$$|\mathbf{E}(\delta_{\nu_{k+1}}^*\,\delta_{\nu_p}^*)| \leq \frac{1}{2^k} \qquad (p = 1, 2, \ldots, k)$$

and

$$\left|\int_{A_l} \delta_{\nu_{k+1}}^*\,\delta_{\nu_p}^*\,d\mathbf{P}\right| \leq \frac{1}{2^k} \quad (p = 1, 2, \ldots, k; \quad l = 1, 2, \ldots, k)$$

where

$$A_l = A_l^{(j_l)}(i_1, i_2, \ldots, i_l) =$$

$$= \left\{\omega : | i_1 \delta^*_{\nu_1} + i_2 \delta^*_{\nu_2} + \ldots + i_l \delta^*_{\nu_l} \geq \frac{1}{2^{j_l}}, | i_1 \delta^*_{\nu_1} + i_2 \delta^*_{\nu_2} + \ldots + i_{l-1} \delta^*_{\nu_{l-1}} | < \right.$$

$$\left. < \frac{1}{2^{j_l}}, \ldots, | i_1 \delta^*_{\nu_1} | < \frac{1}{2^{j_l}} \right\}$$

and

$$i_m = 0, \pm \frac{1}{2^m b_{\nu_m}}, \pm \frac{2}{2^m b_{\nu_m}}, \ldots, \pm \frac{2^m b_{\nu_m} - 1}{2^m b_{\nu_m}}, \pm 1;$$

$$m = 1, 2, \ldots, l; \qquad j_l = 1, 2, \ldots, l.$$

We now prove a lemma analogous to Kolmogorov's inequality:

Lemma 5.1.1. *Let $\eta_l = d_l \delta^*_{\nu_l}$ $(l = 1, 2, \ldots)$ where $\delta^*_{\nu_l}$ is the sequence of random variables defined above and $\{d_l\}$ is an arbitrary sequence of real numbers such that $| d_l | \leq 1$ $(l = 1, 2, \ldots)$. Then, for any ε such that $0 < \varepsilon \leq \frac{1}{2}$ and for any $1 \leq j < k$ we have*

$$\mathbf{P}\left\{ \max_{j \leq l \leq k} \left| \sum_{h=j}^{l} \eta_h \right| \geq \varepsilon \right\} \leq \frac{64 K \sum_{l=j}^{k} d_l^2 + \frac{64(2j+5)}{2^j}}{\varepsilon^2}.$$

Proof of Lemma 5.1.1. First of all suppose that ε is one of the numbers $\frac{1}{2}, \frac{1}{4}, \ldots, \frac{1}{2^j}$ and d_l is one of the numbers

$$0, \pm \frac{1}{2^l b_{\nu_l}}, \pm \frac{2}{2^l b_{\nu_l}}, \ldots, \pm \frac{2^l b_{\nu_l} - 1}{2^l b_{\nu_l}}, \pm 1.$$

Let

$$\Delta_l = \eta_j + \eta_{j+1} + \ldots + \eta_l \qquad (l = j, j+1, \ldots, k),$$

$$B = \{\omega : \max_{j \leq l \leq k} | \Delta_l | \geq \varepsilon\}$$

and

$$B_l = \{\omega : | \Delta_l | \geq \varepsilon, | \Delta_{l-1} | < \varepsilon, \ldots, | \Delta_j | < \varepsilon\} \quad (l = j, j+1, \ldots, k).$$

Then clearly,

$$B_l = A_l^{(\varepsilon)}(0, 0, \ldots, 0, d_{j+1}, \ldots, d_l)$$

and

$$B = \sum_{l=j}^{k} B_l.$$

Then we have

$$\mathbf{E}(\Delta_k^2) = \int_\Omega \Delta_k^2 \, d\mathbf{P} \leqq 4\,K \sum_{l=j}^{k} d_l^2 + \frac{4}{2^j}\,,$$

$$\int_\Omega \Delta_k^2 \, d\mathbf{P} \geqq \int_B \Delta_k^2 \, d\mathbf{P} = \sum_{l=j}^{k} \int_{B_l} \Delta_k^2 \, d\mathbf{P}$$

and

$$\int_{B_l} \Delta_k^2 \, d\mathbf{P} = \int_{B_l} (\eta_j + \eta_{j+1} + \ldots + \eta_k)^2 \, d\mathbf{P} = \int_{B_l} (\eta_j + \eta_{j+1} + \ldots + \eta_l)^2 \, d\mathbf{P} +$$

$$+ \sum_{r=l+1}^{k} \int_{B_l} \eta_r^2 \, d\mathbf{P} + 2 \sum_{r=l+1}^{k} \sum_{q=j}^{r-1} \int_{B_l} \eta_q \eta_r \, d\mathbf{P} \geqq \int_{B_l} (\eta_j + \eta_{j+1} + \ldots + \eta_l)^2 \, d\mathbf{P} -$$

$$- 2 \sum_{r=l}^{\infty} \frac{r}{2^r} \geqq \varepsilon^2 \, \mathbf{P}(B_l) - \frac{l+1}{2^{l-2}}\,.$$

Therefore

$$4\,K \sum_{l=j}^{k} d_l^2 \geqq \varepsilon^2 \, \mathbf{P}(B) - \frac{2\,j+5}{2^{j-2}}.$$

Hence we have proved the lemma in the case $\varepsilon = \dfrac{1}{2^h}$ $(h = 1,\ 2, \ldots, j)$ and $d_l = \pm \dfrac{s}{2^l\, b_{\nu_l}}$ $(s = 0, 1, 2, \ldots, 2^l\, b_{\nu_l})$. We can obtain our inequality in the case $\dfrac{1}{2^{h-1}} \geqq \varepsilon > \dfrac{1}{2^h}$ $(h = 2, 3, \ldots, j)$ by using the inequalities

$$\mathbf{P}\left\{ \max_{j \leqq l \leqq k} |\Delta_l| \geqq \varepsilon \right\} \leqq \mathbf{P}\left\{ \max_{j \leqq l \leqq k} |\Delta_l| \geqq \frac{1}{2^h} \right\} \leqq \frac{4\,K \sum\limits_{l=j}^{k} d_l^2 + \dfrac{2\,j+5}{2^{j-2}}}{\left(\dfrac{1}{2^h}\right)^2} \leqq$$

$$\leqq \frac{16\,K \sum\limits_{l=j}^{k} d_l^2 + 4\,\dfrac{2\,j+5}{2^{j-2}}}{\varepsilon^2}\,.$$

If $\varepsilon \leqq \dfrac{1}{2^j}$ our inequality is evident because its right-hand side is larger than 1.

We can obtain the lemma in the general case by using the fact that for any d_l one can find an integer t $(|\,t\,| \leqq 2^l\, b_{\nu_l})$ such that

$$\left| d_l - \frac{t}{2^l\, b_{\nu_l}} \right| \leqq \frac{1}{2^l\, b_{\nu_l}}\,.$$

Thus the proof of the lemma is complete.

Now we return to the proof of Theorem 5.1.1. Let

$$\sigma_n = \sum_{k=1}^{n} c_k \, \delta^*_{\beta_k}$$

where β_k is an arbitrary reordering of the sequence $\{\nu_k\}$, and let

$$\alpha_m = \sup_k \, |\sigma_{m+k} - \sigma_m|$$

$$\alpha = \inf_m \, a_m .$$

Let ε be an arbitrary but fixed positive number $\left(0 < \varepsilon \leq \frac{1}{2}\right)$ and let m_0 be an integer for which $\frac{1}{2^{m_0}} < \varepsilon$ and $|c_k| \leq 1$ if $k \geq m_0$. Using the lemma for $d_k = c_k$ and any $j \geq m_0$ we obtain

$$\mathbf{P}\{\alpha_j \geq \varepsilon\} \leq \frac{64\,K \sum_{l=\tau_j}^{\infty} c_l^2 + \frac{64(2\tau_j + 5)}{2^{\tau_j}}}{\varepsilon^2}$$

where τ_j is the smallest ν_k in the sequence $\beta_j, \beta_{j+1}, \ldots$.

Since $\sum_{k=1}^{\infty} c_k^2 < \infty$ we have

$$\mathbf{P}(\alpha \geq \varepsilon) = 0 .$$

But ε is any arbitrary positive number $\left(\leq \frac{1}{2}\right)$, and therefore

$$\mathbf{P}(\alpha = 0) = 1 .$$

Thus we have proved the theorem.

Before proving Theorem 5.1.3 we give

Lemma 5.1.2. *If $\{\xi_n\}$ is a sequence of uniformly bounded random variables having a weak limit η and if the series*

$$\sum_{k=1}^{\infty} c_k(\xi_k - \eta^*)$$

is convergent with probability 1 *(where $\{c_k\}$ is a bounded sequence of the real numbers) then either $\mathbf{P}(\eta = \eta^*) = 1$ or the series $\sum_{k=1}^{\infty} c_k$ is convergent and so the series $\sum_{k=1}^{\infty} c_k(\xi_k - \eta)$ is also convergent.*

Proof of Lemma 5.1.2. Denote the limit of $\vartheta_N = \sum_{k=1}^{N} c_k(\xi_k - \eta^*)$ by ϑ. Then by Theorem 0.1.6, ϑ_N converges to ϑ uniformly on a set

F_ε of measure $1-\varepsilon$ (where ε is an arbitrary, but given positive number). Hence

$$(\vartheta_N, \psi) \to (\vartheta, \psi) \qquad (\text{as } N \to \infty)$$

whenever ψ is a square integrable random variable taking the value 0 on $\bar{F}_\varepsilon$. Since

$$(\xi_k, \psi) - (\eta^*, \psi) \to (\eta - \eta^*, \psi) \quad (\text{as } k \to \infty)$$

the convergence of the series $\sum_{k=1}^{\infty} c_k(\xi_k - \eta^*)$ implies the convergence of the series $\sum_{k=1}^{\infty} c_k(\eta - \eta^*, \psi)$. This fact proves the lemma.

PROOF OF THEOREM 5.1.3. Let $\{\xi_{\nu_i}\}$ be a subsequence of $\{\xi_i\}$ having a weak limit η. Let

$$\delta_k = \xi_{\nu_k} - \eta .$$

If

$$\lim_{k\to\infty} \mathbf{E}(\delta_k^2) = 0$$

then the theorem is obvious. Hence we assume that

$$\lim_{k\to\infty} \mathbf{E}(\delta_k^2) > 0 .$$

Now let $\{\delta_{\tau_k}\}$ be a subsequence of $\{\delta_k\}$ such that the series

$$\frac{\delta_{\tau_1}^2}{\mathbf{E}(\delta_{\tau_1}^2)}, \quad \frac{\delta_{\tau_2}^2}{\mathbf{E}(\delta_{\tau_2}^2)}, \ldots$$

has a weak limit ψ^2 $(0 < \mathbf{E}(\psi^2) < \infty)$.

A sequence $\{d_k\}$ of real numbers will be called a "good sequence" if d_k is one of the numbers $\frac{i}{2^k}$ $(k = 0, \pm 1, \pm 2, \ldots, \pm 2^k K_2)$ (where K_2 is defined by $|c_k| \leq K_2$).

Now we choose the sequence $\{n_k\}$ as follows: let $n_1 = \tau_1$. Supposing that $n_1, n_2, \ldots, n_{l-1}$ has already been chosen then we can choose n_l with the following properties:

(a) n_l is an element of the sequence τ_k

(b) $$\left| \int_{G_{l-1}} \frac{\delta_{n_l}^2}{\mathbf{E}(\zeta_{n_l}^2)} dP - \int_{G_{l-1}} \psi^2 \, dP \right| \leq \frac{1}{2^l}$$

and

(c) $$\left| \int_{G_{l-1}} \delta_{n_l} \sigma_{l-1} \, dP \right| \leq \frac{1}{2^l} \quad .$$

where

$$\sigma_0 = 0$$

$$\sigma_l = \sigma_l(d_1, d_2, \ldots, d_l) = \sum_{j=1}^{l} d_j \delta_{n_j} \quad (l = 1, 2, \ldots)$$

and

$$G_l = G_l(d_1, d_2, \ldots, d_l; j) = \prod_{i=1}^{l} \{\omega : \sigma_i \leqq j\}.$$

We require the validity of (b) and (c) for each good sequence and for each j $(j = 1, 2, \ldots, l)$.

Now let us suppose that there exists a sequence $\{c_k\}$ $(|c_k| \leqq K_2)$ and a random variable η^* such that (5.1.1) is convergent with probability 1 where $\{n_k\}$ is that sequence of integers just constructed. By Lemma 5.1.2 the series $\sum_{k=1}^{\infty} c_k(\xi_{n_k} - \eta)$ is also convergent. Further we can find a "good sequence" $\{d_k\}$ such that $|d_l - c_l| \leqq \frac{1}{2^l}$ and since $|\eta| \leqq K_1$, the series

$$\sum_{k=1}^{\infty} d_k(\xi_{n_k} - \eta) \tag{5.1.6}$$

is also convergent with probability 1.

Under this condition, Egorov's theorem implies that for any $\varepsilon > 0$ there exists a measurable subset E of Ω such that $P(\bar{E}) < \varepsilon$ and (5.1.6) is uniformly convergent on E. Similarly Egorov's theorem implies the existence of an integer N such that

$$E = \prod_{l=0}^{\infty} \{\omega : |\sigma_l| \leqq N\}.$$

If we put

$$E_n = \prod_{l=0}^{n} \{\omega : |\sigma_l| \leqq N\}$$

then $E_n = G_n(d_1, d_2, \ldots, d_n; N)$ (provided that $n \geqq N$) and then E_n is a decreasing sequence of sets whose intersection is E. If $F_n = E_{n-1} - E_n$ $(n = 1, 2, \ldots)$ and $\alpha_n = \int_{E_n} \sigma_n \, d\mathbf{P}$ then (if $l > N$)

$$\alpha_l - \alpha_{l-1} = \int_{E_{l-1}} \sigma_l^2 \, d\mathbf{P} - \int_{F_l} \sigma_l^2 \, d\mathbf{P} - \int_{E_{l-1}} \sigma_{l-1}^2 d\mathbf{P} = \int_{E_{l-1}} d_l^2 \delta_{n_l}^2 \, d\mathbf{P} +$$

$$+ 2 \int_{E_{l-1}} d_l \, \delta_{n_l} \sigma_{l-1} \, d\mathbf{P} - \int_{F_l} \sigma_l^2 \, d\mathbf{P} \geqq d_l^2 \, \mathbf{E}(\delta_{n_l}^2) \int_{E_{l-1}} \psi^2 \, d\mathbf{P} -$$

$$- \int_{F_l} \sigma_l^2 \, d\mathbf{P} - \frac{2d_l}{2^l} - \frac{d_l^2 \, \mathbf{E}(\delta_{n_l}^2)}{2^l}$$

and since $E_l \subset E_l$ and $\sigma_l \leqq N + 2K_1 K_2$ on F_l $(l = N, N+1, \ldots)$ it follows that

$$\alpha_l - \alpha_{l-1} \geqq d_l^2 \mathbf{E}(\delta_{n_l}^2) \int_{E_{l-1}} \psi^2 \, d\mathbf{P} - \frac{2\, d_l + d_l^2 \mathbf{E}(\delta_{n_l}^2)}{2^l} - (N + 2K_1K_2)^2 \mathbf{P}(F_l) \geqq$$

$$\geqq d_l^2 \mathbf{E}(\delta_{n_l}^2) \int_{E_{l-1}} \psi^2 \, d\mathbf{P} - \frac{2\, K_2 + 4\, K_1^2 K_2^2}{2^l} - (N + 2\, K_1 K_2)^2 \, \mathbf{P}(F_l).$$

Summing over l from $N + 1$ to k we obtain

$$\alpha_k - \alpha_{N-1} \geqq \int_E \psi^2 \, d\mathbf{P} \sum_{l=N+1}^{k} d_l^2 \mathbf{E}(\delta_{n_l}^2) - \frac{2\, K^2 + 4\, K_1^2 K_2^2}{2^N} - (N + 2\, K_1 K_2)^2.$$

Letting $k \to \infty$ we obtain

$$\sum_{l=1}^{\infty} d_l^2 \mathbf{E}(\delta_{n_l}^2) < \infty$$

which easily implies our statement (using Lemma 5.1.2 again).

In a certain sense the following result is a generalization of Theorem 5.1.2.

THEOREM 5.1.4 (see KOMLÓS [1]). *Let $\xi_1, \xi_2, \ldots$ be a sequence of random variables for which $\mathbf{E}(|\xi_i|) \leqq K$ $(i = 1, 2, \ldots)$. Then there exists a subsequence $n_1, n_2, \ldots$ of the integers and a random variable η such that*

$$\mathbf{P}\left\{\frac{\xi_{n_1} + \xi_{n_2} + \ldots \xi_{n_k}}{k} \to \eta\right\} = 1.$$

The proof of this theorem is omitted.

Using the methods of proof of Theorem 5.1.1 and the paper [1] of M. WEISS we obtain the following:

THEOREM 5.1.5. *Let $\xi_1, \xi_2, \ldots$ be a sequence of uniformly bounded random variables. Then there exists a subsequence $n_1, n_2, \ldots$ of the integers and two random variables μ and σ $(\sigma \geqq 0)$ such that*

$$\mathbf{P}\left\{\overline{\lim_{k\to\infty}} \frac{(\xi_{n_1} - \mu) + (\xi_{n_2} - \mu) + \ldots + (\xi_{n_k} - \mu)}{\sqrt{2\, k \log\log k}\;\, \sigma} = 1 \,\middle|\, \sigma > 0\right\} = 1 \quad (5.1.7)$$

and

$$\mathbf{E}\left\{(\xi_{n_k} - \mu)^2 \,|\, \sigma = 0\right\} \to 0 \quad (k \to \infty). \qquad (5.1.8)$$

(5.1.7), (resp. (5.1.8)) lose all their meaning if $\mathbf{P}(\sigma > 0) = 0$ (resp. $\mathbf{P}(\sigma = 0) = 0$).

We omit the proof.

§ 5.2. Subsequences of stationary sequences

Let $\xi_1, \xi_2, \ldots$ be a stationary sequence. In this § we ask under what condition can we state that any (or a random) subsequence of this sequence obeys the law of large numbers. The difficulty of this question is shown by the fact that a subsequence of a stationary sequence is in general non-stationary, except when the original sequence is a sequence of symmetrically dependent random variables. More exactly, any subsequence of a sequence of symmetrically dependent random variables is a stationary sequence and conversely if any subsequence of a stationary sequence is stationary then the original sequence is a sequence of symmetrically dependent random variables.

The investigation of a random subsequence of a strongly stationary sequence is very easy. (See also BLUM–ROSENBLATT [1,])

DEFINITION. Let $\xi_1, \xi_2, \ldots$ be a sequence of random variables stationary in the strong sense and let $\tau_1, \tau_2, \ldots$ be a sequence of independent random variables with

$$\mathbf{P}(\tau_i = 1) = p\,, \quad \mathbf{P}(\tau_i = 0) = 1 - p \qquad (0 < p < 1\,; i = 1, 2, \ldots)$$

which are independent of the sequence $\xi_1, \xi_2, \ldots$. The sequence $\tau_1\xi_1, \tau_2\xi_2, \ldots$ is called a random subsequence of $\xi_1, \xi_2, \ldots$.

Obviously, a random subsequence of $\xi_1, \xi_2, \ldots$ is a stationary sequence in the strong sense. Therefore we have the following trivial

THEOREM 5.2.1. *If $\xi_1, \xi_2, \ldots$ is a sequence of random variables stationary in the strong sense with $\mathbf{E}(|\xi_i|) < \infty$ and*

$$\frac{\xi_1 + \xi_2 + \ldots + \xi_n}{n} \to \eta$$

then

$$\frac{\tau_1 \xi_1 + \tau_2 \xi_2 + \ldots + \tau_n \xi_n}{n} \to \eta\, p\,.$$

The investigation of the non-random subsequences of a stationary sequence is much more complicated. To formulate our results we use the language of ergodic theory.

THEOREM 5.2.2. *If T is a mixing transformation defined on a probability space $\{\Omega, \mathscr{S}, \mathbf{P}\}$ and $f(\omega)$ is a square-integrable function defined on Ω with $\int_\Omega f(\omega)d\mathbf{P} = 0$*

then

$$\frac{f(T^{n_1}\omega) + f(T^{n_2}\omega) + \ldots + f(T^{n_k}\omega)}{k} \xrightarrow{m} 0 \; (k \to \infty)$$

where $n_1, n_2, \ldots$ is an arbitrary increasing subsequence of integers.

PROOF. To evaluate the expectation of

$$\left(\frac{f(T^{n_1}\omega) + f(T^{n_2}\omega) + \ldots + f(T^{n_k}\omega)}{k}\right)^2$$

and to see that it converges to 0 is very easy.

In some sense we can prove that the condition that T is mixing is necessary.

THEOREM 5.2.3. *If T is a transformation defined on a probability space $\{\Omega, \mathscr{S}, \mathbf{P}\}$ and if for all $f(\omega) \in L^2$ and for all subsequences $n_1, n_2, \ldots$ of the integers we have*

$$\frac{f(T^{n_1}\omega) + f(T^{n_2}\omega) + \ldots + f(T^{n_k}\omega)}{k} \xrightarrow{m} \int_\Omega f(\omega)\, d\mathbf{P} \qquad (5.2.1)$$

then T is mixing.

PROOF. Let $g(\omega)$ be an arbitrary element of $L^2(\Omega, \mathbf{P})$, then by (5.2.1) for *all* $n_1, n_2, \ldots$ we have

$$\frac{1}{k}\sum_{i=1}^{k}\int_\Omega f(T^{n_i}\omega)\, g(\omega)\, d\mathbf{P} \to \int_\Omega f(\omega)\, d\mathbf{P}\int_\Omega g(\omega)\, d\mathbf{P}.$$

This obviously implies

$$\int_\Omega f(T^n\omega)\, g(\omega)\, d\mathbf{P} \to \int f \int g$$

which is our statement.

To find conditions which will imply that any subsequence of a stationary sequence obeys the strong law of large numbers is much more complicated.

§ 5.3. Subsequences of special orthogonal sequences

In § 5.1 we have already seen that any sequence of random variables, bounded in a certain sense, contains a subsequence obeying the law of large numbers and the law of the iterated logarithm. Evidently in the general case one cannot say anything about the density of a "good" sequence.

In this § we investigate this question in the case of Walsh functions $\{w_n(x)\}$ and the sequence $\{\sin nx\}$. We will see that if we consider a subsequence w_{n_k} (resp. $\sin n_k x$) of these sequences for which $n_{k+1}/n_k \geq \geq q > 1$ then we can obtain practically the same results as for independent sequences. The proofs of these facts are very complicated and therefore only the most important results and some ideas of the proofs are given.

The most complete results are which known have been obtained for the trigonometric sequence (see M. WEISS [2] and ERDŐS–GÁL.

THEOREM 5.3.1. *Let us suppose that $\{n_k\}$ is a sequence of integers*[1] *for which $n_{k+1}/n_k \geqq q > 1$ and $\{a_k\}$ and $\{b_k\}$ are sequences of real numbers for which*

$$\max_{1 \leqq k \leqq N} (a_k^2 + b_k^2)^{1/2} = o\left(\frac{B_N}{\sqrt{\log \log B_n}}\right)$$

$$B_N \to \infty$$

where

$$B_N = \sqrt{\frac{1}{2} \sum_{k=1}^{N} (a_k^2 + b_k^2)} \;.$$

Then for almost all x we have

$$\overline{\lim_{N \to \infty}} \frac{S_N(\mathrm{x})}{\sqrt{2 B_N^2 \log \log B_N}} = 1$$

where

$$S_N(x) = \sum_{k=1}^{N} (a_k \cos n_k x + b_k \sin n_k x).$$

This result seems to be quite complete, but recently ERDŐS [3] has proved a central limit theorem for the sequence $\{\sin n_k x\}$ under the condition that n_{k+1}/n_k converges to 1 sufficient slowly. The analogous law of the iterated logarithm is unknown.

The problem of analogues for Walsh functions is treated in RÉVÉSZ–WSCHEBOR [1]. The treatment of Walsh functions seems to be much simpler but the results corresponding to this question are not as complete as the corresponding results for trigonometric functions.

THEOREM 5.3.2. *Let $w_{n_1}, w_{n_2}, \ldots$ be a lacunary subsequence of the Walsh functions (i.e. $n_{k+1}/n_k \geqq q > 1$]. Then we have*

$$\overline{\lim_{N \to \infty}} \frac{\sum_{k=1}^{N} w n_k}{\sqrt{2 N \log \log N}} \leqq 1$$

(almost everywhere).

This result is trivial in the case $\frac{n_{k+1}}{n_k} \geqq 2$ because in this case the elements of the sequence $w_{n_1}, w_{n_2}, \ldots$ are independent.

Here we only give a sketch of the proof which is based on the following

REMARK (a). Let t be the smallest integer for which $q \geqq 1 + \frac{1}{2^t}$. Then at most $2t + 1$ members of the sequence $n_1, n_2, \ldots$ belong to the interval $[2^t, 2^{t+1})$. Therefore if we choose each $(2t+1)$-th member of the sequence $w_{n_1}, w_{n_2}, \ldots$ then we obtain an independent sequence.

[1] Similar results are known dropping the condition that n_k's are integers.

This remark together with the simplest form of the law of the iterated logarithm implies that

$$\overline{\lim_{N\to\infty}} \frac{w_{n_1} + w_{n_2} + \ldots + w_{n_N}}{\sqrt{2N \log\log N}} \leqq 2^{t+1}$$

almost everywhere.

The most important part of the proof of Theorem 5.3.2 is the following

LEMMA 5.3.1. *Let $w_{n_1}, w_{n_2}, \ldots$ be a subsequence of the Walsh functions, such that $n_{k+1}/n_k \geqq q > 1$. Then*

$$\lim_{N\to\infty} \int_0^1 \left[\prod_{k=1}^{N} \left(1 + \frac{\lambda}{\sqrt{N}} w_{n_k}\right)\right] dx = 1$$

where λ is any complex number.

REMARK (b). Among the first $t + 1$ digits in the binary expansion of n_{k+l} $(k = 1, 2, \ldots; l = 1, 2, \ldots)$ there is at least one that differs from the corresponding digit of n_k.

PROOF OF LEMMA 5.3.1. We have

$$\prod_{k=1}^{N} \left(1 + \frac{\lambda}{\sqrt{N}} w_{n_k}\right) = 1 + \frac{\lambda}{\sqrt{N}} \sum_{k=1}^{N} w_{n_k} + \frac{\lambda^2}{N} \sum_{1\leqq i<j\leqq N} w_{n_i} w_{n_j} +$$

$$+ \frac{\lambda^3}{N^{3/2}} \sum_{1\leqq i<j<l\leqq N} w_{n_i} w_{n_j} w_{n_l} + \ldots + \frac{\lambda^N}{N^{N/2}} w_{n_1} w_{n_2} \ldots w_{n_N}.$$

The expectation (the integral) of the second and third terms of the right-hand side of this formula is zero. So, to prove our lemma, it is enough to prove that the limit of the expectation of the following part (i.e. the fourth, fifth, ..., N-th terms) is zero as $N \to \infty$. Consider a term

$$\frac{\lambda^m}{N^{m/2}} \sum_{1\leqq l_1<l_2<\ldots<l_m\leqq N} w_{n_{l_1}} w_{n_{l_2}} \ldots w_{n_{l_m}}.$$

In this sum, the expectation of each term is 0 or 1, and it is 1 if and only if the exponent of each Rademacher function in $w_{n_{l_1}}, w_{n_{l_2}} \ldots w_{n_{l_m}}$ is even. The problem is then, to estimate the number of terms of the sum

$$\sum_{1\leqq l_1<l_2<\ldots<l_m\leqq N} w_{n_{l_1}} w_{n_{l_2}} \ldots w_{n_{l_m}}$$

whose expectation is equal to 1.

Let us try to construct a product $w_{n_{l_1}} w_{n_{l_2}} \ldots w_{n_{l_m}}$ $(l_1 < l_2 < \ldots < l_m)$, whose expectation is equal to 1. First, the number of possibilities to choose the index n_{l_m} is smaller than N. Let us suppose that $n_{l_m} \in [2^\nu, 2^{\nu+1})$. This means that $w_{n_{l_m}}$ contains the Rademacher function $r_{\nu+1}$.

If

$$\int_0^1 w_{n_{l_1}} w_{n_{l_2}} \ldots w_{n_{l_m}} \, dx = 1 \tag{5.3.1}$$

then $w_{nl_1} w_{nl_2} \ldots w_{nl_m}$ contains at least one $r_{\nu+1}$ more, and hence $n_{l_{m-1}} \in [2^\nu, 2^{\nu+1})$ also. But according to remark (a), we have at most 2^{t+1} possibilities to choose the index $n_{l_{m-1}}$. $w_{n_{l_m}} w_{n_{l_{m-1}}}$ is a Walsh function again, and using remark (b), it contains a Rademacher function whose index is larger than $(\nu + 1) - (t + 1) = \nu - t$. This means that we have at most $(t + 1)^2 < 2^{2(t+1)}$ possibilities to choose $n_{l_{m-2}}$.

Thus the number of possibilities to choose the first three Walsh functions of the product $w_{n_{l_1}} w_{n_{l_2}} \ldots w_{n_{l_m}}$ is smaller than $N 2^{3(t+1)}$. Now $w_{n_{l_m}} w_{n_{l_{m-1}}} w_{n_{l_{m-2}}}$ is a Walsh function again, and let us suppose that the Rademacher function of largest index contained by it is r_{k_1+1}. We consider two cases:

1. $$n_{l_{m-3}} \in [2^{k_1}, 2^{k_1+t+1})$$

2. $$n_{l_{m-3}} \notin [2^{k_1}, 2^{k_1+t+1}).$$

In case 1. we have less than $2^{2(t+2)}$ possibilities to choose $n_{l_{m-3}}$.
In case 2. $n_{l_{m-3}} \geqq 2^{k_1+t+1}$. Furthermore we have much fewer than N possibilities to choose $n_{l_{m-3}}$, but if we have already fixed $n_{l_{m-3}}$ then we have again less than $2^{3(t+2)}$ possibilities for the next two Walsh functions.

Hence, in case 1. we have less than $N 2^{5(t+2)}$ possibilities to choose the first four Walsh functions, and in case 2. less than $N^2\ 2^6{}_t{}^+$. for the first six ones. We continue our procedure in a similar way,

Let us suppose that we obtain our m Walsh functions $w_{n_{l_m}}$, $w_{n_{l_{m-1}}}$ $\ldots, w_{nl_1}$ in such a way that we choose them k times using the method 2. and $m - 3k$ times using the method 1. We can do this less than $3^k \binom{\left[\frac{m}{3}\right]}{k}$ ways, and therefore the number of products for which (5.3.1) holds is smaller than

$$3^k \binom{\left[\frac{m}{3}\right]}{k} (N\ 2^{3(t+2)})^k\ (2^{2(t+2)})^{m+3k}.$$

Therefore the total number of possibilities for the choice of w_{nl_m}, $w_{nl_{m-1}}, \ldots, w_{nl_1}$ is bounded by:

$$\sum_{k=0}^{\left[\frac{m}{3}\right]} 3^k \binom{\left[\frac{m}{3}\right]}{k} [N\ 2^{3(t+2)}]^k\ [2^{2(t+2)}]^{m-3k} \leqq [3\,N\ 2^{3(t+2)} + 2^{6(t+2)}]^{\frac{m}{3}}.$$

Then

$$\int \sum_{1 \leq l_1 < l_2 < \ldots < l_m \leq N} w n_{l_1} w n_{l_2} \ldots w n_{l_m} \, dx \leq [3 N \, 2^{3(t+2)} + 2^{6(t+2)}]^{\frac{m}{3}}$$

and

$$\lim_{N \to \infty} \sum_{m=3}^{N} \frac{\lambda^m}{N^{m/2}} \int \sum_{1 \leq l_1 < l_2 < \ldots l_m \leq N} w n_{l_1} w n_{l_2} \ldots w n_{l_m} \, dx <$$

$$< \lim_{n \to \infty} \sum_{m=3}^{N} \frac{|\lambda|^m}{N^{m/2}} [3 N \, 2^{3(t+2)} \, 2^{6(t+2)}]^{\frac{m}{3}}$$

and hence our lemma is proved.

Using the above lemma the proof of Theorem 5.3.2 is essentially the same as the classical proof (see e.g. M. WEISS [1]). The proof of this lemma was given here because it probably should enable us to obtain results similar to those obtained by ERDŐS (n_{k+1}/n_k tends to 1 slowly in this case).

Let us mention here the following

PROBLEM. What is the "smallest" function $f(k)$ for which

$$\frac{w_{n_1} + w_{n_2} + \ldots + w_{n_k}}{f(k)} \to 0 \text{ (almost everywhere)}$$

where $n_1, n_2, \ldots$ is an arbitrary sequence of integers? It is easy to see that for this smallest function one has

$$\sqrt{n} \, (\log \log n)^C \leq f(n) \leq \sqrt{n} \, (\log n)^{3/2} \, (\log \log n)^2$$

for any $C > 0$ (see RÉVÉSZ–WSCHEBOR [1]).

CHAPTER 6

SYMMETRICALLY DEPENDENT RANDOM VARIABLES AND THEIR GENERALIZATIONS

§ 6.1. Symmetrically dependent random variables

A sequence $\xi_1, \xi_2, \ldots$ of symmetrically dependent random variables is a stationary sequence in the strong sense. Therefore by Theorem 4.1.1 the sequence $\xi_1, \xi_2, \ldots$ obeys the strong law of large numbers if $\mathbf{E}(\xi_i)$ exists. This fact also follows easily from Theorem 5.1.4. Stronger results can be obtained by making use of a fundamental theorem of symmetrically dependent random variables (see Révész [3], Loève [1] p. 365).

First we give some lemmas.

The first lemma is a trivial consequence of Theorem 0.4.8.

Lemma 6.1.1. *Let $\xi_1, \xi_2, \ldots$ be a sequence of symmetrically dependent random variables with finite variances. Then ξ_n converges weakly to an element μ of the Hilbert space of square integrable random variables, i.e.*

$$\mathbf{E}(\xi_n \eta) \to \mathbf{E}(\mu \eta) \qquad (n \to \infty)$$

for any square integrable random variable η.

Lemma 6.1.2. *If the random variable $\psi(\omega)$ is a symmetric*[1] *Baire function of the symmetrically dependent random variables $\xi_1, \xi_2, \ldots$ and $g(x, y)$ is a Borel measurable function defined on the Euclidean plane then $g(\xi_1, \psi), g(\xi_2, \psi), \ldots$ is a sequence of symmetrically dependent random variables.*

Proof. The distribution functions[2] $F_1(x_1)$, $F_2(x_1, x_2), \ldots$ uniquely determine the distribution function of $\psi(\omega)$ and the joint distribution function of $g(\xi_{i_1}, \psi), g(\xi_{i_2}, \psi), \ldots, g(\xi_{i_k}, \psi)$. This last mentioned distribution function does not depend on the indices $i_1, i_2, \ldots, i_k$.

Lemma 6.1.3. *Let $\xi_1, \xi_2, \ldots$ be a sequence of symmetrically dependent random variables with finite variances. Then*

$$\mathbf{P}\left(\frac{\xi_1 + \xi_2 + \ldots + \xi_n}{n} \to \mu\right) = 1 \qquad (6.1.1)$$

[1] The function $\psi(x_1, x_2, \ldots)$ is *symmetric* if $\psi(x_1, x_2, \ldots) = \psi(x_{i_1}, x_{i_2}, \ldots)$ where $i_1, i_2, \ldots$ is any permutation of the integers.

[2] $F_k(x_1, x_2, \ldots, x_k) = \mathbf{P}(\xi_1 < x_1, \xi_2 < x_2, \ldots \xi_k < x_k)$.

and

$$\frac{(\xi_1-\mu)^2+(\xi_2-\mu)^2+\ldots+(\xi_n-\mu)^2}{n} \tag{6.1.2}$$

converges to an integrable random variable $\sigma^2(\omega)$ *with probability* 1, *where* μ *is the weak limit of* ξ_n.

PROOF. (6.1.1) and (6.1.2) are trivial consequences of Theorem 4.1.1 and Lemma 2. (Obviously μ is a symmetric Baire function of $\xi_1, \xi_2, \ldots$).

Let $\xi_1, \xi_2, \ldots$ be a sequence of symmetrically dependent random variables. We use the following notations:

1. $A_n(x)$ is the event that $\xi_n < x$, i.e. $A_n(x)$ is the set of those points $\omega \in \Omega$ for which $\xi_n(\omega) < x$.
2. $a_n^{(x)}(\omega)$ is the indicator function of $A_n(x)$, i.e.

$$a_n^{(x)}(\omega) = \begin{cases} 1 \text{ if } \omega \in A_n(x) \\ 0 \text{ if } \omega \notin A_n(x) . \end{cases}$$

The next lemma characterizes the behaviour of the weak limits of the sequences $\{a_n^{(x)}(\omega)\}$ $(-\infty < x < +\infty)$.

LEMMA 6.1.4. *A stochastic process* $\lambda_x(\omega)$ $(-\infty < x < +\infty)$ *can be defined such that*

1°. λ_x *is the weak limit of* $\{a_n^{(x)}\}_{n=1}^{\infty}$ $(-\infty < x < +\infty)$,

2°. $\lambda_x(\omega)$ *is a distribution function for each* $\omega \in \Omega$.

PROOF. Obviously

$$\mathbf{P}(\lambda_x \leqq \lambda_y) = 1$$

if $x < y$. Arrange all rational numbers into a sequence $r_1, r_2, \ldots$ and define the random variable λ_{r_1} as any[1] weak limit of the sequence $\{a_n^{(r_1)}\}$. If λ_{r_1} is already defined for each ω, then define the random variable λ_{r_2} as that weak limit of $\{a_n^{(r_2)}\}$ which is not larger (not smaller) than λ_{r_1} everywhere if $r_1 > r_2$ $(r_2 > r_1)$, respectively. If $\lambda_{r_1}, \lambda_{r_2}, \ldots, \lambda_{r_k}$ are already defined then define the random variable $\lambda_{r_{k+1}}$ such that

(a) $\lambda_{r_{k+1}}$ is the weak limit of $\{a_n^{(r_{k+1})}\}_{n=1}^{\infty}$,

(b) $\lambda_{r_{k+1}} \leqq \lambda_{r_j}$ if $j \leqq k$ and $r_j > r_{k+1}$,

$\lambda_{r_{k+1}} \geqq \lambda_{r_j}$ if $j \leqq k$ and $r_j < r_{k+1}$.

Let λ_t for an irrational t be defined by

$$\lim_j \lambda_{r_j} = \lambda_t$$

where $\{r_j\}$ is an increasing sequence of rational numbers tending to t.

To prove Lemma 6.1.4 we have to show that:

[1] The weak limit of a sequence is uniquely determined *except* on a set of measure 0.

I. λ_t is the weak limit of $\{a_n^{(t)}\}_{n=1}^{\infty}$ (t is irrational),

II. $\mathbf{P}(\lim_{h\searrow 0} \lambda_{t-h} = \lambda_t) = 1$ (for each t),

III. $\mathbf{P}(\lim_{t\to-\infty} \lambda_t = 0) = \mathbf{P}(\lim_{t\to\infty} \lambda_t = 1) = 1$.

The proof of I: denote the weak limit of $a_n^{(t)}$ by β_t. Then

$$\mathbf{P}(\beta_t \geqq \lambda_t \geqq \lambda_r) = 1$$

if $r < t$. For any $\varepsilon > 0$ we can find a rational r such that $r < t$ and

$$\int_\Omega (a_N^{(t)} - a_N^{(r)})\, d\mathbf{P} < \varepsilon \qquad \text{for each N} \tag{6.1.3}$$

and we have

$$\lim_{N\to\infty} \int_\Omega (a_N^{(t)} - a_N^{(r)})\, d\mathbf{P} = \int_\Omega (\beta_t - \lambda_r)\, d\mathbf{P} \geqq \int_\Omega (\beta_t - \lambda_t)\, d\mathbf{P}. \tag{6.1.4}$$

(6.1.3) and (6.1.4) together imply I.

The proofs of II. and III. are similar.

LEMMA 6.1.5.

$$\mathbf{E}(a_{i_1}^{(x_1)} a_{i_2}^{(x_2)} \dots a_{i_k}^{(x_k)} \lambda_{t_1}^{r_1} \lambda_{t_2}^{r_2} \dots \lambda_{t_j}^{r_j}) = \mathbf{E}(\lambda_{x_1} \lambda_{x_2} \dots \lambda_{x_k} \lambda_{t_1}^{r_1} \lambda_{t_2}^{r_2} \dots \lambda_{t_j}^{r_j})$$

provided that the indices $i_1, i_2, \dots, i_k$ are different.

PROOF. In this proof we use many times the fact that the weak limit of $\{a_n^{(x)}\}_{n=1}^{\infty}$ is λ_x. So if $i_1 < i_2 < \dots < i_k < l_{11} < l_{12} < \dots < l_{1r_1} < l_{21} < l_{22} < \dots < l_{2r_2} < \dots < l_{j1} < l_{j2} < \dots < l_{jr_j}$ then we have

$$\mathbf{E}\big(a_{i_1}^{(x_1)} a_{i_2}^{(x_2)} \dots a_{i_k}^{(x_k)} a_{l_{11}}^{(t_1)} a_{l_{12}}^{(t_1)} \dots a_{l_{1r_1}}^{(t)} a_{l_{21}}^{(t_2)} \dots a_{l_{2r_2}}^{(t_2)} \dots a_{l_{j1}}^{(t_j)} \dots a_{l_{jr_j}}^{(t_j)}\big) =$$

$$= \lim_{l_{jr_j}\to\infty} \mathbf{E}\left(a_{i_1}^{(x_1)} \dots a_{i_k}^{(x_k)} a_{l_{11}}^{(t_1)} \dots a_{l_11}^{(t_1)} \dots a_{2r}^{(t_j)} \dots a_{ljrj}^{(t_j)}\right) =$$

$$= \mathbf{E}\left(a_{i_1}^{(x_1)} \dots a_{i_k}^{(x_k)} a_{l_{11}}^{(t_1)} \dots a_{l_{1r_1}}^{(t)} \dots a_{lj_1}^{(t_j)} \dots a_{ljr_{j-1}}^{(t_j)} \lambda_{t_j}\right).$$

Continuing this process $k + r_1 + \dots + r_j$ times we obtain the lemma.

We now formulate the fundamental theorem of symmetrically dependent random variables.

THEOREM 6.1.1. *Let $\xi_1, \xi_2, \dots$ be a sequence of symmetrically dependent random variables, then*

$$\mathbf{P}(\xi_{i_1} < x_1, \xi_{i_2} < x_2, \dots, \xi_{i_k} < x_k \mid \mathscr{F}) =$$

$$\mathbf{P}(\xi_{i_1} < x_1 \mid \mathscr{F})\, \mathbf{P}(\xi_{i_2} < x_2 \mid \mathscr{F}) \dots \mathbf{P}(\xi_{i_k} < x_k \mid \mathscr{F}) = \lambda_{x_1} \lambda_{x_2} \dots \lambda_{x_k}$$

with probability 1, *where $\mathscr{F}$ is the smallest σ-algebra containing the sets*

$$= A = \{\omega : a_1 \leqq \lambda_{x_1} < b_1, a_2 \leqq \lambda_{x_2} < b_2, \dots, a_n \leqq \lambda_{x_n} < b_n\} \tag{6.1.5}$$

and $\lambda_x(\omega)$ is the stochaistic process defined in Lemma 6.1.4.

PROOF. Let us suppose that

$$\mathbf{P}(\xi_{i_1} < x_1, \xi_{i_2} < x_2, \ldots, \xi_{i_k} < x_k \mid \mathscr{F}) = \lambda_{x_1} \lambda_{x_2} \ldots \lambda_{x_k} + \\ + \varepsilon_{i_1 i_2 \ldots i_k} (x_1, x_2, \ldots, x_k) . \tag{6.1.6}$$

Here the random variable $\varepsilon = \varepsilon_{i_1 i_2 \ldots i_k} (x_1, x_2, \ldots, x_k)$ is measurable with respect to $\mathscr{F}$.

Since λ_t $(-\infty < t < +\infty)$ is measurable with respect to $\mathscr{F}$, by Lemma 6.1.5 and condition (6.1.6) we have

$$\mathbf{E}(\lambda_{t_1}^{r_1} \lambda_{t_2}^{r_2} \ldots \lambda_{t_j}^{r_j} \lambda_{x_1} \lambda_{x_2} \ldots \lambda_{x_k}) = \mathbf{E}(a_{i_1}^{(x_1)} a_{i_2}^{(x_2)} \ldots a_{i_k}^{(x_k)} \lambda_{t_1}^{r_1} \lambda_{t_2}^{r_2} \ldots \lambda_{t_j}^{r_j}) =$$

$$= \mathbf{E}(\mathbf{E}(a_{i_1}^{(x_1)} \ldots a_{i_k}^{(x_k)} \lambda_{t_1}^{r_1} \lambda_{t_2}^{r_2} \ldots \lambda_{t_j}^{r_j} \mid \mathscr{F})) =$$

$$= \mathbf{E}(\lambda_{t_1}^{r_1} \lambda_{t_2}^{r_2} \ldots \lambda_{t_j}^{r_j} \mathbf{E}(a_{i_1}^{(x_1)} \ldots a_{ik}^{(x_k)} \mid \mathscr{F})) =$$

$$= \mathbf{E}(\lambda_{t_1}^{r_1} \lambda_{t_2}^{r_2} \ldots \lambda_{t_j}^{r_j} (\lambda_{x_1} \lambda_{x_2} \ldots \lambda_{x_k} + \varepsilon)).$$

Therefore

$$\mathbf{E}(\lambda_{t_1}^{r_1} \lambda_{t_2}^{r_2} \ldots \lambda_{t_j}^{r_j} \varepsilon) = 0 \tag{6.1.7}$$

for any sequence $\{t_i\}_{i=1}^{j}$ of real numbers and for any sequence $\{r_i\}$ of integers.

To prove the theorem it is enough to see that

$$\int_A \varepsilon \, d\mathbf{P} = \int_\Omega \varepsilon \alpha \, d\mathbf{P} = 0 \tag{6.1.8}$$

for any A of type (6.1.5), where α is the indicator function of A. But (6.1.8) follows from (6.1.7) using the fact that α can be approximated in mean by a polynomial

$$\sum c_{r_1 r_2 \ldots r_j} \lambda_{t_1}^{r_1} \lambda_{t_2}^{r_2} \ldots \lambda_{t_j}^{r_j}.$$

As a consequence of this fundamental theorem we can easily prove the following analogue of Theorems 2.9.2, 2.9.3 and 2.8.2.

THEOREM 6.1.2. *If $\xi_1, \xi_2, \ldots$ is a sequence of symmetrically dependent random variables then the sequence $c_1 \xi_1, c_2 \xi_2, \ldots$ obeys the strong law of large numbers, i.e.*

$$\zeta_n = \frac{c_1 \xi_1 + c_2 \xi_2 + \ldots + c_n \xi_n}{n} \to 0 \tag{6.1.9}$$

whenever

$$\mathbf{E}(\xi_k) = 0 \qquad \mathbf{E}(|\xi_k|^p) < \infty \quad (1 \leq p < 2)$$

and

$$k^{2-p} \sum_{n=k^p}^{\infty} \frac{|c_n|^2}{n^2} \leq K$$

where K is a positive constant.

THEOREM 6.1.3. *If (6.1.9) holds with* $|c_n| \geq A n^{\frac{p-1}{p}}$ *(where A is a positive constant) then* $\mathbf{E}(\xi_n) = 0$ *and* $\mathbf{E}(|\xi_n^p|) < \infty$.

THEOREM 6.1.4. *If* $\xi_1, \xi_2, \ldots$ *is a sequence of square-integrable symmetrically dependent random variables and* μ *is the weak limit of* ξ_n *and* σ^2 *is the weak limit of* $(\xi_n - \mu)^2$ *then*

$$\mathbf{P}\left(\overline{\lim_{n\to\infty}} \frac{\xi_1 + \xi_2 + \ldots + \xi_n - n\mu}{\sqrt{2 n \log\log n}\, \sigma} = 1 \,\middle|\, \sigma > 0\right) = 1 \qquad (6.1.10)$$

and

$$\mathbf{P}(\xi_i = \mu \mid \sigma = 0) = 1 . \qquad (6.1.11)$$

(6.1.10) (resp. (6.1.11)) loses all its meaning if $\mathbf{P}(\sigma > 0) = 0$ (resp. $\mathbf{P}(\sigma = 0) = 0$).

Only the proof of Theorem 6.1.4 is given because the proofs of the other two theorems are essentially the same; in fact, they are easier.

Before the proof of Theorem 6.1.4 we give a lemma.

LEMMA 6.1.6. *If* $\xi_1, \xi_2, \ldots$ *is a sequence of symmetrically dependent random variables with finite variances, then*

$$\mathbf{E}(\xi_i \mid \mathscr{F}) = \int_{-\infty}^{+\infty} x\, d\lambda_x = \mu \qquad (i = 1, 2, \ldots) \qquad (6.1.12)$$

and

$$\mathbf{E}\big((\xi_i - \mu)^2 \mid \mathscr{F}\big) = \int_{-\infty}^{+\infty} (x - \mu)^2\, d\lambda_x = \sigma^2 \qquad (6.1.13)$$

with probability 1.

PROOF. We prove only (6.1.12) because the proof of (6.1.13) is exactly the same. (6.1.12) evidently follows from Theorem 6.1.1 and Lemma 6.1.3. In fact, Theorem 6.1.1 and Kolmogorov's strong law of large numbers (Theorem 2.9.2) imply

$$\mathbf{P}\left(\frac{\xi_1 + \xi_2 + \ldots + \xi_n}{n} \to \int_{-\infty}^{+\infty} t\, d\lambda_t \,\middle|\, \mathscr{F}\right) = 1 \qquad (6.1.14)$$

and

$$\mathbf{E}(\xi_k \mid \mathscr{F}) = \int_{-\infty}^{+\infty} t\, d\lambda_t \qquad (6.1.15)$$

with probability 1. (6.1.14) implies

$$\mathbf{P}\left(\frac{\xi_1 + \xi_2 + \ldots + \xi_n}{n} \to \int_{-\infty}^{+\infty} t\, d\lambda_t\right) = 1 . \qquad (6.1.16)$$

(6.1.15), (6.1.16) and (6.1.1) together imply (6.1.12).

PROOF OF THEOREM 6.1.4. (6.1.11) is a trivial consequence of (6.1.13). In fact

$$\int_{\{\omega:\sigma=0\}} \mathbf{E}((\xi_i-\mu)^2\,|\,\mathscr{F})\,d\,\mathbf{P} = \int_{\{\omega:\sigma=0\}} (\xi_i-\mu)^2\,d\,\mathbf{P} = \int_{\{\omega:\sigma=0\}} \sigma^2\,d\mathbf{P} = 0\,.$$

(σ is measurable with respect to $\mathscr{F}$.)

Similarly (6.1.10) is a simple consequence of Lemma 6.1.6, Theorem 6.1.1 and Theorem 2.8.2.

§ 6.2. Quasi-independent events

In this § we find the analogue of the theorems of § 6.1 for quasi-independent events.

First of all we have to prove some lemmas.

LEMMA 6.2.1. *If $A_1, A_2, \ldots$ is a sequence of quasi-independent events with*

$$\frac{1}{n^2}\sum_{k=1}^{n}\frac{1}{\mathbf{P}(A_k)} \leq K\,, \tag{6.2.1}$$

where K is a positive constant, then the sequence

$$\psi_N = \frac{1}{N}\sum_{k=1}^{N}\frac{a_k(\omega)}{\mathbf{P}(A_k)} \tag{6.2.2}$$

has a weak limit $\lambda(\omega)$ in the space of square integrable random variables where $a_k(\omega)$ is the indicator function of A_k.

PROOF. This lemma evidently follows from Theorem 0.4.8 if we can prove that the sequence $\mathbf{E}(\psi_N^2)$ is uniformly bounded and $\mathbf{E}(\psi_N\,\psi_k)$ tends to a limit if k is fixed and N tends to infinity. In fact

$$\mathbf{E}(\psi_n^2) = \frac{1}{n^2}\sum_{k=1}^{n}\frac{1}{\mathbf{P}(A_k)} + \frac{2}{n^2}\sum_{k<j}\frac{\mathbf{P}(A_k\,A_j)}{\mathbf{P}(A_k)\,\mathbf{P}(A_j)} =$$

$$= \frac{1}{n^2}\sum_{k=1}^{n}\frac{1}{\mathbf{P}(A_k)} + \frac{2}{n^2}\binom{n}{2}\alpha_2\,.$$

Similarly we have

$$\lim_{n\to\infty}\mathbf{E}(\psi_n\,\psi_k) = \lim_{n\to\infty}\frac{1}{nk}\,\mathbf{E}\left[\sum_{j=1}^{n}\frac{a_j(\omega)}{\mathbf{P}(A_j)}\sum_{l=1}^{k}\frac{a_l(\omega)}{\mathbf{P}(A_l)}\right] =$$

$$= \lim_{n\to\infty}\frac{1}{nk}\,\alpha_2\,(n-k)\,k = \alpha_2\,.$$

LEMMA 6.2.2. *Under the conditions of Lemma* 6.2.1

$$\lim_{\substack{n_j\to\infty \\ n_j/n_{j-1}\to\infty}} \mathbf{E}\left(\frac{a_{m_1}(\omega)}{\mathbf{P}(A_{m_1})}\frac{a_{m_2}(\omega)}{\mathbf{P}(A_{m_2})}\cdots\frac{a_{m_r}(\omega)}{\mathbf{P}(A_{m_r})}\psi_{n_1}\psi_{n_2}\cdots\psi_{n_k}\right) = \alpha_{k+r}$$

$$(j = 1, 2, \ldots, k) \qquad (k = 1, 2, \ldots; r = 1, 2, \ldots)$$

for any integers $m_1 < m_2 < \ldots < m_r$.

PROOF. We have

$$\lim \mathbf{E}\left(\psi_{n_1}\psi_{n_2}\cdots\psi_{n_k}\frac{a_{m_1}}{\mathbf{P}(A_{m_1})}\cdots\frac{(a_{m_r})}{\mathbf{P}(A_{m_r})}\right) =$$

$$= \lim \mathbf{E}\left(\frac{a_{m_1}}{\mathbf{P}(A_{m_1})}\cdots\frac{a_{m_r}}{\mathbf{P}(A_{m_r})}\frac{1}{n_1}\sum_{i_1=1}^{n_1}\frac{a_{i_1}}{\mathbf{P}(A_{i_1})}\frac{1}{n_2}\left[\sum_{i_2=1}^{n_1}\frac{a_{i_2}}{\mathbf{P}(A_{i_2})} + \right.\right.$$

$$\left.\left. + \sum_{i_2=n_1+1}^{n_2}\frac{a_{i_2}}{\mathbf{P}(A_{i_1})}\right]\cdots\frac{1}{n_k}\left[\sum_{i_k=1}^{n_{k-1}}\frac{a_{i_k}}{\mathbf{P}(A_{i_k})} + \sum_{i_k=n_{k-1}+1}^{n_k}\frac{a_{i_k}}{\mathbf{P}(A_{i_k})}\right]\right). \tag{6.2.3}$$

In this expression consider first the term

$$\frac{1}{n_1 n_2\cdots n_k}\mathbf{E}\left[\frac{a_{m_1}}{\mathbf{P}(A_{m_2})}\cdots\frac{a_{m_r}}{\mathbf{P}(A_{m_r})}\sum_{i_1=1}^{n_1}\frac{a_{i_1}}{\mathbf{P}(A_{i_1})}\sum_{i_2=n_1+1}^{n_2}\frac{a_{i_2}}{\mathbf{P}(A_{i_2})}\cdots\times\right.$$

$$\left.\times\sum_{i_k=n_{k-1}+1}^{n_k}\frac{a_{i_k}}{\mathbf{P}(A_{i_k})}\right]. \tag{6.2.4}$$

The limit of (6.2.4) is α_{k+r} and a simple calculation shows that the limit of the other terms of (6.2.3) is 0.

As a simple consequence of Lemmas 6.2.1 and 6.2.2 we obtain

LEMMA 6.2.3. *Under the conditions of Lemma* 6.2.1

$$\mathbf{E}\left(\frac{a_{m_1}}{\mathbf{P}(A_{m_1})}\frac{a_{m_2}}{\mathbf{P}(A_{m_2})}\cdots\frac{a_{m_r}}{\mathbf{P}(A_{m_r})}\lambda^k\right) = \alpha_{k+r} \quad (k = 1, 2, \ldots; r = 1, 2, \ldots) \tag{6.2.5}$$

LEMMA 6.2.4. *Under the conditions of Lemma* 6.2.1

$$\alpha_k \leq \left(\frac{1}{\mathbf{P}(A_l)}\right)^k \qquad (l = 1, 2, \ldots; k = 1, 2, \ldots). \tag{6.2.6}$$

PROOF. (6.2.6) is trivial for $k = 1$. The proof for $k = 2$ is as follows:

$$\alpha_2 = \frac{\mathbf{P}(A_l A_{l+1})}{\mathbf{P}(A_l)\,\mathbf{P}(A_{l+1})} \leq \frac{\mathbf{P}(A_{l+1})}{\mathbf{P}(A_l)\,\mathbf{P}(A_{l+1})} = \frac{1}{\mathbf{P}(A_l)} \leq \frac{1}{\mathbf{P}^2(A_l)}.$$

For $k = 3$ similarly we have

$$\alpha_3 = \frac{\mathbf{P}(A_l A_{l+1} A_{l+2})}{\mathbf{P}(A_l)\,\mathbf{P}(A_{l+1})\,\mathbf{P}(A_{l+2})} \leq \frac{\mathbf{P}(A_{l+1} A_{l+2})}{\mathbf{P}(A_l)\,\mathbf{P}(A_{l+1})\,\mathbf{P}(A_{l+2})} =$$

$$= \frac{\alpha_2}{\mathbf{P}(A_l)} \leq \frac{1}{\mathbf{P}^3(A_l)}\,.$$

By induction we can obtain (6.2.6) for any k.

As a simple consequence of Lemmas 6.2.3 and 6.2.4 we have

LEMMA 6.2.5. *Under the conditions of Lemma* 6.2.1

$$\mathbf{P}\left(0 \leq \lambda \leq \inf_k \frac{1}{\mathbf{P}(A_k)}\right) = 1.$$

Now we can prove the following analogue of Theorem 6.1.1.

THEOREM 6.2.1. *Under the conditions of Lemma* 6.2.1 *we have*

$$\mathbf{P}(A_{i_1} A_{i_2} \ldots A_{i_k} \mid \lambda) = \mathbf{P}(A_{i_1} \mid \lambda)\,\mathbf{P}(A_{i_2} \mid \lambda) \ldots \mathbf{P}(A_{i_k} \mid \lambda) =$$
$$= \lambda^k\,\mathbf{P}(A_{i_1})\,\mathbf{P}(A_{i_2}) \ldots \mathbf{P}(A_{i_k}) \text{ with probability } 1 \; (i_j \neq i_l \text{ if } j \neq l). \tag{6.2.7}$$

PROOF. Put

$$\eta_k(\omega) = \frac{a_k(\omega)}{\mathbf{P}(A_k)}\,.$$

We assume that

$$\mathbf{E}(\eta_n \mid \lambda) = \lambda + \varepsilon_n. \tag{6.2.8}$$

Here $\varepsilon_n(\omega)$ is a Baire function of λ. Let $\varepsilon_n(\omega) = g_n(\lambda(\omega))$. Then

$$\alpha_2 = \mathbf{E}(\eta_n) = \mathbf{E}(\lambda) = \mathbf{E}(\mathbf{E}(\eta_n \mid \lambda)) = \mathbf{E}(\lambda + \varepsilon_n) = \mathbf{E}(\lambda) + \mathbf{E}(\varepsilon_n)$$

and therefore $\mathbf{E}(\varepsilon_n) = 0$ $(n = 1, 2, \ldots)$. Similarly we have

$$\alpha_2 = \mathbf{E}(\eta_k \eta_l) = \mathbf{E}(\lambda^2) = \mathbf{E}(\lambda \eta_k) = \mathbf{E}(\mathbf{E}(\lambda \eta_k \mid \lambda)) =$$
$$= \mathbf{E}(\lambda(\lambda + \varepsilon_k)) = \mathbf{E}(\lambda^2) + \mathbf{E}(\lambda \varepsilon_k).$$

Therefore $\mathbf{E}(\lambda \varepsilon_k) = 0$. Likewise we obtain

$$\mathbf{E}(\lambda^n \varepsilon_k) = \int_0^K x^n g_k(x)\, dF_\lambda(x) = 0 \qquad (k = 1, 2, \ldots; n = 1, 2, \ldots)$$

where $F_\lambda(x)$ is the distribution function of $\lambda(\omega)$ and $K = \inf_k \frac{1}{\mathbf{P}(A_k)}$.

(Clearly $\mathbf{P}(0 \leq \lambda \leq K) = 1$.) The fact that the sequence $\{x^n\}$ is a complete sequence in the space $L^2_{F_\lambda[0,K]}$ (the space of functions in the interval $[0, K]$ which are square integrable with respect to the measure defined by the distribution function $F_\lambda(x)$) implies that $g_n(x)$

is equal to 0 almost everywhere with respect to the measure defined by $F_\lambda(x)$. Hence

$$\mathbf{P}(\varepsilon_k = 0) = 1 \qquad (k = 1, 2, \ldots)$$

and therefore

$$\mathbf{E}(\eta_n \mid \lambda) = \lambda$$

and

$$\mathbf{P}(A_n \mid \lambda) = \lambda\, \mathbf{P}(A_n)\,. \tag{6.2.9}$$

The proof for $k = 2$ is similar to the above proof. Let

$$\mathbf{E}(\eta_i\, \eta_k \mid \lambda) = \lambda^2 + \varepsilon_{ik}$$

where ε_{ik} is a Baire function of λ. With these notations we have

$$\mathbf{E}(\eta_i\, \eta_k) = \mathbf{E}(\lambda^2) = \mathbf{E}(\mathbf{E}(\eta_i\, \eta_k \mid \lambda)) = \mathbf{E}(\lambda^2 + \varepsilon_{ik})$$

so that

$$\mathbf{E}(\varepsilon_{ik}) = 0.$$

Similarly we have

$$\mathbf{E}(\eta_i\, \eta_j\, \eta_k) = \mathbf{E}(\lambda^3) = \mathbf{E}(\eta_i\, \eta_j\, \lambda) = \mathbf{E}(\mathbf{E}(\eta_i\, \eta_j\, \lambda \mid \lambda)) = \mathbf{E}(\lambda(\lambda^2 + \varepsilon_{ij}))$$

so that

$$\mathbf{E}(\varepsilon_{ij}\, \lambda) = 0$$

and in general we obtain

$$\mathbf{E}(\varepsilon_{ik}\, \lambda^n) = 0 \quad (n = 1,\ 2, \ldots), \text{ i. e. } \mathbf{P}(\varepsilon_{ik} = 0) = 1.$$

Therefore,

$$\mathbf{E}(\eta_i\, \eta_k \mid \lambda) = \lambda^2$$

and

$$\mathbf{P}(A_i\, A_k \mid \lambda) = \lambda^2\, \mathbf{P}(A_i)\, \mathbf{P}(A_k)$$

and using (6.2.9) we obtain (6.2.7) for $k = 2$.

The proof of (6.2.7) for any value of k is essentially the same.

Making use of this theorem we can obtain for example the following version of the law of large numbers.

THEOREM 6.2.2. *Under the condition of Lemma* 6.2.1

$$\mathbf{P}\left(\frac{c_1(a_1 - \lambda\, \mathbf{P}(A_1)) + c_2(a_2 - \lambda\, \mathbf{P}(A_2)) + \ldots + c_n(a_n - \lambda\, \mathbf{P}(A_n))}{n} \to 0\right) = 1$$

if $\sum_{k=1}^{\infty} \frac{c_k^2}{k^2} < \infty$.

This theorem and other analogues of the theorems of Chapter 2 can be proven using the method of the proof of Theorem 6.1.4. We omit the details.

§ 6.3. Quasi-multiplicative systems

As a simple consequence of Theorem 0.4.8 we have

LEMMA 6.3.1. *Let $\xi_1, \xi_2, \ldots$ be a quasi-multiplicative system then ξ_n converges weakly to a random variable μ in the Hilbert space of square integrable random variables.*

Our first aim is to investigate the properties of the sequence

$$\eta_n = \xi_n - \mu . \tag{6.3.1}$$

LEMMA 6.3.2. *Let $\xi_1, \xi_2, \ldots$ be a uniformly bounded quasi-multiplicative system then*

$$\mathbf{E}\left(\xi_{i_1}^{r_1} \xi_{i_2}^{r_2} \ldots \xi_{i_k}^{r_k} \mu^l\right) = \alpha_{j+l,m}^{(k+l)} \qquad (i_1 < i_2 < \ldots < i_k) \tag{6.3.2}$$

where r_i can be equal to 1 or 2, l is an arbitrary integer and j (resp. m) means the number of 1's (resp. 2's) in the sequence $r_1, r_2, \ldots, r_k$. $\alpha_{j,k}^{(n)}$ is defined by (0.6.3).

PROOF. If $i_1 < i_2 < \ldots < i_k < j_1 < j_2 < \ldots j_l$ we have

$$\alpha_{j+l,m}^{(k+l)} = \mathbf{E}\left(\xi_{i_1}^{r_1} \xi_{i_2}^{r_2} \ldots \xi_{i_k}^{r_k} \xi_{j_1} \xi_{j_2} \ldots \xi_{j_l}\right) = \lim_{j_l \to \infty} \mathbf{E}\left(\xi_{i_1}^{r_1} \xi_{i_2}^{r_2} \ldots \xi_{i_k}^{r_k} \xi_{j_1} \xi_{j_2} \ldots \xi_{j_l}\right) =$$

$$= \mathbf{E}\left(\xi_{i_1}^{r_1} \xi_{i_2}^{r_2} \ldots \xi_{i_k}^{r_k} \xi_{j_1} \xi_{j_2} \ldots \xi_{j_{l-1}} \mu\right) = \ldots = \mathbf{E}\left(\xi_{i_1}^{r_1} \xi_{i_2}^{r_2} \ldots \xi_{i_k}^{r_k} \mu^l\right).$$

This implies

LEMMA 6.3.3.

$$\mathbf{E}\left(\eta_{i_1}^{r_1} \eta_{i_2}^{r_2} \ldots \eta_{i_k}^{r_k} \mu^l\right) = \begin{cases} 0 \ \textit{if at least one } r_i \textit{ is equal to } 1, \\ \beta_{kl} \ \textit{if } r_1 = r_2 = \ldots = r_k = 2 . \end{cases}$$

In particular

$$\mathbf{E}\left(\eta_i^2 \eta_j^2\right) = \alpha_{4,0}^{(4)} - 2\,\alpha_{2,1}^{(3)} + \alpha_{0,2}^{(2)}$$

where $\beta_{k,l}$ is a constant which depends only on k and l but does not depend on the indices $i_1, i_2, \ldots, i_k$.

Lemma 6.3.3 and Theorem 0.4.8 together imply

LEMMA 6.3.4. *Let $\xi_1, \xi_2, \ldots$ be a uniformly bounded quasi-multiplicative system. Then $\eta_n^2 = (\xi_n - \mu)^2$ converges weakly to a non-negative random variable σ^2.*

Our next theorem shows the connection between the ESMS and the quasi-multiplicative systems.

THEOREM 6.3.1. *Let $\xi_1, \xi_2, \ldots$ be a uniformly bounded quasi-multiplicative system, then we have*

$$\mathbf{E}\left(\eta_{i_1}^{r_1} \eta_{i_2}^{r_2} \ldots \eta_{i_n}^{r_n} \mid \sigma^2\right) = \begin{cases} \sigma^{2n} \ \textit{if } r_1 = r_2 = \ldots = r_n = 2 \\ 0 \ \textit{otherwise} \end{cases}$$

with probability 1, *if* r_i $(i = 1, 2, \ldots, n)$ *can be equal to* 1 *or* 2. σ *is defined by Lemma* 6.3.4 *and* η_n *bq* (6.3.1).

PROOF. First consider the case when at least one element of the sequence $r_1, r_2, \ldots, r_n$ is equal to 1. Assume that the number of 2's is k and suppose that

$$\mathbf{E}(\eta_{i_1}^{r_1}\eta_{i_2}^{r_2}\ldots\eta_{i_n}^{r_n} \mid \sigma^2) = \varepsilon_{i_1 i_2 \ldots i_n}^{(r_1, r_2, \ldots, r_n)} = \varepsilon$$

where the random variable ε is a Baire function of σ^2. In this case we have

$$\begin{aligned} 0 &= \mathbf{E}(\eta_{i_1}^2\eta_{i_2}^2\ldots\eta_{i_k}^2\eta_{i_{k+1}}\eta_{i_{k+2}}\ldots\eta_{i_n}\eta_{i_{n+1}}^2\eta_{i_{n+2}}^2\ldots\eta_{i_{n+m}}^2) = \\ &= \mathbf{E}(\eta_{i_1}^2\eta_{i_2}^2\ldots\eta_{i_k}^2\eta_{i_{k+1}}\eta_{i_{k+2}}\ldots\eta_{i_n}\sigma^{2m}) = \\ &= \mathbf{E}(\mathbf{E}(\eta_{i_1}^2\eta_{i_2}^2\ldots\eta_{i_k}^2\eta_{i_{k+1}}\eta_{i_{k+2}}\ldots\eta_{i_k}\sigma^{2m} \mid \sigma^2)) = \\ &= \mathbf{E}(\sigma^{2m}\mathbf{E}(\eta_{i_1}^2\eta_{i_2}^2\ldots\eta_{i_k}^2\eta_{i_{k+1}}\eta_{i_{k+2}}\ldots\eta_{i_n} \mid \sigma^2)) = \mathbf{E}(\sigma^{2m}\varepsilon), \end{aligned}$$

i.e. for any integer m,

$$\mathbf{E}(\sigma^{2m}\varepsilon) = 0.$$

This implies that

$$\mathbf{P}(\varepsilon = 0) = 1.$$

The proof of the case: $r_1 = r_2 = \ldots = r_n = 2$ is exactly the same and therefore is omitted.

This theorem evidently implies the

COROLLARY. *If* $\mathbf{P}(\sigma = 0) > 0$ *then we have*

$$\mathbf{P}(\xi_i = \mu \mid \sigma = 0) = 1 \qquad (i = 1, 2, \ldots). \tag{6.3.3}$$

Applying Theorems 6.3.1, 3.3.2 and 3.3.3 we obtain

THEOREM 6.3.2. *Let* $\xi_1, \xi_2, \ldots$ *be a quasi-multiplicative system. The weak limit of* ξ_n *is denoted by* μ *and the weak limit of* $(\xi_n - \mu)^2$ *is denoted by* σ^2. *Then we have*

$$\frac{c_1(\xi_1 - \mu) + c_2(\xi_2 - \mu) + \ldots + c_n(\xi_n - \mu)}{n} \to 0$$

$$\mathbf{P}\left(\overline{\lim_{n\to\infty}}\left(\frac{(\xi_1 - \mu) + (\xi_2 - \mu) + \ldots + (\xi_n - \mu)}{\sqrt{n \log\log n}\,\sigma} \leq 7 \mid \sigma > 0\right)\right) = 1 \tag{6.3.4}$$

and

$$\mathbf{P}(\xi_i = \mu \mid \sigma = 0) = 1$$

provided that $\sum_{k=1}^{\infty} \frac{c_k^2}{k^2} < \infty.$

(6.3.4) (resp. (6.3.3)) loses all its meaning if $\mathbf{P}(\sigma > 0) = 0$ (resp. $\mathbf{P}(\sigma = 0) = 0$).

CHAPTER 7

MARKOV CHAINS

A homogeneous Markov chain with a stationary initial distribution is a stationary sequence in the strong sense. Thus the laws of large numbers for this case are simple consequences of the theorems of Chapter 4. If the intial distribution of a homogeneous Markov chain is non-stationary (but there exists a stationary initial distribution) then the situation is not much more complicated. The real difficulties are in the treatment of non-homogeneous Markov chains.

In this chapter the following notations are used:

(1) $\boldsymbol{\xi} = (\xi_1, \xi_2, \ldots)$ is a Markov chain;

(2) $F_1(x) = \mathbf{P}(\xi_1 < x)$ is the initial distribution of $\boldsymbol{\xi}$;

(3) $F_n(x) = \mathbf{P}(\xi_n < x)$ is the distribution of ξ_n;

(4) $P_{ij}(x, A) = \mathbf{P}(\xi_j \in A \mid \xi_i = x)$ $(i < j)$ is a transition probability distribution of $\boldsymbol{\xi}$; having the following two simple properties (a) $P_{ij}(x, A)$ is a Borel measurable function of x for each Borel measurable set A and (b)$P_{ij}(x, A)$ is a probability measure defined on the Borel measurable sets of the real line for each x; in particular $P_{i,i+1}(x, A) = P_i(x, A)$;

(5) if the Markov chain is homogeneous, then $P_i(x, A) = P(x, A)$ $(i = 1, 2, \ldots)$;

(6) the distribution function $F(x)$ is called a stationary initial distribution corresponding to the transition probability distribution $P(x, A)$ if

$$\int_A dF(x) = \int_{-\infty}^{+\infty} P(x, A)\, dF(x);$$

(7) the homogeneous Markov chain $\boldsymbol{\xi}$ is called an ergodic system if

$$P(x, A) = 1 \text{ for each } x \in A$$

implies

$$A = \Omega \text{ or } \bar{A} = \varnothing;$$

(8) if $\boldsymbol{\xi}$ is a discrete Markov chain (i.e. the number of the possible values is finite or countably infinite) then the transition probability distribution can be characterized by a transition probability matrix Π. The notations $P_{ij}(x, A) \sim \Pi_{ij}$, $P_i(x, A) \sim \Pi_i$, $P(x, A) \sim \Pi$ are used in the obvious sense.

§ 7.1. Homogeneous Markov chains

For homogeneous Markov chains we have

THEOREM 7.1.1. *Let* $\boldsymbol{\xi} = (\xi_1, \xi_2, \ldots)$ *be a homogeneous ergodic Markov chain and denote by* $g(x)$ *a Borel measurable function defined on the real line. Suppose that there exists a stationary initial distribution* $F(x)$ *of* $\boldsymbol{\xi}$. *Finally assume that* $\int_{-\infty}^{+\infty} |g(x)| \, dF(x) < \infty$. *Then*

$$\frac{g(\xi_1) + g(\xi_2) + \ldots + g(\xi_n)}{n} \to \int_{-\infty}^{+\infty} g(t) \, dF(t).$$

REMARK 1. It is not assumed that $\mathbf{P}(\xi_1 < x) = F(x)$, so $\boldsymbol{\xi}$ is generally a non-stationary sequence.

REMARK 2. In general $g(\xi_1), g(\xi_2), \ldots$ is not a Markov chain.

REMARK 3. If $\boldsymbol{\xi}$ is non-ergodic then similar results can be obtained by taking the conditional probabilities with respect to the σ-algebra of the invariant sets of $\boldsymbol{\xi}$.

PROOF (see DOOB [1], p. 220). If $\mathbf{P}(\xi_1 < x) = F(x)$ then $g(\xi_1)$, $g(\xi_2), \ldots$ is a stationary sequence in the strong sense and therefore the theorem immediately follows from Theorem 4.1.1.

Theorem 4.1.1 also implies that

$$\mathbf{P}\left(\frac{g(\xi_1) + g(\xi_2) + \ldots + g(\xi_n)}{n} \to \int_{-\infty}^{+\infty} g(x) \, dF(x) \,\Big|\, \xi_1 = x_0\right) = 1 \qquad (7.1.1)$$

for almost all x_0, i.e. (7.1.1) holds if x_0 does not belong to a set A_0 of F-measure 0, i.e. $\int_{A_0} dF(x) = 0$. First of all we want to show that A_0 is the empty set. The ergodicity of $\boldsymbol{\xi}$ implies that $\mathbf{P}(\xi_n \notin A_0 \mid \xi_1 = x_0) \to 1$ $(n \to \infty)$. Suppose that ν is the least integer for which $\xi_\nu \notin A_0$. Then we have

$$\mathbf{P}\left(\frac{g(\xi_1) + g(\xi_2) + \ldots + g(\xi_n)}{n} \to \int_{-\infty}^{+\infty} g(x) \, dF(x) \,\Big|\, \xi_1 = x_0\right) =$$

$$= \sum_{k=2}^{\infty} \int_{-\infty}^{+\infty} \mathbf{P}\left(\frac{g(\xi_1) + g(\xi_2) + \ldots g(\xi_n)}{n} \to \int_{-\infty}^{+\infty} g(x) \, dF(x) \,\Big|\, \xi_1 = x_0,\right.$$

$$\left. \nu = k,\ \xi_\nu = x' \right) d_x \mathbf{P}(\nu = k, \xi_\nu < x' \mid \xi_1 = x_0) =$$

$$= \sum_{k=2}^{\infty} \int_{x' \notin A_0} \mathbf{P}\left(\frac{g(\xi_1) + g(\xi_2) + \ldots + g(\xi_n)}{n} \to \int_{-\infty}^{+\infty} g(x) \, dF(x) \,\Big|\, \xi_1 = x_0,\right.$$

$$\left. \nu = k,\ \xi_\nu = x' \right) d_x \mathbf{P}(\nu = k, \xi_\nu < x' \mid \xi_1 = x_0).$$

But since

$$\mathbf{P}\left(\frac{g(\xi_1)+g(\xi_2)+\ldots+g(\xi_n)}{n}\to\int_{-\infty}^{+\infty}g(x)\,dF(x)\,|\,\xi_1=x_0,\nu=k,\xi_\nu=x'\right)=1$$

for any $x'\notin A_0$, and for any x_0, A_0, is empty.

To prove the theorem we take the integral of (7.1.1) with respect to F_1.

§ 7.2. Non-homogeneous Markov chains

The laws of large numbers as well as the limit theorems for non-homogeneous Markov chains in general are based on different kinds of measures of ergodicity. First of all we have to introduce some of them.

DEFINITION 1. (DYNKIN [1].) Let $\nu(A)$ be a signed measure on the real line R_1 with $\nu(R_1)=0$ and define the norm of ν by

$$||\nu||=\sup_{A\in\mathscr{B}}|\nu(A)|$$

where $\mathscr{B}$ is the set of Borel measurable sets of R_1. Further let $P=$ $=P(x,A)$ be a transition probability distribution. The norm $N(P)$ of P is defined by

$$N(P)=\sup_{\nu\in\mathscr{N}}||\int_{-\infty}^{+\infty}P(x,A)\,d_x\nu\,||$$

where $\mathscr{N}$ is the set of those signed measures defined on R_1, for which $\nu(R_1)=0$ and $||\,\nu\,||=1$.

The ergodic coefficient $\alpha(P)$ of P is defined as

$$\alpha(P)=1-N(P).$$

DEFINITION 2 (see RÉVÉSZ [1]). Assume that there exists a stationary intial distribution $F(x)$ corresponding to the transition probability distribution $P=P(x,A)$. Define the norm $V(P)$ of P by

$$V(P)=\sup_{f\in\Phi}\int_{-\infty}^{+\infty}\left(\int_{-\infty}^{+\infty}f(x)\,dP(y,dx)\right)^2dF(y)$$

where Φ contains those Borel measurable functions f defined on R_1 for which

$$\int_{-\infty}^{+\infty}f(x)\,dF(x)=0,\qquad\int_{-\infty}^{+\infty}f^2(x)\,dF(x)=1.$$

Define an ergodic coefficient β of P by

$$\beta(P) = 1 - V(P).$$

$V(P_1 + P_2)$ (P_1 and P_2 are probability transition distributions) is defined as

$$V(P_1 + P_2) = \sup_{f \in \Phi} \int_{-\infty}^{+\infty} \left[\int_{-\infty}^{+\infty} f(x)\, d\big(P_1(y, dx) + P_2(y, dx)\big) \right]^2 dF(y).$$

Definition 3. Set

$$U(P, f, G) = \int_{-\infty}^{+\infty} \left[\int_{-\infty}^{+\infty} f(x)\, dP(y, dx) \right]^2 dG(y)$$

where $f(x)$ is a bounded Borel measurable function and G is a distribution function.

It would be interesting to see the connection between $\alpha(P)$ and $\beta(P)$ but it is unknown.

A simple property of α and β is that: $\alpha(P) = \beta(P) = 0$ if P is non-ergodic.

Our first theorem concerns non-homogeneous Markov chains which have a common stationary initial distribution.

Theorem 7.2.1. *Let* $\xi = (\xi_1, \xi_2, \ldots)$ *be a non-homogeneous Markov chain with a common stationary initial distribution* $F(x)$, *i.e.*

$$\int_A dF(x) = \mathbf{P}(\xi_{n+1} \in A) = \int_{-\infty}^{+\infty} \mathbf{P}_n(x, A)\, dF(x) \qquad (n = 1,2,\ldots).$$

for any Borel measurable set A. *Suppose that*

$$F_1(x) = F(x) \tag{7.2.1}$$

and

$$[V(P_{j,j+1} + P_{j,j+2} + \ldots + P_{j,j+n})]^{\frac{1}{2}} \leq Cj^{1-\varepsilon} \; (j = 1,2, \ldots ; n = 1, 2, \ldots) \tag{7.2.2}$$

where $C > 0$ *and* $0 < \varepsilon < 1$. *Then*

$$\sigma_n = \frac{f(\xi_1) + f(\xi_2) + \ldots + f(\xi_n)}{n} \to 0 \; (n \to \infty) \tag{7.2.3}$$

if $f(x)$ *is a bounded Borel measurable function for which* $\int f dF = 0$.

Remark 1. This theorem is a simple consequence of a random ergodic theorem (see Révész [1]) but here we give a direct proof.

Remark 2. It is easy to see that condition (7.2.2) holds if

$$\beta(P_{n,n+1}) \geq \frac{C_1}{n^{1-\varepsilon_1}}$$

where $C_1 > 0$ and $0 < \varepsilon_1 < 1$.

PROOF: Our conditions imply

$$Q_n = \mathbf{E}\left[\frac{1}{n}\sum_{k=1}^{n} f^2(\xi_k)^2\right] = \frac{1}{n^2}\left\{\sum_{k=1}^{n}\mathbf{E}\left(f^2(\xi_k)\right) + 2\sum_{j=1}^{n}\mathbf{E}\left[f(\xi_j)\sum_{k=j+1}^{n} f(\xi_k)\right]\right\} =$$

$$= O\left(\frac{1}{n}\right) + \frac{2}{n^2}\sum_{j=1}^{n}\mathbf{E}\left\{f(\xi_j)\left[\mathbf{E}\left(\sum_{k=j+1}^{n} f(\xi_k)\mid\xi_j\right)\right]\right\} \leq$$

$$\leq O\left(\frac{1}{n}\right) + \frac{2}{n^2}\sum_{j=1}^{n}\left[\mathbf{E}\left(f^2(\xi_j)\right)\ \mathbf{E}\left\{\left[\mathbf{E}\left(\sum_{k=j+1}^{n} f(\xi_k)\mid\xi_j\right)\right]^2\right\}\right]^{\frac{1}{2}}.$$

Since

$$\mathbf{E}\left(\sum_{k=j+1}^{n} f(\xi_k)\mid\xi_j = y\right) = \int_{-\infty}^{+\infty} f(x)\, d\sum_{k=j+1}^{n} P_{jk}(y,dx)$$

we have

$$Q_n \leq O\left(\frac{1}{n}\right) + \frac{2}{n^2}\sum_{j=1}^{n}\mathbf{E}\left(f^2(\xi_j)\right)\, Cj^{1-\varepsilon} = O\left(\frac{1}{n^\varepsilon}\right)$$

which, according to the Beppo-Levi theorem, implies that

$$\sigma_{k^{2\alpha}} \to 0 \qquad (k \to \infty)$$

where $\alpha = \left[\frac{1}{\varepsilon}\right] + 1$. Now let n be an arbitrary integer for which

$$k^{2\alpha} \leq n < (k+1)^{2\alpha}.$$

Then

$$|\sigma_n| \leq \left|\sigma_{k^{2\alpha}}\frac{k^{2\alpha}}{n}\right| + \left|\frac{\xi_{k+1}^{2\alpha} + \xi_{k+2}^{2\alpha} + \ldots + \xi_n}{n}\right| = |\sigma_{k^{2\alpha}}|\, O(1) +$$

$$+ O(1)\,\frac{(k+1)^{2\alpha} - k^{2\alpha}}{n}$$

which proves the theorem.

Condition (7.2.2) easily implies that the Markov chain $\boldsymbol{\xi}$ is ergodic in the following sense: if $\mathbf{P}(\xi_n \in A$ for each $n \mid \xi_1 \in A) \neq 0$ for a Borel A set of R_1 then $\int_A dF(x) = 0$ or $\int_A dF(x) = 1$. However (7.2.2) does not imply that $A = \varnothing$ or $\bar{A} = \varnothing$. If we assume this stronger condition then the condition (7.2.1) of Theorem 7.2.1 can be dropped. More precisely we have

THEOREM 7.2.2. *Let $\boldsymbol{\xi}$ be a non-homogeneous Markov chain with a common stationary initial distribution $F(x)$. Suppose that the condition*

$$\mathbf{P}(\xi_n \in A \text{ for each } n \mid \xi_1 = x_0 \in A) > 0$$

(where A is a Borel set) implies that $A = \emptyset$ *or* $\bar{A} = \emptyset$. *Suppose further that* (7.2.2) *holds. Then we have* (7.2.3) *for any bounded Borel measurable function* $f(x)$ *with* $\int f dF = 0$.

PROOF. This theorem follows from Theorem 7.2.1 making use of the method of proof of Theorem 7.1.1.

Similar results can be obtained by similar methods if the different stationary initial distributions correspond to transition probability distributions.

THEOREM 7.2.3. *Let* $\boldsymbol{\xi}$ *be a non-homogeneous Markov chain. Suppose that* $F_n(x)$ *is a stationary initial distribution corresponding to* $P_n(x, A)$ $(n = 1, 2, \ldots)$ *and* $\mathbf{P}(\xi_1 < x) = F_1(x)$. *Further let* $f(x)$ *be a bounded Borel measurable function. We assume that*

$$U(P_{j,j+1} + P_{j,j+2} + \ldots + P_{j,j+n}, f, F_j) \leqq Cj^{1-\varepsilon} (j = 1, 2 \ldots; n=1, 2, \ldots)$$

where $C > 0$ *and* $0 < \varepsilon < 1$. *Then we have*

$$\frac{f(\xi_1) + f(\xi_2) + \ldots + f(\xi_n)}{n} - \mathbf{E}\left(\frac{f(\xi_1) + f(\xi_2) + \ldots + f(\xi_n)}{n}\right) \to 0 .$$

The proof of this theorem will be omitted because it is essentially the same as the proof of Theorem 7.2.1.

ROTH–ROSENBLATT ([1], [2]) obtained similar results making use of $\alpha(P)$ instead of $\beta(P)$. It seems to us that his results are better than the above theorems if the variance of ξ_n is very large; but if ξ_n is bounded then the above theorems are in general better. We now mention a theorem of ROSENBLATT-ROTH without proof.

THEOREM 7.2.4 (see ROSENBLATT-ROTH [1]). *Let* $\boldsymbol{\xi}$ *be a non-homogeneous Markov chain. Denote by* α_n *the ergodic coefficient of* $P_n(x, A)$ *and let*

$$\alpha^{(n)} = \min_{1 \leqq i \leqq n} \alpha_i .$$

Further, set

$$\omega_i = \sum_{m=u}^{\infty} (l^m \alpha^{(l^{m+1})})^{-1} \quad if \quad l^u \leqq i < l^{u+1}$$

where $l \geqq 2$ *is a fixed integer. We assume that* $n \alpha^{(n)} \to \infty$ $(n \to \infty)$ *and*

$$\sum_{n=1}^{\infty} \omega_n \mathbf{D}^2(\xi_n) < \infty$$

for some l. Then

$$\frac{\xi_1 + \xi_2 + \ldots + \xi_n}{n} - \mathbf{E}\left(\frac{\xi_1 + \xi_2 + \ldots + \xi_n}{n}\right) \to \infty . \qquad (7.2.4)$$

In particular if $\alpha_i > \varrho > 0$ *then the condition*

$$\sum_{n=1}^{\infty} \frac{\mathbf{D}^2(\xi_n)}{n^2} < \infty$$

implies (7.2.4).

Consider two simple examples.

EXAMPLE 1. Let $\boldsymbol{\xi} = (\xi_1, \xi_2, \ldots)$ be a homogeneous Markov chain such that

$$\mathbf{P}(\xi_i = +1 \mid \xi_{i-1} = -1) = \mathbf{P}(\xi_i = -1 \mid \xi_{i-1} = +1) = 1$$
$$\mathbf{P}(\xi_i = +1 \mid \xi_{i-1} = +1) = \mathbf{P}(\xi_i = -1 \mid \xi_{i-1} = -1) = 0$$
$$\mathbf{P}(\xi_i = +1) = \mathbf{P}(\xi_i = -1) = \frac{1}{2}.$$

Then $\boldsymbol{\xi}$ clearly obeys the strong law of large numbers, but since $\alpha^{(n)}(P) = 0$ this does not follow from Theorem 7.2.4. However

$$V(P_{j,j+1} + P_{j,j+2} + \ldots + P_{j,j+n}) \leqq C$$

and therefore Theorem 7.1.1 implies the mentioned convergence.

EXAMPLE 2. Let $\boldsymbol{\xi} = (\xi_1, \xi_2, \ldots)$ be a non-homogeneous Markov chain with

$$\mathbf{P}(\xi_{n+1} = 1 \mid \xi_n = 1) = \mathbf{P}(\xi_{n+1} = -1 \mid \xi_n = -1) = 1 - \frac{1}{n^{1-\varepsilon}}$$

$$\mathbf{P}(\xi_{n+1} = 1 \mid \xi_n = -1) = \mathbf{P}(\xi_{n+1} = -1 \mid \xi_n = +1) = \frac{1}{n^{1-\varepsilon}}$$

$$\mathbf{P}(\xi_1 = +1) = \mathbf{P}(\xi_1 = -1) = \frac{1}{2}.$$

Then clearly

$$\alpha_n = \alpha^{(n)} = \frac{1}{n^{1-\varepsilon}}$$

and

$$\omega_i = \sum_{m=u}^{\infty} \left[2^m \frac{1}{2^{(m+1)1-\varepsilon}} \right]^{-1} \quad \text{if } 2^u \leqq i < 2^{u+1} \text{ and } l = 2.$$

(For other values of l the situation is similar.) Also

$$\beta(P_{n,n+1}) = \frac{2}{n^{1-\varepsilon}}$$

so that both Theorem 7.2.1 and Theorem 7.2.3 imply that $\boldsymbol{\xi}$ obeys the strong law of large numbers (see Remark 2).

§ 7.3. The law of the iterated logarithm

The result of this § is due to CHUNG ([2] p. 101), who proved that the law of the iterated logarithm holds for discrete homogeneous Markov chains under some further restrictions.

Let $\boldsymbol{\xi} = (\xi_1, \xi_2, \ldots)$ be a homogeneous Markov chain with possible values 1, 2, ... Further let $f(n)$ be a real valued function defined on the integers. Assume that the Markov chain returns from a state i to i after a "short time".

More precisely: let $\tau_1(i, \omega) < \tau_2(i, \omega) < \ldots$ be the increasing infinite sequence of all values of $n \geqq 1$ for which $\xi_n(\omega) = i$, i.e.

$$\xi_{\tau_1(i)} = \xi_{\tau_2(i)} \cdots = i$$

and

$$\xi_n \neq i \qquad \text{if} \qquad n \neq \tau_k .$$

Then $\tau_n(i, \omega)$ $(i = 1, 2, \ldots; n = 1, 2, \ldots)$ is a random variable. Now we assume that

$$\mathbf{E}\big((\tau_{n+1}(i) - \tau_n(i))^2\big) < \infty \tag{7.3.1}$$

and

$$\mathbf{E}\left\{\left[\sum_{j=\tau_n(i)}^{\tau_{n+1}(i)} f(\xi_j)\right]^2\right\} < \infty. \tag{7.3.2}$$

We can now formulate

THEOREM 7.3.1. *Under conditions* (7.3.1) *and* (7.3.2)

$$\mathbf{P}\left\{\overline{\lim_{n\to\infty}} \frac{f(\xi_1) + f(\xi_2) + \ldots + f(\xi_n) - M_n}{\sigma_n \sqrt{2\, n \log \log n}} = 1\right\} = 1$$

where

$$M_n = \mathbf{E}\big(f(\xi_1) + f(\xi_2) + \ldots + f(\xi_n)\big)$$

and

$$\sigma_n^2 = \mathbf{D}^2[f(\xi_1) + f(\xi_2) + \ldots + f(\xi_n)] .$$

We do not intend to give the proof of this theorem because it is based on deep properties of Markov chains. We only mention that the proof depends on Theorem 2.8.2 and the fact that the values of $\boldsymbol{\xi}$ after the n-th return to the state i are independent of the values of $\boldsymbol{\xi}$ before the n-th return.

CHAPTER 8

WEAKLY DEPENDENT RANDOM VARIABLES

In Chapters 3–7 the strong laws of large numbers for some different classes of stochastic processes were treated. In each chapter a different kind of stochastic dependence was considered (orthogonality, stationarity, etc.). In this chapter we have no restrictions on the kind of dependence, only on the strength of it. A very suitable condition is the so-called mixing condition. Many different definitions of mixing are used. Roughly speaking, a sequence of random variables is called mixing if those elements which are far from each other in the sequence are nearly independent.

In § 8.1 a general theorem of LOÈVE is given. In § 8.2, the notion of mixing is treated.

§ 8.1. A general theorem on centered random variables

Let ξ_1, .. be a sequence of random variables with finite expectations. The sequence

$$\xi_1^* = \xi_1 - \mathbf{E}(\xi_1)$$

and

$$\xi_n^* = \xi_n = \mathbf{E}(\xi_n \mid \xi_{n-1}, \xi_{n-2}, \ldots \xi_1) \qquad (n = 2, 3, \ldots) \qquad (8.1.1)$$

is called the centered sequence obtained from the sequence $\xi_1, \xi_2, \ldots$. The properties of the sequence $\{\xi_n^*\}$ are similar to the properties of independent random variables. More precisely, Lemma 2.2.1 and Theorem 2.7.5a are valid for centered random variables, i.e. we have

THEOREM 8.1.1 (see LOÈVE [1], p. 386). *If $\xi_1, \xi_2, \ldots$ are random variables with finite variances then*

$$\mathbf{P}\left\{\max_{1 \leq k \leq n} \left| \sum_{j=1}^{k} \xi_j^* \right| \geq \varepsilon \right\} \leq \frac{1}{\varepsilon^2} \sum_{k=1}^{n} \mathbf{E}(\xi_k^{*2})$$

where ξ_k^* is defined by (8.1.1).

THEOREM 8.1.2 (see LOÈVE [1] p. 387). *If $\xi_1, \xi_2, \ldots$ is a sequence of square integrable random variables with*

$$\sum_{k=1}^{\infty} \frac{\mathbf{D}^2(\xi_k)}{k^2} < \infty$$

then

$$\frac{1}{n}\sum_{k=1}^{n}\xi_k^* \to 0 \qquad (n \to \infty) \tag{8.1.2}$$

and if $\sum_{k=1}^{\infty}\mathbf{D}^2(\xi_k) < +\infty$ *then the series* $\sum_{k=1}^{\infty}\xi_k^*$ *is convergent with probability* 1.

These theorems can be proved in the same way as the analogous classical theorems.

Before proving these theorems we note that

$$\sum_{k=1}^{n}\mathbf{E}(\xi_k^{*2}) = \mathbf{E}\left[\left(\sum_{k=1}^{n}\xi_k^*\right)^2\right] \qquad (n = 1, 2, \ldots) \tag{8.1.3}$$

and

$$\mathbf{E}(\xi_n - \mathbf{E}(\xi_n \mid \xi_1 \ldots \xi_{n-1}))^2 \leq \mathbf{D}^2(\xi_n) \qquad (n = 2, 3, \ldots). \tag{8.1.4}$$

(8.1.3) follows from

$$\mathbf{E}(\xi_k^*\xi_j^*) = \mathbf{E}[\mathbf{E}(\xi_k^*\xi_j^* \mid \xi_1, \xi_2, \ldots, \xi_{k-1})] = \mathbf{E}[\xi_j^*\mathbf{E}(\xi_k^* \mid \xi_1, \xi_2, \ldots, \xi_{k-1})] =$$
$$= \mathbf{E}[\xi_j^*\mathbf{E}(\xi_k - \mathbf{E}(\xi_k \mid \xi_1, \xi_2, \ldots, \xi_{k-1}) \mid \xi_1, \xi_2, \ldots, \xi_{k-1})] = \mathbf{E}(\xi_j^* \cdot 0) = 0$$

if $j < k$.

It can be seen in a similar way that

$$\int_A \xi_k^*\xi_j^*\,d\mathbf{P} = 0$$

whenever $j < k$ and $A \in \mathscr{B}(\xi_1, \xi_2, \ldots, \xi_{k-1})$ (the smallest σ-algebra with respect to which the random variables $\xi_1, \xi_2, \ldots, \xi_{k-1}$ are measurable).

Proof of Theorem 8.1.1. Let

$$A = \left\{\omega: \max_{1\leq k\leq n}\left|\sum_{j=1}^{k}\xi_j^*\right| \geq \varepsilon\right\},$$

$$A_k = \{\omega: |\eta_1| < \varepsilon, |\eta_2| < \varepsilon, \ldots, |\eta_k| \geq \varepsilon\}$$

where $\eta_k = \xi_1^* + \xi_2^* + \ldots + \xi_k^*$. Then clearly

$$\sum_{k=1}^{n} A_k = A \quad \text{and} \quad A_i A_j = \emptyset \quad \text{if} \quad i \neq j.$$

Now we have

$$\int_{A_k}\eta_n^2\,d\mathbf{P} = \int_{A_k}\eta_k^2\,d\mathbf{P} + \sum_{l=k+1}^{n}\int_{A_k}\xi_l^{*2}\,d\mathbf{P} + 2\sum_{j=1}^{l-1}\sum_{l=k+1}^{n}\int_{A_k}\xi_j^*\xi_l^*\,d\mathbf{P} =$$

$$= \int_{A_k}\eta_k^2\,d\mathbf{P} + \sum_{l=k+1}^{n}\int_{A_k}\xi_l^{*2}\,d\mathbf{P} \geq \int_{A_k}\eta_k^2\,d\mathbf{P} \geq \varepsilon^2\,\mathbf{P}(A_k)$$

and

$$\sum_{k=1}^{n} \mathbf{D}^2(\xi_k^*) = \mathbf{D}^2(\sum_{k=1}^{n} \xi_k^*) \geq \int_A \eta_n^2 \, d\mathbf{P} = \sum_{k=1}^{n} \int_{A_k} \eta_n^2 \, d\mathbf{P} \geq \sum_{k=1}^{n} \varepsilon^2 \mathbf{P}(A_k) =$$

$$= \mathbf{P}(A)\,\varepsilon^2.$$

This proves the theorem.

PROOF OF THEOREM 8.1.2. Only the second assertion of this theorem will be proved since the first assertion is implied by it.

Let

$$\alpha_m(\omega) = \sup_k \{ | \eta_{m+k} - \eta_m | \},$$

$$\alpha(\omega) = \inf_m \{ \alpha_m(\omega) \}.$$

To show the convergence of the series $\sum_{k=1}^{\infty} \xi_k^*$ it is enough to prove that $\mathbf{P}(\alpha(\omega) = 0) = 1$. By Theorem 8.1.1, for any integers m and n, we have

$$\mathbf{P}(\sup_{1 \leq k \leq n} | \eta_{m+k} - \eta_m | \geq \varepsilon) \leq \frac{1}{\varepsilon^2} \sum_{k=m+1}^{n} \mathbf{D}^2(\xi_k^*).$$

Hence,

$$\mathbf{P}(| \alpha_m | \geq \varepsilon) \leq \frac{1}{\varepsilon^2} \sum_{k=m+1}^{\infty} \mathbf{D}^2(\xi_k^*)$$

and therefore,

$$\mathbf{P}(| \alpha | \geq \varepsilon) \leq \frac{1}{\varepsilon^2} \sum_{k=m+1}^{\infty} \mathbf{D}^2(\xi_k^*)$$

for any integer m, where ε is an arbitrary positive number. Then $\alpha(\omega) = 0$ almost everywhere.

The analogue of Theorem 2.2.1 can be obtained similarly.

The analogue of Theorem 2.9.2 for centered random variables is proved in a way similar to the method employed in the original theorem. We formulate this theorem for the special case in which $p = 1$; $c_1 = c_2 = \ldots = 1$.

THEOREM 8.1.3. *Let $\xi_1, \xi_2, \ldots$ be a sequence of identically distributed random variables with finite excpectation. Then*

$$\frac{1}{n} \sum_{k=1}^{n} \xi_k^* \to 0.$$

The proof is omitted.

§ 8.2. Mixing

Let $\xi_1, \xi_2, \ldots$ be a sequence of random variables and denote by $\mathscr{B}_n^m$ the smallest σ-algebra with respect to which $\xi_n, \xi_{n+1}, \ldots, \xi_m$ are measurable, i.e. $\mathscr{B}_n^m$ is the smallest σ-algebra which contains the sets

$$\{\omega: \xi_n(\omega) < x_n, \ \xi_{n+1}(\omega) < x_{n+1}, \ldots, \xi_m(x) < x_m\}$$

where $x_n, x_{n+1}, \ldots, x_m$ is an arbitrary sequence of real numbers.

In general the mixing conditions assume that

$$|\mathbf{P}(A \mid \mathscr{B}_1^m) - \mathbf{P}(A)|$$

is small if $A \in \mathscr{B}_{m+n}^\infty$ where n is large. A concrete mixing condition that can replace independence in Theorem 2.7.5a. is introduced in Blum–Hanson–Koopman [1] and called *-mixing.

Definition. The sequence $\xi_1, \xi_2, \ldots$ will be called *-mixing if there exists a positive integer N and a function $f(n)$ defined for the integers $n \geq N$ such that f is non-increasing with $\lim_{n\to\infty} f(n) = 0$ and such that if $n \geq N$, $A \in \mathscr{B}_1^m$, $B \in \mathscr{B}_{m+n}^{m+n}$ then

$$|\mathbf{P}(AB) - \mathbf{P}(A)\,\mathbf{P}(B)| \leq f(n)\,\mathbf{P}(A)\,\mathbf{P}(B). \tag{8.2.1}$$

for any integer m.

Clearly condition (8.2.1) is equivalent to the following condition:

$$|\mathbf{P}(B \mid \mathscr{B}_1^m) - \mathbf{P}(B)| \leq f(n)\,\mathbf{P}(B) \qquad (B \in \mathscr{B}_{m+n}^{m+n})$$

with probability 1. This implies

$$|\mathbf{E}(\xi_{m+n} \mid \xi_1, \xi_2, \ldots, \xi_m) - \mathbf{E}(\xi_{m+n})| \leq f(n)\,\mathbf{E}(|\xi_{m+n}|) \tag{8.2.2}$$

with probability 1.

Now we can give

Theorem 8.2.1 (see Blum–Hanson–Koopman [1][1]). *Let $\xi_1, \xi_2, \ldots$ be a *-mixing sequence such that $\mathbf{E}(\xi_n) = 0$, $\mathbf{E}(\xi_n^2) < \infty$ $(n = 1, 2, \ldots)$. Suppose that $\mathbf{E}(|\xi_n|) \leq K$ $(n = 1, 2, \ldots;\ K > 0$ is constant) and $\sum_{n=1}^\infty \frac{\mathbf{E}(\xi_n^2)}{n^2} < \infty$. Then*

$$\frac{\xi_1 + \xi_2 + \ldots + \xi_n}{n} \to 0. \tag{8.2.3}$$

Proof. Let $\varepsilon > 0$ be an arbitrary positive number and choose an integer n_0 such that $f(n_0) < \varepsilon$. We will show that

$$\mathbf{P}\left\{\lim_{\nu\to\infty} \left| \frac{1}{\nu} \sum_{d=1}^{\nu} \xi_{dn_0+t} \right| \leq \varepsilon K \right\} = 1 \tag{8.2.4}$$

[1] In this paper the conditions are somewhat stronger than ours. Our proof is due to P. Bártfai.

for any $t = 0, 1, 2, \ldots, n_0-1$. This implies (8.2.3). By Theorem 8.1.2, in order to prove (8.2.4), it is enough to prove that

$$\mathbf{P}\left\{\overline{\lim_{\nu\to\infty}}\left|\frac{1}{\nu}\sum_{d=1}^{\nu}\mathbf{E}(\xi_{dn_0+t}\mid\xi_{(d-1)n_0+t},\xi_{(d-2)n_0+t},\ldots,\xi_{n_0+t})\right|\leqq\varepsilon K\right\}=1.$$

This immediately follows from (8.2.2).

The proof shows that the condition (8.2.1) (*-mixing) can be replaced by condition (8.2.2).

H. Cohn [1] proposed to investigate the sequences $\{\xi_n\}$ for which it is not assumed that

$$|\mathbf{P}(A\mid\mathscr{B}_1^m)-\mathbf{P}(A)|\qquad(A\in\mathscr{B}_{m+n}^{\infty})\tag{8.2.5}$$

is small if n is large. It is only assumed that the difference (8.2.5) is not near to 1. More precisely he proved.[1]

Theorem 8.2.2 (Cohn [1]). *Let $\xi_1, \xi_2, \ldots$ be a sequence of square integrable random variables with $\mathbf{E}(\xi_i) = 0$ $(i = 1, 2, \ldots)$ for which there exists an integer $s \geqq 1$ and a real number $0 < \delta < 1$ such that*

$$|\mathbf{P}(A\mid\mathscr{B}_1^m)-\mathbf{P}(A)|\leqq\delta\tag{8.2.6}$$

if $A\in\mathscr{B}_{m+s}^{\infty}$. Further we assume that

$$\mathbf{D}^2\left(\sum_{k\in A}\frac{\xi_k}{k}\right)\leqq C\sum_{k\in A}\mathbf{D}^2\left(\frac{\xi_k}{k}\right)$$

where C is a positive constant and A is a subset of the integers. Then

$$\frac{1}{n}\sum_{k=1}^{n}\xi_k\to 0$$

if

$$\sum_{k=1}^{\infty}\frac{\mathbf{D}^2(\xi_k)}{k^2}<\infty.$$

Condition (8.2.6) does not imply that $|\mathbf{P}(A\mid\mathscr{B}_1^m)-\mathbf{P}(A)|$, $(A\in\mathscr{B}_{m+s}^{\infty})$, tends to 0 as $s\to\infty$, unless $\delta<{}^1/_2$. It would be interesting to investigate whether condition (8.2.6) can be replaced by the following one:

$$|\mathbf{P}(A\mid\mathscr{B}_1^m)-\mathbf{P}(A)|\leqq\delta<1\quad\text{if}\quad A\in\mathscr{B}_{m+s}^{m+s}.$$

Without loss of generality it can be assumed that $s = 1$.

The proof of this theorem is based on the following

[1] For some other properties of the mixing sequences in this sense see Bártfai–Révész [1].

LEMMA 8.2.1. *Let $\xi_1, \xi_2, \ldots, \xi_n$ be square integrable random variables with $\mathbf{E}(\xi_i) = 0$ $(i = 1, 2, \ldots)$. Suppose that there exists a real number $0 < \delta < 1$ such that*

$$|\mathbf{P}(B \mid \mathscr{B}_1^m) - \mathbf{P}(B)| \leq \delta \tag{8.2.7}$$

if $B \in \mathscr{B}_{m+1}^n$ $(m = 1, 2, \ldots, n-1)$. Then for any $\varepsilon > 0$ we have

$$\mathbf{P}\left\{\max_{1 \leq k \leq n} |\eta_k| \geq \varepsilon\right\} \leq \frac{\left(\frac{2}{\varepsilon}\right)^2 \mathbf{E}(\eta_n^2)}{v - \left(\frac{2}{\varepsilon}\right)^2 K(\xi_1, \xi_2, \ldots, \xi_n)}$$

(provided that the denominator of the right-hand side is positive) where

$$v = 1 - \delta; \quad \eta_k = \xi_1 + \xi_2 + \ldots + \xi_k$$

and

$$K(\xi_1, \xi_2, \ldots, \xi_n) = \max_{1 \leq m \leq n} \mathbf{E}\left[(\xi_m + \xi_{m+1} + \ldots + \xi_n)^2\right].$$

PROOF. Let

$$A = \left\{\omega : \max_{1 \leq k \leq n} |\eta_k| \geq \varepsilon\right\},$$

$$A_j = \{\omega : |\eta_1| < \varepsilon, |\eta_2| < \varepsilon, \ldots, |\eta_{j-1}| < \varepsilon, |\eta_j| \geq \varepsilon\} \quad (j = 1, 2, \ldots n),$$

$$B_j = \left\{\omega : |\eta_n - \eta_j| \leq \frac{\varepsilon}{2}\right\} \quad (j = 1, 2, \ldots, n-1)$$

and

$$D = \left\{\omega : |\eta_n| \geq \frac{\varepsilon}{2}\right\}.$$

Then clearly

$$\sum_{j=1}^n A_j = A \quad \text{and} \quad A_j A_k = \varnothing \quad \text{if} \quad j \neq k,$$

and

$$\sum_{m=1}^n A_m B_m \subset D.$$

Hence by condition (8.2.7) we get

$$\mathbf{P}\left(\sum_{m=1}^n A_m B_m\right) = \sum_{m=1}^n \mathbf{P}(A_m B_m) \geq \sum_{m=1}^n [\mathbf{P}(A_m)\mathbf{P}(B_m) - \delta \mathbf{P}(A_m)], \tag{8.2.8}$$

By the Chebyshev inequality we have

$$\mathbf{P}(B_m) = \mathbf{P}\left(\left|\sum_{i=m+1}^{n} \xi_i\right| \leq \frac{\varepsilon}{2}\right) \geq 1 - \frac{4\,\mathbf{E}\left[\left(\sum_{i=m+1}^{n} \xi_i\right)^2\right]}{\varepsilon^2} \geq$$

$$\geq 1 - \frac{4\,K(\xi_1, \xi_2, \ldots, \xi_n)}{\varepsilon^2}$$

and so

$$\min_{1 \leq m \leq n} \mathbf{P}(B_m) \geq 1 - \frac{4\,K(\xi_1, \xi_2, \ldots, \xi_n)}{\varepsilon^2}. \tag{8.2.9}$$

(8.2.8) and (8.2.9) together imply

$$\mathbf{P}\left(\sum_{m=1}^{n} A_m B_m\right) \geq \left[v - \frac{4\,K(\xi_1, \xi_2, \ldots, \xi_n)}{\varepsilon_n}\right] \sum_{m=1}^{n} \mathbf{P}(A_m) =$$

$$= \left[v - \frac{4\,K(\xi_1, \xi_2, \ldots, \xi_n)}{\varepsilon^2}\right] \mathbf{P}(A).$$

Therefore, making use of the Chebyshev inequality again

$$\mathbf{P}(A) \leq \frac{\mathbf{P}(C)}{v - \dfrac{4\,K(\xi_1, \xi_2, \ldots, \xi_n)}{\varepsilon^2}} \leq \frac{\dfrac{4}{\varepsilon^2}\,\mathbf{E}\left[(\xi_1 + \xi_2 + \ldots + \xi_n)^2\right]}{v - \dfrac{4\,K(\xi_1, \xi_2, \ldots, \xi_n)}{\varepsilon^2}}.$$

Hence the lemma is proved.

We can now prove Theorem 8.2.2 by using the same method that was used in the proof of Theorem 8.1.2.

CHAPTER 9

INDEPENDENT RANDOM VARIABLES TAKING VALUES IN AN ABSTRACT SPACE

Up to now we have considered random variables taking values on the real line. In general similar results can be obtained for random variables taking values in a finite dimensional Banach space. This statement can be formulated more precisely in the independent case, since in this case the coordinates of the random variables are also independent. In particular Theorem 2.9.2 is true in the case $p = 1$. (The expectation of a finite dimensional random vector is the vector of the expectations of the coordinates of the random vector.)

The situation is not much more complicated if the values of the random variables are in a Hilbert space, because in this case the variance of the sum of independent random variables is equal to the sum of the variances. The real difficulty is in the treatment of the random variables taking values in a Banach space.

The most fundamental theorems in this case were obtained by MOURIER [1] and FORTET [2], Here we follow the treatment of BECK [1].

First of all we have to give some definitions.

Let $\{\Omega, \mathscr{S}, \mathbf{P}\}$ be a probability space and let B be a Banach space. A function $\xi(\omega)$ $(\omega \in \Omega)$ is called B-random variable, or a random variable taking values in B, if $\xi(\omega) \in B$ for each $\omega \in \Omega$ and

$$\{\omega: \xi(\omega) \in U\} \in \mathscr{S}$$

for any open subset U of B ("open" is with respect to the strong topology) or in other words, if $\xi(\omega)$ is measurable.

If $\| \xi(\omega) \|$ is integrable (with respect to $\mathbf{P}$) then there exists an element $\mathbf{E}(\xi)$ of B, called the expectation of ξ, for which

$$f(\mathbf{E}(\xi)) = \int_{\Omega} f(\xi)\, d\mathbf{P} = \mathbf{E}(f(\xi))$$

for any bounded linear functional f defined on B (see PETTIS [1]).

The variance of ξ is defined as

$$\mathbf{D}^2(\xi) = \int_{\Omega} \| \xi - \mathbf{E}\,\xi \|^2\, d\mathbf{P}\,.$$

The B-random variables $\xi_1, \xi_2, \ldots, \xi_n$ are called independent if

$$\mathbf{P}(\xi_1 \in U_1, \xi_2 \in U_2, \ldots, \xi_n \in U_n) = \mathbf{P}(\xi_1 \in U_1)\,\mathbf{P}(\xi_2 \in U_2) \ldots \mathbf{P}(\xi_n \in U_n)$$

for any open sets $U_1, U_2, \ldots, U_n$ of B

The following definition is due to RIESZ:

A Banach space B is called *uniformly convex* if for every $\varepsilon > 0$ there is a $\delta > 0$ such that for all $x \in B, y \in B$ with $\| x \| \leq 1, \| y \| \leq 1$ we have that

$$\left\| \frac{x+y}{2} \right\| \geq 1 - \delta \quad \text{implies} \quad \| x - y \| \leq \varepsilon .$$

As a generalization of this, BECK has introduced the following;

A Banach space B is called convex in the sense of Beck if there is an integer k and an $\varepsilon > 0$ such that for every sequence $x_1, x_2, \ldots, x_k$ of the elements of B with $\| x_i \| \leq 1$ $(i = 1, 2, \ldots, k)$ we have

$$\| \pm x_1 \pm x_2 \pm \ldots \pm x_k \| \geq k(1 - \varepsilon)$$

for some choice of the signs $+$ and $-$.

§ 9.1. Independent random variables taking values in a Hilbert space

Theorems 2.7.5a and 2.1.1 and Lemma 2.2.1 hold if the values of the random variables are from a Hilbert space, i.e. we have

THEOREM 9.1.1. *Let $\xi_1, \xi_2, \ldots$ be a sequence of independent random variables taking values in a Hilbert space H for which*

$$\mathbf{E}(\xi_i) = 0$$

(0 is the zero element of H) and

$$\sum_{i=1}^{\infty} \frac{\mathbf{D}^2(\xi_i)}{i^2} < \infty .$$

Then

$$\mathbf{P}\left(\left\| \frac{1}{n} \sum_{k=1}^{n} \xi_k \right\| \to 0 \right) = 1$$

and if

$$\sum_{i=1}^{\infty} \mathbf{D}^2(\xi_i) < \infty \quad \text{and} \quad \mathbf{E}(\xi_i) = 0$$

then $\sum_{k=1}^{\infty} \xi_k$ is convergent with probability 1, *i.e. there exists a random variable η (taking values in H) such that*

$$\mathbf{P}\left(\left\| \sum_{k=1}^{n} \xi_k - \eta \right\| \to 0 \right) = 1 .$$

THEOREM 9.1.2. *Let $\xi_1, \xi_2, \ldots, \xi_n$ be a sequence of independent random variables taking values in a Hilbert space H for which $\mathbf{E}(\xi_i) = 0$ $(i = 1, 2, \ldots, n)$. Then we have*

$$\mathbf{P}\left(\sup_{1 \leq k \leq n} \left\| \sum_{i=1}^{k} \xi_i \right\| \geq \varepsilon \right) \leq \frac{\sum_{k=1}^{n} \mathbf{D}^2(\xi_k)}{\varepsilon^2}$$

for any $\varepsilon > 0$.

The proofs of these theorems follow the same lines as the proofs of Theorems 8.1.1 and 8.1.2; they use the simple fact that

$$\int_A (\xi_k, \xi_j)\, d\mathbf{P} = 0 \qquad (j < k)$$

if A belongs to the smallest σ-algebra with respect to which the random variables $\xi_1, \xi_2, \ldots, \xi_{j-1}$ are measurable.

§ 9.2. Independent random variables taking values in a Banach space

Our first aim is to give the analogue of Theorem 2.9.2.

THEOREM 9.2.1. *Let $\xi_1, \xi_2, \ldots$ be a sequence of independent, identically distributed B-random variables for which $\mathbf{E}(\xi_i) = 0$. Then*

$$\mathbf{P}\left(\left\| \frac{1}{n} \sum_{k=1}^{n} \xi_k \right\| \to 0 \right) = 1.$$

PROOF. As was mentioned in the first part of the present chapter this theorem is quite clear if B is a finite dimensional Banach space.

Let ε be an arbitrary positive number and let $x_1, x_2, \ldots$ be a dense sequence in B. Set $K_j = \{x : \| x - x_j \| < \varepsilon \}$ and $A_j = K_j - \sum_{i=1}^{j-1} K_j$. Define the B-random variable ξ_i^* as

$$\xi_i^*(\omega) = x_j \text{ whenever } \xi_i(\omega) \in A_j \quad (i = 1, 2, \ldots; \; j = 1, 2, \ldots).$$

Then $\| \xi_i^*(\omega) - \xi_i(\omega) \| \leq \varepsilon$ and

$$\sum_{j=1}^{\infty} \| x_j \| \, \mathbf{P}(\xi_i \in A_j) = \mathbf{E}(\| \xi_i^* \|) \leq \mathbf{E}(\| \xi_i \|) + \varepsilon < \infty.$$

Choose the integer N such that

$$\sum_{j=N}^{\infty} \| x_j \| \, \mathbf{P}(\xi_i \in A_j) < \varepsilon \qquad (i = 1, 2, \ldots).$$

Let

$$\zeta_i^* = \begin{cases} x_j & \text{if } \xi_i \in A_j \quad j \geq N \\ 0 & \text{if } j < N \end{cases}$$

and

$$\eta_i = \xi_i^* - \zeta_i^*, \quad \zeta_i = \xi_i - \eta_i.$$

Then $\{\xi_i^*\}$ and $\{\eta_i\}$ are sequences of independent B-random variables for which

$$\| \mathbf{E}(\zeta_i^*) \| \leq \mathbf{E}(\| \zeta_i^* \|) \sum_{j=N}^{\infty} \| x_j \| \, \mathbf{P}(\xi_i \in A_j) < \varepsilon \quad (i = 1, 2, \ldots)$$

and

$$\| \mathbf{E}(\eta_i) \| \leq \| \mathbf{E}(\xi_i^*) \| + \| \mathbf{E}(\zeta_i^*) \| = \| \mathbf{E}(\xi_i^* - \xi_i) + \mathbf{E}(\xi_i) \| + \| \mathbf{E}(\zeta_i^*) \| =$$
$$= \| \mathbf{E}(\xi_i - \xi_i^*) \| + \| \mathbf{E}(\zeta_i^*) \| \leq \varepsilon + \varepsilon = 2\varepsilon.$$

Further

$$\zeta_i = \xi_i - \eta_i = (\xi_i - \xi_i^*) + (\xi_i^* - \eta_i) = (\xi_i - \xi_i^*) + \zeta_i^*,$$

and hence

$$\mathbf{E}(\| \zeta_i \|) \leq \mathbf{E}(\| \xi_i - \xi_i^* \|) + \mathbf{E}(\| \zeta_i^* \|) < 2\varepsilon.$$

Clearly, since $\mathbf{E}(\xi_i) = 0$

$$\xi_i = (\eta_i - \mathbf{E}(\eta_i)) + (\zeta_i - \mathbf{E}(\zeta_i)).$$

$\{\eta_i - \mathbf{E}(\eta_i)\}$ is a sequence of independent identically distributed random variables, taking only $N-1$ distinct values. Thus it obeys the strong law of large numbers.

Since

$$\left\| \frac{1}{n} \sum_{i=1}^{n} (\zeta_i - \mathbf{E}(\zeta_i)) \right\| \leq \frac{1}{n} \sum_{i=1}^{n} \| \zeta_i \| + \frac{1}{n} \sum_{i=1}^{n} \| \mathbf{E}(\zeta_i) \| \leq$$
$$\leq \frac{1}{n} \sum_{i=1}^{n} \| \zeta_i \| + \frac{1}{n} \sum_{i=1}^{n} \mathbf{E}(\| \zeta_i \|) \leq \frac{1}{n} \sum_{i=1}^{n} \| \zeta_i \| + 2\varepsilon,$$

by Theorem 2.9.2, we have our statement.

To obtain an analogue, of Theorem 2.7.5a for B-random variables (at least in the case when B is "good" in some sense) seems to be very difficult. Beside several negative results, a positive result can be obtained if the variance is bounded and the Banach space B is convex in the sense of Beck. More precisely we have

THEOREM 9.2.2 (see BECK [1]). *Let B be a Banach space, convex in the sense of Beck and let $\xi_1, \xi_2, \ldots$ be a sequence of independent random variables taking values in B with $\mathbf{E}(\xi_i) = 0$, $\mathbf{D}^2(\xi_i) \leq K$ $(i = 1, 2, \ldots)$ (K is a positive constant). Then*

$$\mathbf{P}\left(\left\| \frac{1}{n} \sum_{k=1}^{n} \xi_k \right\| \to 0 \right) = 1.$$

If B is not convex in the sense of Beck, then there exists a sequence of independent B-random variables with $\mathbf{E}(\xi_i) = 0$, $\mathbf{D}^2(\xi_i) \leq 1$ $(i = 1, 2, \ldots)$ not obeying the strong law of large numbers.

The proof of this theorem is too long to be given here.

CHAPTER 10

SUM OF A RANDOM NUMBER OF INDEPENDENT RANDOM VARIABLES

In general, a law of large numbers states that the average of the first n terms of a sequence of random variables is practically constant if n is large enough. In many practical applications the number of the experiments (i.e. the integer n) depends on chance. More precisely, let $\xi_1, \xi_2, \ldots$ be a sequence of independent random variables and let $\nu_1, \nu_2, \ldots$ be a sequence of positive integer-valued random variables. We intend to investigate the properties of the sequence

$$\zeta_{\nu_n} = \frac{\eta_{\nu_n}}{\nu_n} = \frac{\xi_1 + \xi_2 + \ldots + \xi_{\nu_n}}{\nu_n}.$$

Clearly, the interesting case is when ν_n tends to infinity (in some sense). We restrict our attention to the case where the $\xi_1, \xi_2, \ldots$ are independent. The situation is simple when $\{\nu_n\}$ is independent of $\{\xi_n\}$ (see DOBRUSHIN [1]). The general case has been treated by many authors[1] (see e.g. ANSCOMBE [1], RÉNYI [4], MOGYORÓDI [1], [2]).

The following theorem is clear without any proof.

THEOREM 10.1. *Let $\boldsymbol{\xi} = (\xi_1, \xi_2, \ldots)$ be a sequence of independent random variables and let $\nu_1, \nu_2, \ldots$ be a sequence of positive integer-valued random variables. Then*

$$\zeta_n = \frac{\xi_1 + \xi_2 + \ldots + \xi_n}{n} \to 0 \text{ and } \nu_n \to \infty \text{ imply } \zeta_{\nu_n} \to 0, \tag{10.1}$$

$$\zeta_n = \frac{\xi_1 + \xi_2 + \ldots + \xi_n}{n} \to 0 \text{ and } \nu_n \Rightarrow \infty \text{ imply } \zeta_{\nu_n} \Rightarrow 0, \tag{10.2}$$

but

$$\zeta_n = \frac{\xi_1 + \xi_2 + \ldots + \xi_n}{n} \Rightarrow 0 \text{ and } \nu_n \to \infty \text{ do not imply } \zeta_{\nu_n} \Rightarrow 0. \tag{10.3}$$

[1] The mentioned papers (except MOGYORÓDI [1]) are dealing mostly with limit distribution theorems.

According to this theorem, the most interesting question is to find conditions on $\{\nu_n\}$ under which $\zeta_n \Rightarrow 0$ implies $\zeta_{\nu_n} \Rightarrow 0$. The usual restriction is that ν_n/n tends to a positive constant (or a positive random variable) in probability. This condition easily implies that $a < \nu_n < b$ (for some constants $0 < a < b < \infty$) with probability close to 1. This second restriction by itself is enough for most purposes. Here we will use a weaker version of this restriction.

THEOREM 10.2. *Let* $\xi_1, \xi_2, \ldots$ *be a sequence of independent random variables and let* $\nu_1, \nu_2, \ldots$ *be a sequence of positive integer-valued random variables. Denote by* $f(n)$ *a positive monotonically increasing function defined on the integers with* $\lim_{n\to\infty} f(n) = \infty$. *Suppose that*

$$\zeta_n = \frac{\eta_n}{n} = \frac{\xi_1 + \xi_2 + \ldots + \xi_n}{n} \Rightarrow 0 \tag{10.4}$$

and that for any $\varepsilon > 0$ *there exists* $0 < a = a(\varepsilon) < b = b(\varepsilon) < \infty$ *such that*

$$\mathbf{P}\big(a\,f(n) < \nu_n < b\,f(n)\big) \geq 1 - \varepsilon\,. \tag{10.5}$$

for $n > n_0(\varepsilon)$. *Then*

$$\zeta_{\nu_n} = \frac{\eta_{\nu_n}}{\nu_n} = \frac{\xi_1 + \xi_2 + \ldots + \xi_{\nu_n}}{\nu_n} \Rightarrow 0\,.$$

REMARK. This theorem is proved in MOGYORÓDI [1] except that condition (10.5) is replaced by the somewhat stronger condition

$$\frac{\nu_n}{n} \Rightarrow \lambda \qquad (n \to \infty)$$

where λ is a positive random variable, i.e. $\mathbf{P}(\lambda > 0) = 1$.

However we can still follow the method of MOGYORÓDI [1] to obtain the theorem.

PROOF. Set

$$A_n = A_n(\varepsilon) = \{\omega : af(n) \leqq \nu_n \leqq bf(n)\}\,.$$

Then for any $\delta > 0$ we have

$$\mathbf{P}(|\zeta_{\nu_n}| \geqq \delta) = \mathbf{P}(|\zeta_{\nu_n}| \geqq \delta, A_n) + \mathbf{P}(|\zeta_{\nu_n}| \geqq \delta, \bar{A}_n) \leqq$$
$$\leqq \mathbf{P}(|\zeta_{\nu_n}| \geqq \delta, A_n) + \varepsilon\,. \tag{10.6}$$

Since the inequality $|\zeta_{\nu_n}| \geqq \delta$ implies that either

$$|\zeta_{[af(n)]}|\,\frac{[af(n)]}{\nu_n} \geqq \frac{\delta}{2}$$

or

$$\left|\frac{\eta_{\nu_n} - \eta_{[af(n)]}}{\nu_n}\right| \geqq \frac{\delta}{2}$$

we have

$$\mathbf{P}(|\zeta_{\nu_n}| \geqq \delta) = \mathbf{P}(|\zeta_{\nu_n}| \geqq \delta, A_n) + \mathbf{P}(|\zeta_{\nu_n}| \geqq \delta, \bar{A}_n) \leqq$$

$$\leqq \mathbf{P}(|\zeta_{\nu_n}| \geqq \delta, A_n) + \varepsilon \leqq \mathbf{P}\left(|\zeta_{[af(n)]}| \frac{[af(n)]}{\nu_n} \geqq \frac{\delta}{2}, A_n\right) +$$

$$+ \mathbf{P}\left(\left|\frac{\eta_{\nu_n} - \eta_{[af(n)]}}{\nu_n}\right| \geqq \frac{\delta}{2}, A_n\right) + \varepsilon. \qquad (10.7)$$

By (10.4) the first member of the right-hand side tends to 0 (as $n \to \infty$). To show that the second member also tends to 0 we apply Theorem 2.5.2. By this theorem, condition (10.4) implies that

$$\sum_{k=1}^{n} \int_{|x|>\varepsilon n} d\mathbf{P}(\xi_k < x) \to 0, \qquad (10.8)$$

$$\frac{1}{n} \sum_{k=1}^{n} \int_{|x|<\varepsilon n} x\, d\mathbf{P}(\xi_k < x) \to 0, \qquad (10.9)$$

$$\sum_{k=1}^{n} \frac{1}{n^2}\left\{\int_{|x|<n\varepsilon} x^2\, dF_k(x) - \left(\int_{|x|<\varepsilon n} x\, dF_k(x)\right)^2\right\} \to 0. \qquad (10.10)$$

Let

$$\xi_k^* = \begin{cases} \xi_k & \text{if } |\xi_k| \leqq f(n)\, b \\ 0 & \text{if } |\xi_k| > f(n)\, b \end{cases} \qquad (k = 1, 2, \ldots, [f(n)\, b]$$

and

$$\eta_k^* = \xi_1^* + \xi_2^* + \ldots + \xi_k^* .$$

Then by (10.8)

$$\mathbf{P}\left\{\max_{[f(n)a] \leqq k \leqq [f(n)b]} |\eta_k^* - \eta_{[f(n)a]}^*| \neq \max_{[f(n)a] \leqq k \leqq [f(n)b]} |\eta_k - \eta_{[f(n)a]}|\right\} \leqq$$

$$\leqq \sum_{k=[f(n)a]}^{[f(n)b]} \int_{|x|>f(n)b} d\mathbf{P}(\xi_k < x). \qquad (10.11)$$

Now it is enough to prove that

$$\mathbf{P}\left(\max_{[f(n)a] \leqq k \leqq [f(n)b]} |\eta_k^* - \eta_{[f(n)a]}^*| \frac{1}{f(n)a} \geqq \varepsilon\right) \to 0$$

which easily follows from (10.10) and the Kolmogorov inequality (Theorem 2.1.1).

CHAPTER 11

APPLICATIONS

§ 11.1. Applications in number theory

Let the i-th digit of the dyadic expansion of $x \in [0,1]$ be $\varepsilon_i = \varepsilon_i(x)$, i.e.

$$x = 0, \varepsilon_1 \varepsilon_2 \ldots$$

or in other words

$$x = \sum_{i=1}^{\infty} \frac{\varepsilon_i(x)}{2^i}.$$

E. Borel asked what the relative frequency of the digit 1 is in the sequence $\varepsilon_1, \varepsilon_2, \ldots$. More precisely, if $\nu_n(x)$ is the number of the 1's among the first n digit of x (i.e. $\nu_n = \varepsilon_1 + \varepsilon_2 + \ldots + \varepsilon_n$) then the question is to find the limit of the sequence

$$\frac{\nu_n(x)}{n} = \frac{\varepsilon_1(x) + \varepsilon_2(x) + \ldots + \varepsilon_n(x)}{n}.$$

In a somewhat more general form, if $\varepsilon_i^{(t)}(x)$ is the i-th digit of the number x in its t-adic expansion, i.e.

$$x = \sum_{i=1}^{\infty} \frac{\varepsilon_i^{(t)}(x)}{t^i},$$

then we ask what the relative frequency of the digit k ($k = 0, 1, 2, \ldots, t-1$) is in the sequence $\varepsilon_1^{(t)}, \varepsilon_2^{(t)}, \ldots$. Then, setting

$$\varphi_{i,k}^{(t)}(x) = \begin{cases} 1 & \text{if } \varepsilon_i^{(t)}(x) = k \\ 0 & \text{if } \varepsilon_i^{(t)}(x) \neq k, \end{cases}$$

our question is to find the limit of the sequence

$$\psi_{k,n}^{(t)}(x) = \frac{\varphi_{1,k}^{(t)}(x) + \varphi_{2,k}^{(t)}(x) + \ldots + \varphi_{n,k}^{(t)}(x)}{n}.$$

Borel introduced the following

Definition. The number $x \in [0,1]$ is called *normal* if

$$\lim_{n\to\infty} \psi_{k,n}^{(t)}(x) = \frac{1}{t} \qquad (k = 0, 1, 2, \ldots, t-1;\ t = 2, 3, \ldots).$$

Clearly the random variables $\varphi_{1,k}^{(t)}(x), \varphi_{2,k}^{(t)}(x), \ldots$ are independent and

$$\int_0^1 \varphi_{n,k}^{(t)}(x)\,dx = \frac{1}{t} \qquad (k = 0, 1, 2, \ldots, t-1\,;\, n = 1, 2, \ldots)\,.$$

Therefore, by Theorem 2.7.5a, we have

THEOREM 11.1.1. (BOREL [1]). *Almost every $x \in [0,1]$ is normal.*

We mention that making use of Theorem 2.8.2 we can obtain the following stronger

THEOREM 11.1.2. *One has*

$$\overline{\lim_{n\to\infty}} \sqrt{\frac{nt^2}{2(t-1)\log\log n}} \left| \psi_{k,n}^{(t)}(x) - \frac{1}{t} \right| = 1$$

almost everywhere.

Similar questions have been raised for other expansions of the numbers $x \in [0,1]$. Here we study two classes of such expansions. The first is the so-called Cantor's series, the second is a very general expansion, introduced by RÉNYI which contains many classical expansions, for example the continued fraction expansion. In connection with this second expansion only the case of the continued fractions will be treated in detail.

First of all we give the definition of the Cantor's series.

Let $\{q_n\}$ denote a sequence of positive integers $q_n \geq 2$ $(n = 1, 2, \ldots)$. It has been shown by G. CANTOR [1], [2] that every real number $x \in (0,1)$ can be represented in the form

$$x = \sum_{n=1}^{\infty} \frac{\varepsilon_n(x)}{q_1 q_2 \cdots q_n} \tag{11.1.1}$$

where the n-th digit $\varepsilon_n(x)$ can take on the values $0, 1, 2, \ldots, q_n - 1$. The series (11.1.1) is called Cantor's series. (This representation is unique, except for some rational numbers.) The statistical properties of the sequence $\varepsilon_1, \varepsilon_2, \ldots$ were investigated by RÉNYI [5].

He obtained the following

THEOREM 11.1.3. *Let $q_1, q_2, \ldots$ be a sequence of positive integers for which $q_n \geq 2$ $(n = 1, 2, \ldots)$ and $\sum_{n=1}^{\infty} \frac{1}{q_n} = \infty$ and let $\varepsilon_i(x)$ be the i-th digit of $x \in (0,1)$ in its Cantor's series i.e.*

$$x = \sum_{n=1}^{\infty} \frac{\varepsilon_n(x)}{q_1 q_2 \cdots q_n}\,.$$

Further let us denote by $N_n(r, x)$ the number of occurrences of the non-

negative number r among the first n digits of x in its expansion (11.1.1) *Then for almost all $x \in [0,1]$ and for those k' s for which*

$$\lim_{n\to\infty} \sum_{\substack{k=1\\ r<q_k}}^{n} \frac{1}{q_k} = \infty$$

we have

$$\lim_{n\to\infty} \frac{N_n(r, x)}{\sum\limits_{\substack{k=1\\ r<q_k}}^{n} \frac{1}{q_k}} = 1.$$

PROOF. Let

$$\varphi_{i,r}(x) = \begin{cases} 1 \text{ whenever } \varepsilon_i(x) = r \\ 0 \text{ whenever } \varepsilon_i(x) \neq r. \end{cases}$$

Then clearly the random variables $\varphi_{1,r}(x), \varphi_{2,r})(x), \ldots$ are independent with

$$\mathbf{E}(\varphi_{i,r}(x)) = \frac{1}{q_i}, \quad \mathbf{D}^2(\varphi_{i,r}(x)) = \frac{1}{q_i}\left(1 - \frac{1}{q_i}\right) \quad (r = 0, 1, 2, \ldots, q_i - 1)$$

and

$$\varphi_{1,n}(x) + \varphi_{2,r}(x) + \ldots + \varphi_{n,r}(x) = N_n(r,x).$$

Hence by Theorem 2.8.3 we have

$$\overline{\lim_{n\to\infty}} \frac{N_n(r, x) - \Sigma^* \frac{1}{q_k}}{\sqrt{2 \Sigma^* \frac{1}{q_k}\left(1 - \frac{1}{q_k}\right) \log\log \Sigma^* \frac{1}{q_k}\left(1 - \frac{1}{q_k}\right)}} =$$

$$= \overline{\lim_{n\to\infty}} \frac{\Sigma^* \frac{1}{q_k}}{\sqrt{2 \Sigma^* \frac{1}{q_k}\left(1 - \frac{1}{q_k}\right) \log\log \Sigma^* \frac{1}{q_k}\left(1 - \frac{1}{q_k}\right)}} \left[\frac{N_n(r, x)}{\Sigma^* \frac{1}{q_k}} - 1\right] = 1$$

which implies (11.1.3) since

$$\overline{\lim_{n\to\infty}} \frac{\Sigma^* \frac{1}{q_k}}{\sqrt{2 \Sigma^* \frac{1}{q_k}\left(1 - \frac{1}{q_k}\right) \log\log \Sigma^* \frac{1}{q_k}\left(1 - \frac{1}{q_k}\right)}} = \infty$$

where

$$\Sigma^* = \sum_{\substack{k=1\\ r>q_k}}^{n}.$$

Now let us turn to the second class of expansions.

Let $f(x)$ be a positive monotone function defined on the interval $(0, +\infty)$. The infinite iteration

$$x = \varepsilon_0 + f(\varepsilon_1 + f(\varepsilon_2 + f(\varepsilon_3 + \ldots)\ldots) \tag{11.1.2}$$

is called the f-expansion of x where the numbers $\varepsilon_n = \varepsilon_n(x)$ are called the digits of x and

$$r_n(x) = f(\varepsilon_{n+1} + f(\varepsilon_{n+2} + f(\varepsilon_{n+3} + \ldots)\ldots)$$

is called the remainder. One can define the digits and the remainders by the following recursive relations:

$$\varepsilon_0(x) = [x], \qquad r_0(x) = (x)$$
$$\varepsilon_{n+1} = [\varphi(r_n(x))], \quad r_{n+1}(x) = (\varphi(r_n(x))) \quad (n = 0, 1, 2, \ldots)$$

where $[z]$ denotes the integral part and (z) the fractional part of the real number z (i.e. $z = [z] + (z)$) and $x = \varphi(y)$ is the inverse function of $y = f(x)$.

In particular if
$$f(x) = \frac{x}{t} \quad (t = 2, 3, \ldots)$$

then the f-expansion reduces to the t-adic expansion and if $f(x) = \dfrac{1}{x}$ we obtain the continued fraction representation of x.

The first question in connection with any f-expansion is whether any real number x can be represented in the form (11.1.2).

A positive answer was obtained by Rényi [6] under the following conditions:

(a1) $f(1) = 1$.

(a2) $f(t)$ is positive, continuous and strictly decreasing for $1 \leq t \leq T$ and $f(t) = 0$ for $t \geq T$ where $T = 2, 3, \ldots, +\infty$ ($T = +\infty$ means that $\lim_{t\to\infty} f(t) = 0$).

(a3) $|f(t_2) - f(t_1)| \leq |t_2 - t_1|$ for $1 \leq t_1 < t_2$ and there is a constant λ such that $0 < \lambda < 1$ and

$$|f(t_2) - f(t_1)| \leq \lambda |t_2 - t_1| \text{ if } 1 \leq t_1 < t_2.$$

The answer is similarly positive under the following different set of conditions:

(b1) $f(0) = 0$.

(b2) $f(t)$ is continuous and strictly increasing for $0 \leq t \leq T$ and $f(t) = 1$ if $t \geq T$ where $T = 2, 3, \ldots, +\infty$. ($T = \infty$ means $\lim_{t\to\infty} f(t) = 1$.)

(b3) $$\frac{f(t_2) - f(t_1)}{t_2 - t_1} < 1 \text{ for } 0 \leq t_1 < t_2.$$

Before the formulation of the theorem of RÉNYI on the statistical properties of the digits of an f-expansion we introduce some notations. Let us define

$$f_1(z_1) = f(z_1),$$

$$f_n(z_1, z_2, \ldots, z_n) = f_{n-1}(z_1, z_2, \ldots, z_{n-2}, z_{n-1} + f(z_n))$$

for $n = 2, 3, \ldots$. Let us put further

$$C_n(x) = f_n(\varepsilon_1(x)_1\, \varepsilon_2(x), \ldots, \varepsilon_n(x))$$

where $\varepsilon_1, \varepsilon_2, \ldots$ are the digits of x in its f-expansion. Finally we put

$$H_n(x, t) = \frac{\partial}{\partial t} f_n(\varepsilon_1(x), \varepsilon_2(x), \ldots, \varepsilon_{n-1}(x), \varepsilon_n(x) + t).$$

Now we can give the following

THEOREM 11.1.4. *If $f(x)$ satisfies the conditions* (a1), (a2), (a3), *or the conditions* (b1), (b2), (b3) *and*

$$\frac{\sup\limits_{0<t<1} H_n(x, t)}{\inf\limits_{0<t<1} H_n(x, t)} < C \tag{11.1.3}$$

where the constant $C > 0$, then for any intergrable function g, defined in the interval (0, 1), *and for almost all x*

$$\lim_{n\to\infty} \frac{1}{n} \sum_{k=0}^{n-1} g(r_k(x)) = M(g)$$

where

$$M(g) = \int_0^1 g(x)\, h(x)\, dx$$

$h(x)$ being a measurable function, depending only on $f(x)$ and satisfying the inequality

$$\frac{1}{C} \leqq h(x) \leqq C$$

where the constant C is the same as that in (11.1.3).

Here we do not give the proof of this theorem but turn to the investigation of the special case $f(x) = \dfrac{1}{x}$, i.e. the case of continued fractions. This problem was investigated by RYLL-NARDZEWSKI [1]. He used the following method.

Let the transformation T be defined on the interval (0,1) as follows:

$$T_x = \frac{1}{x} - \left[\frac{1}{x}\right].$$

This transformation is measurable but not measure-preserving. The fundamental idea of RYLL-NARDZEWSKI is to find a measure ν, defined on the Borel sets of [0,1], such that T would be measure-preserving with respect to ν. He introduces the measure

$$\nu(E) = \frac{1}{\log 2} \int_E \frac{dx}{1+x},$$

where E is any Borel measurable subset of [0,1]. To prove that T is really measure-preserving with respect to this ν it is enough to check that

$$\nu\left(T^{-1}(0,\alpha)\right) = \nu\left(\sum_{n=1}^{\infty}\left(\frac{1}{n+a}, \frac{1}{n}\right)\right) = \sum_{n=1}^{\infty} \frac{1}{\log 2} \int_{\frac{4}{n+\alpha}}^{\frac{1}{4}} \frac{dx}{1+x} =$$

$$= \frac{1}{\log 2} \int_0^{\alpha} \frac{dx}{1+\alpha} = \nu\left((0,a)\right)$$

for any $\alpha \in (0,1)$. It is a slightly more difficult to prove that this transformation is ergodic, but knowing this fact, as a consequence of Theorem 0.5.1 we obtain

THEOREM 11.1.5. (RYLL-NARDZEWSKI [1]). *For each integrable f we have*

$$\frac{1}{n}\left[f(x) + f(Tx) + \ldots + f(T^{n-1}x)\right] \to \frac{1}{\log 2} \int_0^1 \frac{f(t)}{1+t}\, dt$$

for almost all x. In particular, if

$$f(x) = f_p(x) = \begin{cases} 1 \ \textit{whenever} \ \dfrac{1}{p+1} < x < \dfrac{1}{p} \ (p = 1, 2, \ldots) \\ 0 \ \textit{otherwise} \end{cases}$$

(i.e. $f_p(x) = 1$ if the first digit of x is p) then we find that the limit of the relative frequency of the digit p among the digits of x is

$$\frac{1}{\log 2} \log \frac{(p+1)^2}{p(p+2)}$$

for almost all x, similarly if

$$f(x) = p \quad \textit{whenever} \quad \frac{1}{p+1} < x < \frac{1}{p} \quad (p = 1, 2, \ldots)$$

(i.e. $f(x)$ is the first digit of x) then we find that

$$\frac{f(x)+f(Tx)+\ldots+f(T^{n-1}x)}{n}\to\infty$$

almost everywhere, where $f(T^i x)$ is equal to the $(i+1)$-th digit of x.

For further results see Erdős–Rényi [1], [2], Erdős–Rényi–Szüsz [1].

§ 11.2. Applications in statistics

One of the fundamental problems of statistics is to estimate unknown parameters, e.g. mean value, variance, of a distribution function $F(x)$ from a sample $\xi_1, \xi_2, \ldots$ where, at least in the simplest case, $\xi_1, \xi_2, \ldots$ are independent, identically distributed random variables with $\mathbf{P}(\xi_i < x) = F(x)$. The simplest answers to this question are given by the different forms of the laws of large numbers. For example, if $\xi_1, \xi_2, \ldots$ are independent identically distributed random variables then by Theorem 2.9.2 we have

$$\bar{\xi}_n = \frac{\xi_1+\xi_2+\ldots+\xi_n}{n}\to m = \int_{-\infty}^{+\infty} x\,dF(x)$$

and

$$\bar{\sigma}_n^2 = \frac{(\xi_1-\bar{\xi}_n)^2+(\xi_2-\bar{\xi}_n)^2+\ldots+(\xi_n-\bar{\xi}_n)^2}{n} =$$

$$= \frac{1}{n}\sum_{k=1}^{n}\xi_k^2 - \bar{\xi}_n^2 \to \sigma^2 = \int_{-\infty}^{+\infty}(x-m)^2\,dF(x)$$

provided that the integrals of the right hand sides are finite. This means, in the language of statistics, that $\bar{\xi}_n$ and $\bar{\sigma}_n^2$ are consistent estimators of m and σ^2, respectively. Similarly, each law of large numbers can be formulated as a theorem of estimation theory.

Here we want to investigate the estimation of the distribution and of the density functions. The laws of large numbers immediately imply some results on the estimations of these functions but the most interesting and sharpest results are not straightforward consequences of the laws of large numbers.

Let $\xi_1, \xi_2, \ldots$ be a sequence of independent indentically distributed random variables with $\mathbf{P}(\xi_i < x) = F(x)$ $(i = 1, 2, \ldots)$. The function

$$F_n(x) = F_n(x, \omega) = \frac{\varphi_x(\xi_1)+\varphi_x(\xi_2)+\ldots+\varphi_x(\xi_n)}{n} \qquad (11.2.1)$$

is called the *n-th empirical distribution function* where

$$\varphi_x(t) = \begin{cases} 1 \text{ if } t_i < x \\ 0 \text{ if } t_i \geqq x. \end{cases}$$

By Theorem 2.9.2 we have

$$\mathbf{P}(F_n(x, \omega) \to F(x)) = 1 \quad \text{and} \quad \mathbf{P}(F_n(x+0) \to F(x+0)) = 1 \tag{11.2.2}$$

for each fixed $x \in (-\infty, +\infty)$. Similarly it can be shown that

$$\mathbf{P}\left(\int_A dF_n(x) \to \int_A dF(x)\right) = 1$$

for any Borel measurable set A.

The following result shows that (11.2.2) holds uniformly in x.

THEOREM 11.2.1 (GLIVENKO [1], CANTELLI [1]).

$$\mathbf{P}\left(\lim_{n\to\infty} \sup_{-\infty<x<\infty} |F_n(x) - F(x)| = 0\right) = 1. \tag{11.2.3}$$

Before the proof of this theorem, we mention some ways in which the Theorem has been generalized.

The most straightforward generalizations concern the estimation of n-dimensional distribution functions, or of probability measures defined on abstract spaces (see BLUM [1], RAO [1], WOLFOWITZ [1],). More precisely: let $\xi_1, \xi_2, \ldots$ be a sequence of independent, identically distributed random variables taking values in a Banach space B. The distribution of ξ_i is characterized by the measure:

$$\mu(A) = \mathbf{P}(\xi_i \in A) \quad (i = 1,2, \ldots)$$

where A is any Borel set of B. Let the measure μ_i be defined as follows:

$$\mu_i(A) = \begin{cases} 1 \text{ if } \xi_i \in A \\ 0 \text{ otherwise} \end{cases}$$

where A is any Borel set of B. The measure

$$\mu^{(n)} = \frac{\mu_1 + \mu_2 + \ldots + \mu_n}{n}$$

seems to be the most natural estimator of μ. In the above mentioned papers it is proved that $\mu^{(n)}$ tends to μ in some sense.

Another way of generalizing Theorem 11.2.1 is the following: let $\mathfrak{A}$ be the set of half-lines, i.e. the elements of $\mathfrak{A}$ are the intervals $(-\infty, x)$. Then by Theorem 11.2.1 we have

$$\mathbf{P}\left(\lim_{n\to\infty} \sup_{A\in\mathfrak{A}} |\mu^{(n)}(A) - \mu(A)| = 0\right) = 1. \tag{11.2.4}$$

where

$$\mu^{(n)}(A) = \int_A dF_n(x)\ ; \ \mu(A) = \int_A dF(x).$$

A natural question is: does (11.2.2) remain correct if $\mathfrak{A}$ is replaced by a larger class of Borel sets. The analogous problem can be raised in the higher dimensional case (see BLUM [1]). It is clear (already in the one-dimensional case) that if $\mathfrak{A}$ is replaced by the set of all Borel measurable set then (11.2.4) is false. It will be shown that a positive result can be obtained by a little modification of the definition of $\mu^{(n)}$ (or F_n), if $F(x)$ is absolutely continuous. (See the remark after Theorem 11.2.2.)

A third way of generalizing Theorem 11.2.1 is to investigate the rate of the convergence. This question was studied by SETHURAMAN [1] who obtained an analogue of Theorem 2.6.6, proving that $\mathbf{P}(\sup_{-\infty<x<\infty} |F_n(x) - F(x)| \geq \varepsilon)$ tends to 0 exponentially. An analogue of the law of the iterated logarithm was found by SMIRNOV [1].

The last generalization to be mentioned here is the non-independent case. For example, let $\xi_1, \xi_2, \ldots$ be a strictly stationary ergodic sequence with $\mathbf{P}(\xi_i < x) = F(x)$. Define the sample distribution function $F_n(x)$ by (11.2.1). Then Theorem 11.2.1 holds. The proof of this fact is quite similar to the proof of Theorem 11.2.1, making use of Theorem 4.1.1. This question was studied in detail by TUCKER [1].

Of all these results only Theorem 11.2.1 will be proved.

PROOF OF THEOREM 11.2.1. Let r be a positive integer. Denote by x_{rk} $(k = 1, 2, \ldots, r)$ the smallest real number x for which

$$F(x) \leq \frac{k}{r} \leq F(x+0).$$

Set

$$A_r = \left\{\omega : \max\left\{|F_n(x_{rk}) - F(x_{rk})|, |F_n(x_{rk}+0) - F(x_{rk}+0)|\right\} \to 0\right\}.$$

Then by (11.2.2)

$$\mathbf{P}(A_r) = 1 \qquad (r = 1, 2, \ldots).$$

Hence, we have

$$\mathbf{P}\left(\prod_{r=1}^{\infty} A_r\right) = 1. \tag{11.2.5}$$

Taking into account the monotony of $F_n(x)$ and $F(x)$ we obtain (11.2.3) as a clear consequence of (11.2.5).

The estimation of a density function was considered in the paper of PARZEN [1].

Let $\xi_1, \xi_2, \ldots$ be a sequence of independent identically distributed random variables with density function $f(x)$. Further let

$$\ldots < x_{-2} < x_{-1} < x_0 < x_1 < x_2 < \ldots$$

be a partition of the real line, the indicator function of the interval [a, b] is denoted by $\mathcal{I}_{a,b}(t)$. Then clearly,

$$\frac{\mathcal{I}_{x_1,x_2}(\xi_1) + \mathcal{I}_{x_1,x_2}(\xi_2) + \ldots + \mathcal{I}_{x_1,x_2}(\xi_n)}{n} \to \int_{x_1}^{x_2} f(x)\,dx. \quad (11.2.6)$$

So in this way a good enough estimator of $f(x)$ can be obtained if the partition is fine enough. Therefore, it seems that the natural estimator of $f(x)$ is (11.2.6), where finer and finer partitions of the real line are taken.

Here we give the following

THEOREM 11.2.2. *Let $\xi_1, \xi_2, \ldots$ be a sequence of independent, identically distributed random variables with density function $f(x)$. Suppose that $f(x)$ is uniformly continuous and there exist a $\delta > 0$ such that*

$$\int_{-\infty}^{+\infty} |x|^\delta f(x)\,dx > \infty . \quad (11.2.7)$$

Further let

$$\ldots < x_{-2}^{(1)} < x_{-1}^{(1)} < x_0^{(1)} < x_1^{(1)} < x_2^{(1)} < \ldots$$
$$\ldots < x_{-2}^{(2)} < x_{-1}^{(2)} < x_0^{(2)} < x_1^{(2)} < x_2^{(2)} < \ldots$$
$$\ldots\ldots\ldots\ldots\ldots\ldots\ldots\ldots\ldots\ldots$$
$$\ldots\ldots\ldots\ldots\ldots\ldots\ldots\ldots\ldots\ldots$$

be a sequence of the partitions of the real line for which

$$\frac{C_1}{n^{1-\varepsilon}} < x_{k+1}^{(n)} - x_k^{(n)} < \frac{C_2}{n^{1-\varepsilon}} \qquad (k = 0, \pm 1, \pm 2, \ldots)$$

where $0 < \varepsilon < 1$ and C_1 and C_2 are positive numbers.

Denote the indicator function of the interval $[a, b]$ by $\mathcal{I}_{ab}(x)$ and define the n-th empirical density function $f_n(t)$ as follows:

$$f_n(t) = f_n(t, \omega) = \frac{\mathcal{I}_{x_k^{(n)}, x_{k+1}^{(n)}}(\xi_1) + \mathcal{I}_{x_k^{(n)}, x_{k+1}^{(n)}}(\xi_2) + \ldots + \mathcal{I}_{x_k^{(n)}, x_{k+1}^{(n)}}(\xi_n)}{n(x_{k+1}^{(n)} - x_k^{(n)})}$$

$$\text{if } x_k^{(n)} \le t < x_{k+1}^{(n)} .$$

Then we have

$$\mathbf{P}\left(\lim_{n\to\infty} \sup_{-\infty<t<\infty} |f_n(t) - f(t)| = 0\right) = 1. \quad (11.2.8)$$

REMARK 1. This theorem easily implies that

$$\mathbf{P}\left(\sup_{A\in\mathcal{B}} \left| \int_A dF_n(x) - \int_A dF(x) \right| \to 0\right) = 1$$

if $F(x)$ is absolutely continuous and its derivative $f(x)$ obeys the conditions of Theorem 11.2.2 where $\mathcal{B}$ is the set of all Borel measurable sets of the real line and $F_n(x)$ is defined by

$$F_n(x) = F_n(x, \omega) = \int_{-\infty}^{x} f_n(t)dt.$$

REMARK 2. Condition 11.2.7 probably is not necessary to the validity of this Theorem but is easy to see that without a condition about the smoothness of $f(x)$ the statement (11.2.8) does not hold in general. This fact can be shown by the following example: let the density function $f(x)$ be defined as follows:

$$f(x) = h_2(x) + h_3(x) + \dots$$

where

$$h_i(x) = \begin{cases} 2^i\left[x - \left(2^i - \dfrac{1}{2^i}\right)\right] & \text{if } 2^i - \dfrac{1}{2^i} \leqq x \leqq 2^i \\ 2^i\left[2^i + \dfrac{1}{2^i} - x\right] & \text{if } 2^i \leqq x \leqq 2^i + \dfrac{1}{2^i} \\ 2^i\left[x - \left(-2^i - \dfrac{1}{2^i}\right)\right] & \text{if } -2^i - \dfrac{1}{2^i} \leqq x \leqq -2^i \\ 2^i\left[-2^i + \dfrac{1}{2^i} - x\right] & \text{if } -2^i \leqq x \leqq -2^i + \dfrac{1}{2^i} \\ 0 & \text{otherwise.} \end{cases}$$

Since for any n the random variables $\xi_1, \xi_2, \dots \xi_n$ belong to a finite interval (with probability 1), $f_n(x,\omega)$ is equal to 0 if x does not belong to this interval. This implies that

$$\mathbf{P}\left(\lim_{n\to\infty} \sup_{-\infty<x<\infty} |f_n(t) - f(t)| = 1\right) = 1.$$

PROOF OF THEOREM 11.2.2. The conditions of our theorem imply that $f(x)$ is a bounded function; let C be an upper bound of $f(x)$, i.e.

$$f(x) \leqq C \qquad (C > 0).$$

Set

$$f_n^*(t) = \frac{1}{x_{k+1}^{(n)} - x_k^{(n)}} \int_{x_k^{(n)}}^{x_{k+1}^{(n)}} f(u)\,du \qquad \text{if } x_k^{(n)} \leqq t < x_{k+1}^{(n)}$$

$$\mathcal{I}\, x_k^{(n)}, x_{k+1}^{(n)}(t) = \mathcal{I}_k^{(n)}(t)$$

$$\mathcal{I}_k^{(n)}(\xi_j) - \mathbf{E}\left(\mathcal{I}_k^{(n)}(\xi_j)\right) = \mathcal{I}_k^{(n)}(\xi_j) - \int_{x_k^{(n)}}^{x_{k+1}^{(n)}} f(u)\, du = \alpha_k^{(n)}(j).$$

Since

$$\sup_{-\infty < t < \infty} |f(t) - f_n^*(t)| \to 0$$

it is enough to study the difference $|f_n(t) - f_n^*(t)|$. In this investigation the following estimations will be used:

$$\mathbf{E}\left[(\alpha_k^{(n)}(j))^{2T}\right] \leq \int_{x_k^{(n)}}^{x_{k+1}^{(n)}} f(u)\, du \leq C\, (x_{k+1}^{(n)} - x_k^{(n)})$$

$$\mathbf{E}\left[(f_n(t) - \mathbf{E}(f_n(t))^{2K}\right] = \mathbf{E}\left[(f_n(t) - f_n^*(t))^{2K}\right] = O\left(\frac{1}{n^{\varepsilon K}}\right)$$

where K and T are arbitrary positive integers and t is between $x_k^{(n)}$ and $x_{k+1}^{(n)}$.

By the Markov inequality it can be obtained

$$\mathbf{P}\left(|f_n(t) - f_n^*(t)| \geq \varepsilon^*\right) = O\left(\frac{1}{n^{\varepsilon K}}\right)$$

and

$$\mathbf{P}\left(\sup_{-n^{1/\delta} \leq t \leq n^{1/\delta}} |f_n(t) - f_n^*(t)| \geq \varepsilon^*\right) = 2n^{1/\delta}\, n^{1-\varepsilon}\, O\left(\frac{1}{n^{\varepsilon K}}\right)$$

where δ is the constant defined by (11.2.7).

Since K is an arbitrary integer (large as we like) we have

$$\sum_{n=1}^{\infty} \mathbf{P}\left(\sup_{-n^{1/\delta} \leq t \leq n^{1/\delta}} |f_n(t) - f_n^*(t)| \geq \varepsilon^*\right) < \infty$$

for any $\varepsilon^* > 0$. Hence by the Borel–Cantelli lemma we have

$$\mathbf{P}\left(\sup_{-n^{1/\delta} \leq t \leq n^{1/\delta}} |f_n(t) - f_n^*(t)| \to 0\right) = 1.$$

Now we have to study the difference $|f(x) - f_n(x)|$ when x is an element of the set

$$A_n = (-\infty, -n^{1/\delta})\, V\, (n^{1/\delta}, +\infty)$$

Let B_n be the event that the n-th element of the sample is in A_n, i.e.

$$B_n = \{w : \xi_n(w) \in A_n\}.$$

Clearly

$$\sum_{n=1}^{\infty} \mathbf{P}(B_n) = \sum_{n=1}^{\infty} n \left[\int_{n^{1/\delta}}^{(n+1)^{1/\delta}} f(x)\, dx + \int_{-(n+1)^{1/\delta}}^{-n^{1/\delta}} f(x)\, dx\right] \leq \int_{-\infty}^{+\infty} x^{\delta} f(x)\, dx.$$

So by the Borel–Cantelli lemma among the events B_n only finitely many will be occured which together with the fact that $f(x)$ is small enough if $x \in A_n$ and n is large enough implies the theorem.

In our next theorem we investigate the rate of the convergence: $f_n(t) - f(t)$. More precisely we ask about the functions $\chi(n)$ for which

$$\mathbf{P}\left(\chi(n) \sup_{-\infty < t < \infty} |f_n(t) - f(t)| \to 0\right) = 1$$

where $f_n(t)$ is an empirical density function constructed by a suitable partition sequence

$$\cdots < x_{-2}^{(n)} < x_{-1}^{(n)} < x_0^{(n)} < x_1^{(n)} < x_2^{(n)} < \cdots \qquad (n = 1, 2, \ldots).$$

In connection with this question we give the following

THEOREN 11.2.3. *Let $\xi_1, \xi_2, \ldots$ be a sequence of independent, identically distributed random variables with density function $f(x)$ vanishes outside a finite interval* [a, b]. *Suppose that $f(x)$ has a uniformly bounded derivative*

$$|f'(x)| \leqq K.$$

Further let

$$\cdots < x_{-2}^{(n)} < x_{-1}^{(n)} < x_0^{(n)} < x_1^{(n)} < x_2^{(n)} < \cdots \qquad (n = 1, 2, \ldots)$$

be a sequence of the partitions of the real line for which

$$C_1 \frac{1}{n^{1/3}} < x_{k+1}^{(n)} - x_k^{(n)} < C_2 \frac{1}{n^{1/3}}$$

where C_1 and C_2 are positive numbers.

Denote the indicator function of the interval (α, β) by $\mathcal{I}_{\alpha\beta}(x)$ and define the n-th empirical density function $f_n(t)$ as follows

$$f_n(t) = \frac{\mathcal{I}_k^{(n)}(\xi_1) + \mathcal{I}_k^{(n)}(\xi_2) + \cdots + \mathcal{I}_k^{(n)}(\xi_n)}{n(x_{k+1}^{(n)} - x_k^{(n)})} \qquad \text{if } x_k^{(n)} \leqq t < x_{k+1}^{(n)}.$$

Then we have

$$\mathbf{P}\left(\frac{\sqrt[3]{n}}{\log^2 n} \sup_{a<t<b} |f_n(t) - f(t)| \to 0\right) = 1. \qquad (11.2.9)$$

REMARK 1. Knowing the law of the iterated logarithm one can think that the function

$$\chi(n) = \frac{\sqrt[3]{n}}{\log^2 n}$$

can be replaced by a function

$$\chi(n) = o\left(\sqrt{\frac{n}{\log\log n}}\right).$$

It will be shown by an example that it is hopeless to wait a better result than $\chi(n) = \sqrt[3]{n}$.

Let the density function $f(x)$ defined as

$$f(x) = \begin{cases} 2x \text{ if } 0 \leq x \leq 1 \\ 0 \text{ otherwise} \end{cases}$$

Further let

$$0 = x_0^{(n)} < x_1^{(n)} < \cdots < x_{h(n)}^{(n)} = 1 \qquad (n = 1, 2, \cdots)$$

be a sequence of partitions of the interval $[0, 1]$ where $h(n)$ is an integer valued function tending monotonically to $+\infty$. For the sake of simplicity we assume that $n_{k+1}^{(n)} - x_k^{(n)} = \frac{1}{h(n)}$. Now define the empirical density function by

$$f_n(t) = \frac{\mathcal{J}_k^{(n)}(\xi_1) + \mathcal{J}_k^{(n)}(\xi_2) + \cdots + \mathcal{J}_k^{(n)}(\xi_n)}{n\,(x_{k+1}^{(n)} - x_k^{(n)})} \qquad \text{if } x_k^{(n)} \leq t < x_{k+1}^{(n)} \tag{11.2.10}$$

where $\mathcal{J}_k^{(n)}(t)$ is the indicator function of the interval $[x_k^{(n)}, x_{k+1}^{(n)})$.

In the proof of Theorem 11.2.3 we have seen that

$$\mathbf{D}\left(f_n^*(t) - f_n(t)\right) = O\left(\sqrt{\frac{h(n)}{n}}\right)$$

where

$$f_n^*(t) = \frac{1}{x_{k+1}^{(n)} - x_k^{(n)}} \int_{x_k^{(n)}}^{x_{k+1}^{(n)}} f(u)\,du = \mathbf{E}\left(f_n(t)\right) \quad \text{if } x_k^{(n)} \leq t < x_{k+1}^{(n)}.$$

This fact together with the central limit theorem implies

$$\mathbf{P}\left(f_n(t) - f_n^*(t) < -\sqrt{\frac{h(n)}{n}}\right) \geq p > 0$$

where p is a constant (not depending on n).

Lot now t be a point of the interval $(x_k^{(n)}, x_{k+1}^{(n)})$ lying very near to $x_{k+1}^{(n)}$. Then we obtain

$$\mathbf{P}\left(\sqrt[3]{n}\,|f_n(t) - f(t)| \geq \sqrt[3]{n}\left[\frac{1}{2h(n)} + \sqrt{\frac{h(n)}{n}}\right]\right) \geq p > 0.$$

Since the sequence

$$\sqrt[3]{n}\left[\frac{1}{2h(n)} + \sqrt{\frac{h(n)}{n}}\right]$$

does not tend to 0 for any sequence $h(n)$, we obtain that

$$\chi(n) \sup_{0 \leq t \leq 1} |f_n(t) - f(t)|$$

does not converge to 0 *with probability* 1 *(even in probability) if* $\chi(n) \geq \sqrt[3]{n}$ *where* $f_n(t)$ *is the empirical density function defined by* (11.2.10) *and* $h(n)$ *is an arbitrary function.*

Remark 2. Roughly speaking our theorem and Remark 1 state that the "best" estimation of a smooth density function can be obtained by (11.2.10) where

$$x_{k+1}^{(n)} - x_k^{(n)} = \frac{1}{\sqrt[3]{n}}$$

and in this case the rate of convergence is $\dfrac{\log^2 n}{\sqrt[3]{n}}$.

Proof of Theorem 11.2.3. Set

$$\lambda_n = \sqrt[3]{n}\sqrt{\log n}$$

$$\mu_n = 3 \log n$$

$$\mathcal{I}_{x_k^{(n)}, x_{k+1}^{(n)}}(t) = \mathcal{I}_k^{(n)}(t)$$

$$f_n^*(t) = \frac{1}{x_{k+1}^{(n)} - x_k^{(n)}} \int_{x_k^{(n)}}^{x_{k+1}^{(n)}} f(u)\, du \quad \text{if} \quad x_k^{(n)} \leq t < x_{k+1}^{(n)}.$$

$$\mathcal{I}_k^{(n)}(\xi_j) - \mathbf{E}\left(\mathcal{I}_k^{(n)}(\xi_j)\right) = \alpha_k^{(n)}(j)$$

$$f_n(t) - f_n^*(t) = \beta(n) = \beta_k(n) = \frac{\alpha_k^{(n)}(1) + \alpha_k^{(n)}(2) + \cdots + \alpha_k^{(n)}(n)}{n\,(x_{k+1}^{(n)} - x_k^{(n)})}$$

$$\text{if } x_k^{(n)} \leq t < x_{k+1}^{(n)}.$$

Since

$$\frac{\sqrt[3]{n}}{\log^2 n} \sup_{-\infty < t < \infty} |f(t) - f_n^*(t)| \to 0$$

it is enough to study the difference $|f_n(t) - f_n^*(t)|$. In this investigation the following estimations will be used:

$$\mathbf{E}\,(e^{\lambda_n\beta(n)-\mu_n}) = e^{-\mu_n}\prod_{j=1}^{n}\mathbf{E}\left(e^{\lambda_n\frac{\alpha_k^{(n)}(j)}{n(x_{k+1}^{(n)}-x_k^{(n)})}}\right) \leqq$$

$$\leqq e^{-\mu_n}\prod_{j=1}^{n}\mathbf{E}\left(1+\frac{\lambda_n\,\alpha_k^{(n)}(j)}{n(x_{k+1}^{(n)}-x_k^{(n)})}+\frac{\lambda_n^2}{n^2(x_{k+1}^{(n)}-x_k^{(n)})^2}(\alpha_k^{(n)}(j))^2\right) = O\left(\frac{1}{n^2}\right).$$

By the Markov inequality we have

$$\mathbf{P}\,(e^{\lambda n\beta(n)-\mu_n} \geqq e^{\varepsilon}) = \mathbf{P}\,(\lambda_n\beta_n - \mu_n \geqq \varepsilon) = O\left(\frac{1}{n^2}\right).$$

Hence

$$\mathbf{P}\left(\frac{\sqrt[3]{n}}{\log^2 n}\sup_{a\leqq t\leqq b}(f_n(t)-f_n^*(t)) \geqq \frac{\varepsilon}{\log^2 \mathrm{n}}+\frac{\varepsilon}{\log \mathrm{n}}\right) = \sqrt[3]{n}\,(b-a)\,O\left(\frac{1}{n^2}\right)$$

and by the Borel–Cantelli lemma we obtain

$$\mathbf{P}\lim_{n\to\infty}\sup\frac{\sqrt[3]{n}}{\log^2 n}\sup_{a\leqq t\leqq b}(f_n(t)-f_n^*(t)) = 0\Bigg) = 1.$$

In a similar way it can be obtained that

$$\mathbf{P}\left(\lim_{n\to\infty}\inf\frac{\sqrt[3]{n}}{\log^2 n}\inf_{a\leqq t\leqq b}(f_n(t)-f_n^*(t)) = 0\right) = 1$$

what implies our theorem.

§ 11.3. Applications in information theory

In information theory the following type of theorems play an important role:

Let $\xi_1, \xi_2, \ldots$ be a sequence stationary in the strong sense, taking the values $a_1, a_2, \ldots, a_n$. Then the limit of the sequence

$$-\frac{1}{N}\log_2 \mathbf{P}(\xi_1 = a_{i_1}, \xi_2 = a_{i_2}, \ldots, \xi_N = a_{i_N})$$

exists in some sense.

These types of theorems were obtained by SHANNON [1], MCMILLAN [1], FEINSTEIN [1], BREIMAN [2].

To formulate precisely one of these theorems, we introduce the following notations:

for any sequence $(a_{i_1}, a_{i_2}, \ldots, a_{i_N})$ of elements of $(a_1, a_2, \ldots, \xi_N)$, let $p(i_1, i_2, \ldots, i_N) = \mathbf{P}(\xi_1 = a_{i_1}, \ldots, \xi_N = a_{i_N})$. Then $p(\xi_1, \xi_2, \ldots, \xi_N)$ is the probability of the sequence $\{\xi_1, \xi_2, \ldots, \xi_N\}$ actually observed or in other words $p(\xi_1, \xi_2, \ldots, \xi_N)$ is a random variable defined as

$$p(\xi_1, \xi_2, \ldots, \xi_N) = p(i_1, i_2, \ldots, i_N) \quad \text{if} \quad \xi_1 = a_{i_1}, \xi_2 = a_{i_2}, \ldots, \xi_N = a_{i_N}.$$

Then we have

THEOREM 11.3.1.

$$-\frac{1}{N} \log p(\xi_1, \xi_2, \ldots \xi_N) \to \eta \qquad (N \to \infty) \tag{11.3.1}$$

where η is a non-negative random variable.

This theorem is a trivial consequence of Theorem 2.9.2 if the random variables $\xi_1, \xi_2, \ldots$ are independent (and stationary). Another simple case is when $\xi_1, \xi_2, \ldots$ is a Markov chain. The general case was proved by BREIMAN [2].

Also a simple case is when $\xi_1, \xi_2, \ldots$ are symmetrically dependent random variables. In this case $\xi_1, \xi_2, \ldots$ are independent with respect to a σ-algebra $\mathcal{F}$ (see Theorem 6.1.1). Therefore,

$$\mathbf{P}\left(-\frac{1}{N} \log p(\xi_1, \xi_2, \ldots, \xi_N) = -\frac{1}{N} \sum_{k=1}^{N} \log p(\xi_k) \mid \mathcal{F}\right) = 1$$

and then by Theorem 6.1.2

$$\frac{1}{N} \sum_{k=1}^{N} \log p(\xi_k)$$

tends to a limit λ with probability 1.

REFERENCES

ALEXITS, G. [1] *Convergence Problems of Orthogonal Series.* Akadémiai Kiadó, Budapest, 1961.

ALEXITS, G. and TANDORI, K. [1] Über das Konvergenzverhalten einer Klasse von Orthogonalreihen. *Annales Univ. Sci. Bp. de R. Eötvös nom. Sect. Math.* **3** (1961) 15–19.

ANSCOMBE, F. I. [1] Large sample theory of sequential estimation. *Proc. Cambridge Phyl. Soc.* **48** (1952) 600–607.

BÁRTFAI, P. and RÉVÉSZ, P. [1] On a zero-one law. *Zeitschr. f. Wahrscheinlichkeitstheorie* **7** (1967) 43–47.

BAUM, L. E. [1] On convergence to $+\infty$ in the law of large numbers, *Ann. Math. Stat.* **34** (1963) 219–222.

BAUM, L. E. and KATZ, M. [1] Convergence rates in the law of large numbers. *Bull. Amer. Math. Soc.* **69** (1963) 771–773.

BAUM, L. E., KATZ, M. and READ, R. R. [1] Exponential convergence rates for the law of large numbers. *Trans. Amer. Math. Soc.* **102** (1961) 187–199.

BAXTER, G. [1] A general ergodic theorem with weighted averages. *J. of Math. and Mech.* **14** (1965) 277–288.

[2] An ergodic theorem with weighted averages. *J. of Math. and Mech.* **13** (1964) 481–488.

BECK, A. [1] On the strong law of large numbers. *Ergodic Theory* (edited by F. B. Wright). Academic Press, New York–London, 1963, 21–53.

BENTON, J., OREY, S. and PRUIT, W. [1] Convergence of weighted averages of independent random variables. *Zeitschr. f. Wahrscheinlichkeitstheorie* **4** (1965) 40–44.

BLUM, J. R. [1] On the convergence of empiric distribution functions. *Ann. Math. Stat.* **26** (1955) 527–529.

BLUM, J. R. and ROSENBLATT, J. [1] On random sampling from stochastic processes. *Ann. Math. Stat.* **35** (1964) 1713–1717.

BLUM, J. R., HANSON, D. L. and KOOPMAN, L. [1] On the strong law of large numbers for a class of stochastic processes. *Zeitschr. f. Wahrscheinlichkeitstheorie* **2** (1963) 1–11.

BOREL, É. [1] Sur lés probabilités dénombrables et leurs applications arithmétiques. *Rendiconti del Circolo Mat. di Palermo* **26** (1909) 247–271.

BREIMAN, L. [1] A counterexample to a theorem of Kolmogorov. *Ann. Math. Stat.* **28** (1957) 811–814.

[2] The individual ergodic theorem of information theory. *Ann. Math. Stat.* **28** (1957) 809–811.

BRUNK, H. D. [1] The strong law of large numbers. *Duke Math. Journ.* **15** (1948) 181–195.

CANTELLI, F. P. [1] Sulla probabilità come limita della frequenza. *Rend. Accad. Lincei.* **26** (1917) 39.

CANTOR, G. [1] Über die einfachen Zahlensysteme. *Zeitschrift f. Math. u. Phys.* **14** (1869).

CARLESON, L. [1] On convergence and growth of partial sum of Fourier series *Acta Math.* **115** (1966).

Chover, J. [1] A law of the iterated logarithm for stable summands *Proc. Am. Math. Soc.* **17** (1966) 441–443.

Chow, Y. S. [1] Some convergence theorems for linear combinations of independent random variables. *Ann. Math. Stat.* **37** (1966) 540.

Chung, K. L. [1] The strong law of large numbers. *Proc. of the Second Berkeley Symp.* Univ. Calif. 1951, 341–352.

[2] *Markov Chains with Stationary Transition Probabilities.* Springer, Berlin, 1960.

Cohn, H. [1] On a class of dependent random variables. *Rev. Roum. Math. Pures et Appl.* **10** (1965) 1593–1606.

Derman, C. and Robbins, H. [1] The strong law of large numbers when the first moment does not exist. *Proc. Nat. Acad. Sci. USA* **41** (1955) 586–587.

(Dobrushin) Добрушин, Р. А. [1] Лемма о ирeделе сложной функции. *Успехи Мат. Наук* **10** (1955) 157–159.

Doob, J. L. [1] *Stochastic Processes.* John Wiley, New York, 1953.

(Dynkin) Дынкин, Е. В. [1] О некоторых предельных теоремах для цепей Маркова. *Укранский Мат. Журн.* **6** (1954) 21–29.

Ehrenfeucht, A. and Fisz, M. [1] A necessary and sufficient condition for the validity of the weak law of large numbers. *Bull. de l'Acad. Polonaise des Sci. Ser. Math.* **8** (1960) 583–585.

Erdős, P. [1] On a theorem of Hsu and Robbins. *Ann. Math. Stat.* **20** (1949) 286–291.

[2] On the law of the iterated logarithm. *Ann. of Math.* **43** (1942) 419–436.

[3] On trigonometric sums with gaps. *Publ. Math. Inst. Hung. Acad. Sci.* **7** A (1962) 37–42.

Erdős, P. and Rényi, A. [1] On Cantor's series with convergent $\Sigma \frac{1}{q_k}$. *Annales Univ. Sci. Bp. de R. Eötvös nom. Sect. Math.* **2** (1959) 93–109.

[2] Some further statistical properties of the digits in Cantor's series. *Acta Math. Acad. Sci. Hung.* **10** (1959) 21–29.

Erdős, P., Rényi, A. and Szüsz, P. [1] On Engel's and Sylvester's series. *Annales Univ. Sci. Bp. de R. Eötvös nom. Sect. Math.* **1** (1958) 7–32.

Feinstein, A. [1] A new basic theorem of information theory. *IRE Trans. P. G. I. T.* (1954) 2–22.

Feller, W. [1] Generalization of a probability limit theorem of Cramér. *Trans. Amer. Math. Soc.* **54** (1943) 361–372.

[2] The general form of the so-called law of the iterated logarithm. *Trans. Amer. Math. Soc.* **54** (1943) 373–402.

Fisz, M. [1] *Probability theory and mathematical statistics.* J. Wiley, New York–London, 1963.

[2] On necessary and sufficient conditions for the validity of the strong law of large numbers expressed in terms of moments. *Bull. Ac. Pol. Sci. Math.* **7** (1959) 221–225.

Fortet, R. and Mourier, E. [1] Convergence de la répartition empirique vers la répartition théorique. *Ann. Scientifiques de l'École Norm. Sup.* **60** (1953) 267–285.

[2] Resultats complementaires sur les elements aleatoires dans une espace de Banach. *Bull. Sci. Math.* **78** (1954) 14.

Franck, W. E. and Hanson, D. L. [1] Some results giving rates of convergence in the law of large numbers for weighted sums of independent random variables. *Bull. Amer. Math. Soc.* **72** (1966) 266–268.

Glivenko, V. I. [1] Sulla determinazione empirica delle leggi di probabilità. *Giorn. Ist. Ital. Attuari* **4** (1933) 92.

(Gnedenko) [1] Гнеденко, В. И. [1] *Курс теории вероятностей.* Гостехиздат, Москва–Ленинград, 1950. (English translation: *The Theory of Probability,* Chelsea Publ. Co. New York 1962.)

Gnedenko, V. I. and Kolmogorov, A. N. [1] *Limit Distributions for Sums of Independent Random Variables.* Addison-Wesley, Publ. Co. Cambridge, U. S., 1954.

HÁJEK, I. and RÉNYI, A. [1] A generalization of an inequality of Kolmogorov. *Acta Math. Acad. Sci. Hung.* **6** (1955) 281–284.

HALMOS, P. R. [1] *Measure Theory.* Van Nostrand, New York, 1950.
[2] *Lectures on Ergodic Theory.* Math. Soc. of Japan, Tokyo, 1956.

HARTMAN, P. and WINTNER, A. [1] On the law of iterated logarithm. *Amer. J. Math.* **63** (1941) 169–176.

HAUSDORFF, F. [1] *Grundzüge der Mengenlehre.* Leipzig, 1913.

JACOBS, K. [1] *Neuere Methoden und Ergebnisse der Ergodentheorie.* Springer, Berlin, 1960.
[2] *Lecture Notes on Ergodic Theory,* I–II. Aarhus Universität, 1962–1963.

KAKUTANI, S. [1] Random ergodic theorems and Markoff processes with a stable distribution. *Proc. of the Second Berkeley Symp.* Univ. Calif., 1950, 247–262.

KHINCHIN, A. [1] Über dyadische Brüche. *Math. Zeitschr.* **18** (1923) 109–116.

KOLMOGOROV, A. N. [1] *Grundbegriffe der Wahrscheinlichkeitsrechnung,* Springer, Berlin, 1933.
[2] Über die Summen durch den Zufall bestimmter unabhängiger Grössen. *Math. Ann.* **99** (1928) 309–319.
[3] On the tables of random numbers. *Sankhya* **25** (1963) 369–376.
[4] Bemerkungen zu meiner Arbeit "Über die Summen zufälliger Grössen". *Math. Ann.* **102** (1929) 484–488.
[5] Über das Gesetz des iterierten Logarithmus. *Math. Ann.* **101** (1929) 126–135.

KOMLÓS, J. [1] A generalization of a problem of Steinhaus. *Acta Math. Acad. Sci. Hung.*

KOMLÓS, J. and RÉVÉSZ, P. [1] On the weighted averages of independent random variables. *Publ. Math. Inst. Hung. Acad. Sci.* **9** A (1964) 583–587.

LÉVY, P. [1] Sur un théorème de M. Khintchine. *Bull. Sci. Math.* **55** (1931) 145–160.

(LINNIK) [1] Линник, Ю. В. [1] Пять лекций о некоторых вопросах теории чисел и теории вероятностей, Лекция 5. *MTA Mat. Kut. Int. Közl.* **4** (1959) 251–258.

LOÈVE, M. [1] *Probability Theory.* Van Nostrand, New York, 1955.

MARCINKIEWICZ, J. and ZYGMUND, A. [1] Sur les fonctions indépendantes. *Fund. Math.* **29** (1937) 60–90.

MARTIN-LÖF, P. [1] *Algorithmen im zufälligen Folgen,* gehalten am Math. Institut der Univ. Erlangen-Nürnberg, 1966.

MCMILLAN, B. [1] The basic theorems of information theory. *Ann. Math. Stat.* **24** (1953) 169–219.

VON MISES, R. [1] Grundlagen der Wahrscheinlichkeitsrechnung. *Math. Zeitschr.* **5** (1919) 52–99.
[2] *Wahrscheinlichkeit, Statistik und Wahrheit.* Springer, Wien, 1936.

MENSOV, D. [1] Sur les séries de fonctions orthogonales, I. *Fund. Math.* **4** (1923) 82–105.

MOGYORÓDI, J. [1] On the law of large numbers for the sum of a random number of independent random variables. *Annales Univ. Sci. Bp. de R. Eötvös nom. Sect. Math.* **8** (1965) 33–38.
[2] A central limit theorem for the sum of a random number of independent random variables. *Publ. of Math. Inst. of Hung. Acad. Sci.* **7** (1962) 409–429.

MOURIER, E. [1] *L*-random elements and *L**-random elementns in Banach spaces. *Proc. of the Third Berkeley Symp.* Univ. Calif. 1956, **2** 231–242.

OBRETENOV, A. [1] On the strong law of large numbers (Bulgarian) *Bulgar. Akad. Nauk. Izv. Mat. Inst.* **6** (1962) 5–13.

PARZEN, E. [1] On estimation of a probability density function and modes. *Ann. Math. Stat.* **33** (1962) 1065–1076.

(PETROV) Петров, В. В. [1] К закону повторного логарифма. *Вестник Ленинградского Унив.* **7** (1966) 63–67.

PETTIS, B. J. [1] On integration in vector space. *Trans. Amer. Math. Soc.* **44** (1938) 277–304.

PITMAN, E. J. G. [1] On the derivation of a characteristic function at the origin. *Ann. Math. Stat.* **27** (1956) 1156–1160.

(PROKHOROV) Прохоров, Ю. В. [1] Об усиленном законе больших чисел. *Известия Акад. Наук СССР* **14** (1950) 523–536. (English translation: *Theory of Probability*, **3** 141–153.)

[2] Усиленная устойчивость сумм и неограниченно делимые распределения. *Теор. Вероятностей и ее прим.* **3** (1958) 153–165.

RADEMACHER, H. [1] Einige Sätze über Reihen von allgemeinen Orthogonalfunctionen. *Math. Ann.* **87** (1922) 112–138.

RAO, R. RANGA. [1] Relations between weak and uniform convergence of measures with applications. *Ann. Math. Stat.* **33** (1962) 659–680.

RÉNYI, A. [1] *Wahrscheinlichkeitsrechnung mit einem Anhang über Informationstheorie.* VEB Deutscher Verl. d. Wiss., Berlin, 1962.

[2] On stable sequences of events. *Sankhya* **25** (1963) 293–302.

[3] On a conjecture of H. Steinhaus. *Annales Soc. Pol. de Math.* **25** (1952) 279–287.

[4] On the central limit theorem for the sum of a random number of independent random variables. *Acta Math. Ac. Sci. Hung.* **11** (1960) 97–162.

[5] A számjegyek eloszlása valós számok Cantor-féle előállításaiban (Distribution of numerals in the Cantor productions of real numbers). *Mat. Lapok* **7** (1956) 77–100.

[6] Representations for real numbers and their ergodic properties. *Acta Math. Ac. Sci. Hung.* **8** (1957) 477–493.

RÉNYI, A. and ZERGÉNYI, E. [1] An inequality for uncorrelated random variables *Чехословацкий Мат. Жури.* **6** (1956) 415–419.

RÉVÉSZ, P. [1] A random ergodic theorem and its application in the theory of Markov chains. *Ergodic Theory* 217–250. (Ed. by F. B. Wright.) Acad. Press, New York–London, 1963.

[2] On a problem of Steinhaus. *Acta Math. Ac. Sci. Hung.* **16** (1965) 311–318.

[3] A central limit theorem for equivalent random variables. *Publ. Math.* **12** (1965) 295–302.

[4]–[5] On sequences of quasi-equivalent events, I–II. *Publ. Math. Inst. Hung. Ac. Sci.* **8** A (1963) 73–83, **9** A (1964) 227–233.

[6] On momentum equivalent systems. *Transaction of the fourth Prague conference* (1965) 471–477.

[7] Some remarks on strongly multiplicative systems. *Acta Math. Acad. Sci. Hung.* **16** (1965) 441–446.

[8] A convergence theorem of orthogonal series. *Acta Sci. Math.* **27** (1966) 253–259.

RÉVÉSZ, P. and WSCHEBOR, M. [1] On the statistical properties of the Walsh functions. *Publ. Math. Inst. Hung. Acad. Sci.* **9** A (1965) 543–554.

RIESZ, F. and SZŐKEFALVI-NAGY, B. [1] *Functional Analysis.* Blockie, London–Glasgow, 1956.

ROGERS, H. [1] A note on the law of large numbers. *Proc. Amer. Math. Soc.* **8** (1957) 518–520.

ROSENBLATT-ROTH, M. [1] Some theorems concerning the strong law of large numbers for non-homogeneous Markov-chains. *Ann. Math. Stat.* **35** (1964) 566–576.

[2] Some theorems concerning the strong law of large numbers for non-homogeneous Markov-chain.s *Z. f. Wahrscheinlichkeitstheorie* **1** (1963) 433–445.

RYLL-NARDZEWSKI, C. [1] On the ergodic theorems, II. *Studia Math.* **12** (1951) 74–79.

SCHMEIDLER, W. [1] *Lineare Operatoren im Hilbertschen Raum*, Teubner, Stuttgart, 1954.

SETHURAMAN, J. [1] On the probability of large deviations of families of sample means. *Ann. Math. Stat.* **35** (1964) 1304–1316.

SHANNON, C. [1] A mathematical theory of communications. *Bell System. Techn. Journ.* **27** (1948) 379–423, 623–656.

(SINAI) Синай, Я. Г. [1] О спектральных мерах высщих порядков ергодические стационарных процессов. *Теор. Вероят. и ее Прим.* **8** (1963) 463—470. (English translation: *Theory of Probability*, **8** 429—436.)

(SHIRYAEV) Ширяев, А. Н. [1] Об условиях эргодичности стационарных процессов в моменте старных порядков. *Теор. Вероят. и ее Прим.* **8** (1963) 470—473. (English translation: *Theory of Probability*, **8** 436—439.)

(SMIRNOV) Смирнов, И. В. [1] Приближение законов распрегеления случйных величин по эмпирическим данным. *Успехи Мат. Наук.* **10** (1944) 179—205.

SPITZER, F. [1] A combinatorial lemma and its application to probability theory. *Trans. Am. Math. Soc.* **82** (1956) 323–339.

STEINHAUS, H. [1] *The New Scottish Book*. Wroclaw, 1946–1958.

STRASSEN, V. [1] A converse to the law of the iterated logarithm. *Zeitschr. f. Wahrscheinlichkeitstheorie* **4** (1966) 205–268.

[2] An invariance principle for the law of the iterated logarithm. *Zeitschr. f. Wahrscheinlichkeitstheorie* **3** (1964) 221–226.

TANDORI, K. [1] Über die orthogonalen Funktionen, I. *Acta Sci. Math.* **18** (1957) 57–130.

TUCKER, H. G. [1] A generalization of the Glivenko-Cantelli theorem. *Ann. Math. Stat.* **30** (1959) 828–830.

WALSH, I. L. [1] A closed set of normal orthogonal functions. *Amer. J. Math.* **55** (1923) 5–24.

WEISS, M. [1] On the law of iterated logarithm. *Trans. Amer. Math. Soc.* **92** (1959) 531–553.

[2] On the law of iterated logarithm for lacunary trigonometric series. *Trans. Amer. Math. Soc.* **91** (1959) 444–469.

WITTENBERG, H. [1] Limiting distributions for random sums of independent random variables. *Zeitschr. f. Wahrscheinlichkeitstheorie* **3** (1964) 7–18.

WOLFOWITZ, J. [1] Generalization of the theorem of Glivenko-Cantelli. *Ann. Math. Stat.* **25** (1954) 131–138.

YOSIDA, K. [1] *Functional Analysis*. Springer, Berlin, 1965.

AUTHOR INDEX